ANALYTIC GEOMETRY
WITH AN INTRODUCTION TO
VECTORS and MATRICES

Also by D. C. Murdoch
Linear Algebra for Undergraduates

ANALYTIC GEOMETRY
WITH AN INTRODUCTION TO
VECTORS and MATRICES

D. C. MURDOCH

Professor of Mathematics
The University of British Columbia

JOHN WILEY & SONS, INC.   New York · London · Sydney

PREFACE

The place of analytic geometry in the college and high school curriculum has been the subject of a good deal of controversy in recent years. The basic question has been whether it should be taught in a separate course or amalgamated with the calculus by using a "unified" textbook covering both subjects. The tendency in recent years has been toward a unified course in analytic geometry and calculus. This tendency has culminated in the production of textbooks that attempt to put all of analytic geometry, most of linear algebra, and several semesters' work in calculus between two covers. The result is often a massive text of approximately one thousand pages which is rather forbidding to the beginning student. In my opinion this material can be more effectively taught in two sequences of courses, one in calculus and one in analytic geometry and linear algebra.

The dissatisfaction with the traditional course in analytic geometry, which led to the widespread introduction of the unified course, was real and well founded. The traditional course *was* unsatisfactory. It included many topics, for example, curve tracing and tangents, etc., that *are* better done in the calculus course. It often included chapters on "higher plane curves," geometric properties of conics and quadrics, poles and polars, duality, etc., that could well be omitted or postponed to a specialized course in projective geometry. On the other hand, since the course was designed in the days when matrix algebra was an esoteric subject taught only in the graduate school, the basic relationship between analytic geometry and linear algebra was largely ignored.

My purpose in writing this book has been to provide an alternative

v

to the unified course that seems to me to make better sense both mathematically and pedagogically. The book is designed for a course that may still be called analytic geometry but which will meet the mathematical needs of today much better than the traditional course in that subject. Ideally it should precede the first course in calculus but it could be taken concurrently with it. The book is not designed for a course in analytic geometry of the traditional type although the change in spirit is perhaps greater than the change in subject matter. Some topics, such as geometric (especially projective) properties of conics, tangents, systematic curve sketching, and the so-called higher plane curves have been omitted or soft-pedaled for the reasons already stated. Polar coordinates have been treated briefly but there is no extensive discussion of special curves from their polar equations.

Vector and matrix methods have been used extensively and have been developed to the point where the student will be well prepared both for the more abstract concepts and methods of linear algebra and for the use of vector methods in the calculus. The two- and three-dimensional cases have been treated together with an occasional excursion into n dimensions. There seems little reason why, for example, when the distance formula has been developed in the plane, it should not immediately be developed in space also.

A section on linear inequalities with simple applications to linear programming has been included in Chapter 5 but can be omitted without destroying the continuity of the rest of the book. The material on the conics and quadrics in Chapter 6 can be covered quite quickly by an instructor who so wishes, by omitting Section 6.5 and all but the routine problems in the Exercises. On the other hand the chapter can also be used for a much more intensive treatment of the conics by including or expanding Section 6.5 and by working through all the Exercises in detail. In Chapters 7 and 8 I have developed enough of the theory of vector spaces, matrices, and determinants so that transformations of coordinates, rotations of axes, and discussion of the general quadratic equation can be treated in the spirit of linear algebra. On the other hand Chapters 7, 8, and 9 are not intended as a substitute for a course in linear algebra. Rather they are intended to lay a firm foundation for such a course by showing the power of vector-matrix methods in solving basic problems in analytic geometry.

The last chapter contains a section on polar coordinates and a treatment of the complex numbers. The latter seems to me to fit in well with a vector treatment of analytic geometry. This chapter could be done earlier if desired, for example after Chapter 6, or even after Chapter 4 if a few examples and problems are omitted. If Section 10.6 were omitted as well, the chapter could even be inserted immediately after Chapter 2.

I have written the book with the intention and anticipation that the problem sets will be a vital part of the teaching and learning process. Sometimes an idea is developed through a series of problems in an exercise and a good many important results are introduced in this way rather than in the text. I have not hesitated to make use of such results later with appropriate references. Some of the results that the student is asked to establish for himself may be quite as important as those explained fully in the text. I do not consider that relegation to the exercises downgrades the importance of a theorem. On the contrary a theorem that the student establishes for himself may stay with him better than those set out in the text or explained by a teacher. Ideally, students should work virtually all the exercises in the book. Answers or hints to about half of them are given.

I would like to thank all those who have helped in intangible ways with the production of this book. This includes many friends, colleagues, students, and members of my family, most of whom might be surprised to hear that they had helped at all. For help of a more tangible kind I am primarily indebted to my colleague, Mr. J. E. Smith, who read a large part of the manuscript and suggested many improvements, and to Mr. S. Alan Smith for assistance in checking the problems. I would also like to thank the publishers and their staff, and especially their editorial consultants whose constructive criticism and suggestions, in both the planning and later stages, have materially improved the book.

D. C. Murdoch

Vancouver, B.C.
December, 1965

CONTENTS

CHAPTER 1

SOME BASIC CONCEPTS

1.1 Sets

The idea of a *set* or a collection of objects is a convenient starting place in many branches of mathematics, because many important concepts are most easily defined in the language of sets. We make no attempt to define the term *set* itself. This is not primarily because everyone has an intuitive idea of its meaning, but because there is no simpler concept in terms of which set can be defined. The following are examples:

1. The set of all points on a given line.
2. The set of all points inside a given circle.
3. The set of all whole numbers greater than 10.
4. The set of all fractions with numerator 1.
5. The set of all real numbers between 2 and 5.
6. The set of all unmarried female students at X University.
7. The set of all tomcats.

Although in most of our applications we shall be dealing with prosaic things like sets of numbers or sets of points, the algebra of sets will be developed in quite general terms and will not exclude the more colorful sets exemplified in (6) and (7).

The individual objects of which a set is composed are called the *elements* of the set. It is assumed that these objects all belong to some (usually) larger set $\mathfrak{U}$ and that all the sets with which we are concerned are composed of elements of $\mathfrak{U}$. The set $\mathfrak{U}$ is called the *universal set*. It is also assumed that if $\mathfrak{A}$ is a set and x is an element of $\mathfrak{U}$, an unambiguous answer exists to the question "is x an element of $\mathfrak{A}$?" We use the notation $x \in \mathfrak{A}$ to mean "x is an element of $\mathfrak{A}$." The statement $x \in \mathfrak{A}$ may also be read simply as "x is in $\mathfrak{A}$." The elements of $\mathfrak{U}$ that do not belong to $\mathfrak{A}$ constitute a set called the complement of $\mathfrak{A}$, which is denoted by $\mathfrak{A}'$. For example, if $\mathfrak{U}$ is the set of all books in a certain library and $\mathfrak{A}$ is the set of all those books written in English, then $\mathfrak{A}'$ is the set of all those books in the library that are not written in English. The fact that x is not an element of $\mathfrak{A}$ may therefore be written either $x \notin \mathfrak{A}$ or $x \in \mathfrak{A}'$.

If $\mathfrak{A}$ and $\mathfrak{B}$ are sets, the set of all elements of $\mathfrak{U}$ that belong either to $\mathfrak{A}$ or to $\mathfrak{B}$ (or to both) is called the *union*[*] of $\mathfrak{A}$ and $\mathfrak{B}$ and is denoted by $\mathfrak{A} \cup \mathfrak{B}$. The set of all elements of $\mathfrak{U}$ that belong to both $\mathfrak{A}$ and $\mathfrak{B}$ is called the *intersection*[*] of $\mathfrak{A}$ and $\mathfrak{B}$ and is denoted by $\mathfrak{A} \cap \mathfrak{B}$. Thus $x \in \mathfrak{A} \cup \mathfrak{B}$ implies either $x \in \mathfrak{A}$ or $x \in \mathfrak{B}$, and $x \in \mathfrak{A} \cap \mathfrak{B}$ implies both $x \in \mathfrak{A}$ and $x \in \mathfrak{B}$. In order to take care of the possibility that no elements of $\mathfrak{U}$ belong to both $\mathfrak{A}$ and $\mathfrak{B}$, we introduce the concept of the empty, or *null set*, denoted by $\emptyset$. This is a set that contains no elements, and the statement $\mathfrak{A} \cap \mathfrak{B} = \emptyset$ means that $\mathfrak{A}$ and $\mathfrak{B}$ have no elements in common. In this case we say that $\mathfrak{A}$ and $\mathfrak{B}$ are *disjoint*. Relationships between sets are conveniently represented diagramatically by pictures of the type shown in Fig. 1.1, called Venn diagrams.

Subsets. If $\mathfrak{A}$ and $\mathfrak{B}$ are two sets and every element x of $\mathfrak{U}$ belonging to $\mathfrak{A}$ is also an element of $\mathfrak{B}$, we say that $\mathfrak{A}$ is a *subset* of $\mathfrak{B}$ or $\mathfrak{A}$ is contained in $\mathfrak{B}$. This is written $\mathfrak{A} \subseteq \mathfrak{B}$. If $\mathfrak{A} \subseteq \mathfrak{B}$ and also $\mathfrak{B} \subseteq \mathfrak{A}$, then $\mathfrak{A}$ and $\mathfrak{B}$ consist of precisely the same elements and we write $\mathfrak{A} = \mathfrak{B}$. If $\mathfrak{A} \subseteq \mathfrak{B}$ and it is known that $\mathfrak{B}$ contains at least one element that is not an element of $\mathfrak{A}$, we write $\mathfrak{A} \subset \mathfrak{B}$ which is read "$\mathfrak{A}$ is properly contained in $\mathfrak{B}$" or "$\mathfrak{A}$ is a proper subset of $\mathfrak{B}$." The inclusion relation $\subseteq$

---

[*] The terms *sum* and *join* are used in some books in place of union and the terms *crosscut* and *meet* are often used for intersection.

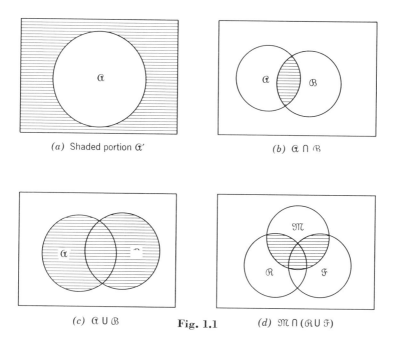

(*a*) Shaded portion $\mathcal{A}'$

(*b*) $\mathcal{A} \cap \mathcal{B}$

(*c*) $\mathcal{A} \cup \mathcal{B}$ **Fig. 1.1**   (*d*) $\mathfrak{M} \cap (\mathcal{R} \cup \mathcal{F})$

may also be written the other way. Thus $\mathcal{A} \supseteq \mathcal{B}$ means the same as $\mathcal{B} \subseteq \mathcal{A}$. Similarly, $\mathcal{A} \supset \mathcal{B}$ may be read "$\mathcal{A}$ properly contains $\mathcal{B}$." Since all the sets under discussion contain only elements of the universal set $\mathcal{U}$, we have for every such set $\mathcal{A}$, $\mathcal{A} \subseteq \mathcal{U}$. Moreover, the empty set $\emptyset$ is assumed to be contained in every set. We may therefore write $\emptyset \subseteq \mathcal{A} \subseteq \mathcal{U}$ for all $\mathcal{A}$. A chain of inclusions such as $\mathcal{A} \subseteq \mathcal{B} \subseteq \mathcal{C} \subseteq \mathcal{D} \subseteq \cdots$ means that $\mathcal{A}$ is a subset of $\mathcal{B}$, $\mathcal{B}$ a subset of $\mathcal{C}$, $\mathcal{C}$ a subset of $\mathcal{D}$, and so on. Any set appearing in such a chain relation is a subset of all those sets appearing after it in the chain. From the definitions of intersection and union, we have for any sets $\mathcal{A}$ and $\mathcal{B}$

$$\emptyset \subseteq (\mathcal{A} \cap \mathcal{B}) \subseteq \mathcal{A} \subseteq (\mathcal{A} \cup \mathcal{B}) \subseteq \mathcal{U}$$

and

$$\emptyset \subseteq (\mathcal{A} \cap \mathcal{B}) \subseteq \mathcal{B} \subseteq (\mathcal{A} \cup \mathcal{B}) \subset \mathcal{U}.$$

Example 1. *Let $\mathcal{U}$ be the set of all students at a certain university, let $\mathfrak{M}$ be the set of all male students, $\mathcal{W}$, all female students, $\mathcal{R}$, all students* *with red hair, and* $\mathfrak{F}$, *all students registered in the first year. Prove the following.*

(a) $\mathfrak{M} \cup \mathfrak{W} = \mathfrak{U}$ and $\mathfrak{M} \cap \mathfrak{W} = \emptyset$.

(b) $(\mathfrak{M} \cap \mathfrak{R}) \cap \mathfrak{F} = \mathfrak{M} \cap (\mathfrak{R} \cap \mathfrak{F})$.

(c) *If there are female first-year students,*

$$(\mathfrak{M} \cap \mathfrak{R}) \cup \mathfrak{F} \neq \mathfrak{M} \cap (\mathfrak{R} \cup \mathfrak{F}).$$

Solution. (a) Since all students are either male or female,

$$\mathfrak{M} \cup \mathfrak{W} = \mathfrak{U}.$$

Because none is both male and female, $\mathfrak{M} \cap \mathfrak{W} = \emptyset$.

(b) To belong to the set $(\mathfrak{M} \cap \mathfrak{R}) \cap \mathfrak{F}$ a student must be male *and* redhaired *and* registered in first year. Moreover the set contains only such students. The same conditions apply to membership in the set $\mathfrak{M} \cap (\mathfrak{R} \cap \mathfrak{F})$. The two sets are therefore equal and both may be unambiguously designated by $\mathfrak{M} \cap \mathfrak{R} \cap \mathfrak{F}$, that is, those students that belong to each of the three sets $\mathfrak{M}$, $\mathfrak{R}$, and $\mathfrak{F}$.

(c) All first-year students belong to $(\mathfrak{M} \cap \mathfrak{R}) \cup \mathfrak{F}$, whereas all members of $\mathfrak{M} \cap (\mathfrak{R} \cup \mathfrak{F})$ are in $\mathfrak{M}$ and therefore male. Hence if there are female first-year students, they belong to the first set but not to the second and the two sets are different.

Sets are sometimes designated by displaying their elements inside brackets of the form $\{\cdots\}$. Thus if $\mathfrak{U}$ is the set of natural numbers $1, 2, 3, \ldots$, the set consisting of the elements 2, 7, 10, 53 is written

$$\{2, 7, 10, 53\}.$$

Example 2. *Let* $\mathfrak{U}$ *be the set of the twenty six letters of the English alphabet,* $\mathfrak{A}$ *the set of vowels* $\{a, e, i, o, u, y\}$, $\mathfrak{B}$ *the set of consonants (including* y), *and* $\mathfrak{C}$ *the set of letters from a through m. Write down the sets* $\mathfrak{A} \cap \mathfrak{B}$, $\mathfrak{A} \cap \mathfrak{C}$, *and* $(\mathfrak{C} \cup \mathfrak{A}) \cap \mathfrak{C}'$.

Solution. Since only y belongs to both $\mathfrak{A}$ and $\mathfrak{B}$, $\mathfrak{A} \cap \mathfrak{B} = \{y\}$. Similarly, $\mathfrak{A} \cap \mathfrak{C} = \{a, e, i\}$, the set of vowels in $\mathfrak{C}$. Finally $\mathfrak{C} \cup \mathfrak{A}$ consists of the letters from a through m and the additional vowels o, u, y. Intersecting this with $\mathfrak{C}'$ (the letters from n through z), we get $(\mathfrak{C} \cup \mathfrak{A}) \cap \mathfrak{C}' = \{o, u, y\}$.

EXERCISE 1.1

1. Let 𝒰 be the set of natural numbers, namely,

$$1, 2, 3, 4, \ldots .$$

(a) If 𝒜 is the set of numbers greater than 6, and ℬ is the set of numbers less than 10, describe each of the sets 𝒜′, 𝒜 ∩ ℬ, 𝒜 ∩ ℬ′, 𝒜 ∪ ℬ, 𝒜′ ∩ ℬ′.

(b) If 𝒜 is the set of all multiples of 15, and ℬ is the set of all multiples of 12, describe the set 𝒜 ∩ ℬ.

2. If 𝔐, ℛ, 𝔉 are the sets described in Example 1, use Fig. 1.1d to verify that 𝔐 ∩ (ℛ ∪ 𝔉) = (𝔐 ∩ ℛ) ∪ (𝔐 ∩ 𝔉). Can you prove this result without a diagram by showing both 𝔐 ∩ (ℛ ∪ 𝔉) ⊆ (𝔐 ∩ 𝔉) ∪ (𝔐 ∩ 𝔉) and (𝔐 ∩ ℛ) ∪ (𝔐 ∩ 𝔉) ⊆ 𝔐 ∩ (ℛ ∪ 𝔉)?

3. In Fig. 1.2 let 𝒰 be the set of points inside the large rectangle, 𝒜 the set of points inside the circle, ℬ the points outside the triangle, and 𝒞 the points inside the square.

(a) Show that the shaded area represents the set (𝒜 ∩ ℬ) ∩ 𝒞.

(b) Shade vertically the area (𝒜′ ∩ ℬ′) ∩ 𝒞′.

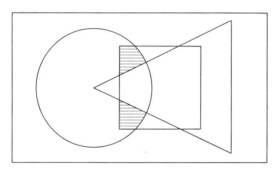

Fig. 1.2

4. In Fig. 1.3

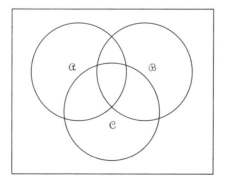

Fig. 1.3

(a) Shade horizontally the area representing the set $(\alpha \cap \mathcal{B}') \cap \mathcal{C}'$.

(b) Shade vertically the area representing the set $(\alpha \cap \mathcal{B}) \cup \mathcal{C}$.

(c) Shade diagonally that part of the set $\mathcal{B}$ that is not yet shaded and write a formula for it in terms of α, $\mathcal{B}$ and $\mathcal{C}$.

5. Write a formula for the set represented by each of the shaded areas in Fig. 1.4.

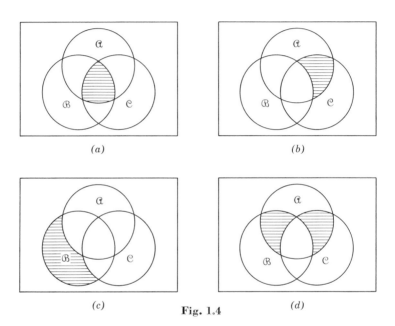

(a)   (b)

(c)   **Fig. 1.4**   (d)

6. Let $\mathfrak{U}$ be a set of individuals each one of which can be classified as (1) blonde or brunette, (2) male or female, and (3) married or single. Let α be the set of all blondes, $\mathcal{B}$ the set of all males, and $\mathcal{C}$ the set of all married individuals.

(a) Describe the set $\alpha \cap \mathcal{B}' \cap \mathcal{C}'$.

(b) Into how many distinct categories are the members of $\mathfrak{U}$ divided? List them all as intersections of three of the sets, α, $\mathcal{B}$, $\mathcal{C}$, α', $\mathcal{B}'$, $\mathcal{C}'$.

We now state the general laws of set algebra in the form of a theorem.

Theorem 1.1. *The three set operations* $\cup$, $\cap$, *and* ' *and the inclusion relation* $\subseteq$ *satisfy the following rules, where* α, $\mathcal{B}$, *and* $\mathcal{C}$ *are any three sets whose elements belong to the universal set* $\mathfrak{U}$.

(a) Commutative laws. $\alpha \cup \mathcal{B} = \mathcal{B} \cup \alpha,$
$\alpha \cap \mathcal{B} = \mathcal{B} \cap \alpha.$

(b) Associative laws. $(\alpha \cup \mathcal{B}) \cup \mathcal{C} = \alpha \cup (\mathcal{B} \cup \mathcal{C}),$
$(\alpha \cap \mathcal{B}) \cap \mathcal{C} = \alpha \cap (\mathcal{B} \cap \mathcal{C}).$

(c) Idempotent laws. $\alpha \cup \alpha = \alpha,$
$\alpha \cap \alpha = \alpha.$

(d) Universal set. $\alpha \cup \mathcal{U} = \mathcal{U},$
$\alpha \cap \mathcal{U} = \alpha.$

(e) Null set. $\alpha \cup \emptyset = \alpha,$
$\alpha \cap \emptyset = \emptyset.$

(f) Distributive laws.

1. $\alpha \cap (\mathcal{B} \cup \mathcal{C}) = (\alpha \cap \mathcal{B}) \cup (\alpha \cap \mathcal{C})$
2. $\alpha \cup (\mathcal{B} \cap \mathcal{C}) = (\alpha \cup \mathcal{B}) \cap (\alpha \cup \mathcal{C})$

(g) Rules for complements.

1. $(\alpha')' = \alpha, \quad \mathcal{U}' = \emptyset, \quad \emptyset' = \mathcal{U}.$
2. $\alpha \cap \alpha' = \emptyset, \quad \alpha \cup \alpha' = \mathcal{U}.$
3. $(\alpha \cup \mathcal{B})' = \alpha' \cap \mathcal{B}'.$
4. $(\alpha \cap \mathcal{B})' = \alpha' \cup \mathcal{B}'.$

(h) Rules for inclusion.

1. If $\alpha \subseteq \mathcal{B}$ and $\mathcal{B} \subseteq \alpha$, then $\alpha = \mathcal{B}$.
2. If $\alpha \subseteq \mathcal{B}$, then $\mathcal{B}' \subseteq \alpha'$.
3. If $\alpha \subseteq \mathcal{B}$ and $\mathcal{B} \subseteq \mathcal{C}$, then $\alpha \subseteq \mathcal{C}$ (transitive law).

Most of the items in Theorem 1.1 are obvious consequences of the definitions and the student should check these item by item with the aid of Venn diagrams if necessary. Exceptions are item (f) and (g)3 and (g)4, which are a little more difficult.

Proof of (f)1.

1. We first prove that $\alpha \cap (\mathcal{B} \cup \mathcal{C}) \subseteq (\alpha \cap \mathcal{B}) \cup (\alpha \cap \mathcal{C})$. Suppose x is any element of $\alpha \cap (\mathcal{B} \cup \mathcal{C})$. Then

$$x \in \alpha$$

and either

$$x \in \mathcal{B} \quad \text{or} \quad x \in \mathcal{C}.$$

Hence either

$$x \in \mathcal{A} \quad \text{and} \quad x \in \mathcal{B}, \quad \text{or} \quad x \in \mathcal{A} \quad \text{and} \quad x \in \mathcal{C}.$$

This is equivalent to

$$x \in \mathcal{A} \cap \mathcal{B} \quad \text{or} \quad x \in \mathcal{A} \cap \mathcal{C}.$$

Hence

$$x \in (\mathcal{A} \cap \mathcal{B}) \cup (\mathcal{A} \cap \mathcal{C})$$

and therefore

$$\mathcal{A} \cap (\mathcal{B} \cup \mathcal{C}) \subseteq (\mathcal{A} \cap \mathcal{B}) \cup (\mathcal{A} \cap \mathcal{C}).$$

2. We next prove that $(\mathcal{A} \cap \mathcal{B}) \cup (\mathcal{A} \cap \mathcal{C}) \subseteq \mathcal{A} \cap (\mathcal{B} \cup \mathcal{C})$. Suppose y is any element of $(\mathcal{A} \cap \mathcal{B}) \cup (\mathcal{A} \cap \mathcal{C})$. Then either

$$y \in \mathcal{A} \quad \text{and} \quad y \in \mathcal{B}, \quad \text{or} \quad y \in \mathcal{A} \quad \text{and} \quad y \in \mathcal{C}.$$

Thus in all cases $y \in \mathcal{A}$ and $y \in$ either $\mathcal{B}$ or $\mathcal{C}$. Hence $y \in \mathcal{A}$ and $y \in \mathcal{B} \cup \mathcal{C}$. Therefore

$$y \in \mathcal{A} \cap (\mathcal{B} \cup \mathcal{C}) \quad \text{and} \quad (\mathcal{A} \cap \mathcal{B}) \cup (\mathcal{A} \cap \mathcal{C}) \subseteq \mathcal{A} \cap (\mathcal{B} \cup \mathcal{C}).$$

From the two inclusions proved it follows that

$$\mathcal{A} \cap (\mathcal{B} \cup \mathcal{C}) = (\mathcal{A} \cap \mathcal{B}) \cup (\mathcal{A} \cap \mathcal{C})$$

and $(f)1$ is proved.

The student should make no attempt to memorize the different items in Theorem 1.1, but he should notice a few of the more interesting patterns that these items display. (Mathematics consists of finding and creating such patterns.) First he should notice that if the union $\mathcal{A} \cup \mathcal{B}$ is written if necessary $\mathcal{A} + \mathcal{B}$ and if the intersection $\mathcal{A} \cap \mathcal{B}$ is written $\mathcal{A}\mathcal{B}$ (this notation is actually used in some of the older textbooks), then rules (a) and (b) and $(f)1$ become the same basic rules that are obeyed by addition and multiplication of ordinary numbers, namely,

$$\mathcal{A} + \mathcal{B} = \mathcal{B} + \mathcal{A}, \qquad\qquad \mathcal{A}\mathcal{B} = \mathcal{B}\mathcal{A}.$$

$$(\mathcal{A} + \mathcal{B}) + \mathcal{C} = \mathcal{A} + (\mathcal{B} + \mathcal{C}), \qquad (\mathcal{A}\mathcal{B})\mathcal{C} = \mathcal{A}(\mathcal{B}\mathcal{C}).$$

$$\mathcal{A}(\mathcal{B} + \mathcal{C}) = \mathcal{A}\mathcal{B} + \mathcal{A}\mathcal{C}.$$

Moreover, the null set plays the role of 0 and the universal set that of 1:

$$\mathcal{A} + \emptyset = \mathcal{A}, \qquad \mathcal{A}\emptyset = \emptyset, \qquad \mathcal{A}\mathcal{U} = \mathcal{A}.$$

In addition to these similarities, the differences between the algebra of sets and the algebra of numbers should be noted:

$$\alpha + \alpha = \alpha, \quad \alpha\alpha = \alpha, \quad \alpha + \mathfrak{U} = \mathfrak{U}, \quad \text{and finally, from } (f)2$$
$$\alpha + \mathfrak{B}\mathfrak{C} = (\alpha + \mathfrak{B})(\alpha + \mathfrak{C}).$$

These relations definitely do not hold in general for numbers.

The second pattern that should be noted is the symmetry between the operations $\cup$ and $\cap$ that is displayed throughout. From any relationship between sets α, $\mathfrak{B}$, . . . another true relationship can be derived by performing the following three changes:

1. Replacing each set α, $\mathfrak{B}$, . . . by its complement α', $\mathfrak{B}'$, ...
2. Replacing $\cup$ by $\cap$ and $\cap$ by $\cup$.
3. Replacing $\subseteq$ by $\supseteq$ and $\supseteq$ by $\subseteq$.

This statement is called the principle of duality and a relationship obtained in this way from another is called its *dual*. For example, the dual of $(g)3$

$$(\alpha \cup \mathfrak{B})' = \alpha' \cap \mathfrak{B}'$$

is
$$(\alpha' \cap \mathfrak{B}')' = \alpha'' \cup \mathfrak{B}'' = \alpha \cup \mathfrak{B},$$

which is clearly equivalent to $(g)4$ since the sets α and $\mathfrak{B}$ are arbitrary and so also therefore are α' and $\mathfrak{B}'$.

Although the algebra of sets is quite interesting in its own right and has interesting applications to such diverse fields as the study of logic and of electrical switching circuits, we cannot take time to develop it further. The main purpose in introducing the basic set operations here is to enable us to make use of these ideas and notations in what follows. There is one further operation on sets that is fundamental in analytic geometry: the formation of the Cartesian product of two sets. Let α and $\mathfrak{B}$ be any two sets. We construct the set consisting of all ordered pairs (a, b) where $a \in \alpha$ and $b \in \mathfrak{B}$ and $(a, b) = (c, d)$ if and only if $a = c$ and $b = d$. This set is denoted by $\alpha \times \mathfrak{B}$ and is called the Cartesian product of α and $\mathfrak{B}$. Two things should be noted concerning the Cartesian product. First, the elements of $\alpha \times \mathfrak{B}$ are not elements of the same universal set to which the elements of α and $\mathfrak{B}$ belong. Second, since the elements of $\alpha \times \mathfrak{B}$ are the *ordered* pairs (a, b), the Cartesian product $\mathfrak{B} \times \alpha$ is not the same set as $\alpha \times \mathfrak{B}$.

A *one-to-one correspondence* between the elements of a set $\mathcal{A}$ and those of a set $\mathcal{B}$ is a correspondence or mapping of the elements of $\mathcal{A}$ onto the elements of $\mathcal{B}$ such that

1. to every element of $\mathcal{A}$ there corresponds exactly one element of $\mathcal{B}$;
2. every element of $\mathcal{B}$ is the corresponding element (image) of exactly one element of $\mathcal{A}$.

For example, there is a one-to-one correspondence between the set of people in a room and the set of chairs in the room if there is one chair for every person and if for each chair there is exactly one person. For two sets that contain only a finite number of elements it is clear that a one-to-one correspondence between them exists if and only if each set contains the same number of elements. In the case of infinite sets, however, it is possible (in fact it always happens) that a set can be put into one-to-one correspondence with a proper subset of itself. For example, to each natural number n there corresponds a number (namely, n^2) in the set of all perfect squares. Conversely to each perfect square there corresponds one natural number whose square it is. Thus the mapping $n \leftrightarrow n^2$ sets up a one-to-one correspondence between the set $\{1, 2, 3, 4, \ldots\}$ of all natural numbers and the set $\{1, 4, 9, 16, \ldots\}$ of all perfect squares. The second set is clearly a proper subset of the first. Two sets that can be put into one-to-one correspondence with each other are said to have the same *cardinal number*.

EXERCISE 1.2

1. Convince yourself of the truth of each item in Theorem 1.1 either by drawing Venn diagrams or by arguing from the definitions of the set operations as in the above proof of $(f)1$.
2. Prove the following, where $\mathcal{A}, \mathcal{B}, \mathcal{C}, \ldots$ are any subsets of $\mathcal{U}$.

   (a) $(\mathcal{A} \cap \mathcal{B}) \cup (\mathcal{A} \cap \mathcal{B}') = \mathcal{A}$.
   (b) $\mathcal{A} \cup (\mathcal{B} \cap \mathcal{A}') = \mathcal{A} \cup \mathcal{B}$.
   (c) $\mathcal{A} \cup (\mathcal{B} \cap \mathcal{C}) \cup (\mathcal{A}' \cap \mathcal{B}) = \mathcal{A} \cup \mathcal{B}$.
3. If $\mathcal{A}$ and $\mathcal{B}$ are sets, $\mathcal{A} - \mathcal{B}$ is defined to be the set of all elements of $\mathcal{A}$ that are not in $\mathcal{B}$. Prove that

   (a) $(\mathcal{A} - \mathcal{B}) - \mathcal{C} = \mathcal{A} - (\mathcal{B} \cup \mathcal{C})$.
   (b) $(\mathcal{A} - \mathcal{B}) \cup (\mathcal{A} - \mathcal{C}) = \mathcal{A} - (\mathcal{B} \cap \mathcal{C})$.

1.2   The real numbers

It will be necessary from time to time to use the words integer, rational number, irrational number, and real number. It is therefore important that the reader understand the meaning of these terms. The *integers* are the whole numbers 1, 2, 3, 4, . . . together with their negatives and zero. The set of all integers will be denoted by $\mathcal{I}$ and hence

$$\mathcal{I} = \{0, \pm 1, \pm 2, \pm 3, \ . \ . \ .\}.$$

A *rational* number is any number that can be expressed as a quotient a/b of two integers a and b, it being understood that the denominator b is not zero. Since we may have $b = 1$, it follows that all the integers are rational numbers. In fact, $\mathcal{I} \subset \mathcal{F}$ where $\mathcal{F}$ is the set of all rational numbers. In addition to the integers, the rational numbers include all the positive and negative fractions and therefore all numbers that can be expressed as finite or repeating decimals, with a plus or minus sign attached. For purposes of practical or physical measurement the rational numbers are sufficient. But for ideal or theoretical measurement they are not sufficient. For example, if the side of a square is 1 unit, the diagonal of the square has length $\sqrt{2}$ in terms of the same unit, and it has been known since ancient times that there is no rational number whose square is 2.* For most mathematical purposes it is necessary to enlarge the rational number system to include all such *irrational numbers* as $\sqrt{2}$, $\sqrt{15}$, $\sqrt[3]{7}$, and many others that cannot be expressed as radicals at all. There are several different ways of doing this so that the resulting set of *real numbers* is adequate for all "ideal measurements." The one that is to some extent familiar to most people is to identify each real number with a positive or negative infinite decimal and conversely. It is necessary to identify a terminating decimal such as 2.76 with the infinite decimal $2.75\dot{9}$, but if this is done the correspondence becomes one-to-one. Whatever method is used, a completely satisfactory definition of the real numbers in terms of the rational numbers, and a derivation of their properties, is quite a long process which will not be undertaken here. For further discussion of this topic see [2], Chapter 7 or [4], Chapter 2.

---

* The proof of this fact is quite simple. See, for example [1] ,p. 18 or [2], p. 224. (Numbers in square brackets refer to references listed at the back of the book.)

If $\mathfrak{R}$ is the set of all real numbers, we note that $\mathscr{I} \subset \mathfrak{F} \subset \mathfrak{R}$. We also record the fact, although we shall have no occasion to use it, that whereas a one-to-one correspondence can be set up between the elements of $\mathscr{I}$ and those of $\mathfrak{F}$, such a correspondence does not exist between the elements of $\mathfrak{F}$ and $\mathfrak{R}$. That is, $\mathscr{I}$ and $\mathfrak{F}$ have the same cardinal number but $\mathscr{I}$ and $\mathfrak{R}$ do not. For the very interesting and simple proof of these statements see [4], p. 81.

It is convenient to associate with every real number x a positive real number denoted by $|x|$ and called the *absolute value* of x. If x is positive $|x|$ is defined to be equal to x, whereas if x is negative $|x| = -x$, which is then positive. Thus, for example, $|5| = |-5| = 5$. We complete the definition by defining $|0|$ to be 0.

Theorem 1.2. *If x and y are any two real numbers, then*

(a) $|xy| = |x| \, |y|$ *and*
(b) $|x + y| \le |x| + |y|$.

The truth of (a) is obvious. In (b), if x and y have the same sign or if either x or y is 0, then it is clear that $|x + y| = |x| + |y|$. If x and y differ in sign, then $|x + y|$ is clearly less than the greater of $|x|$ and $|y|$ and hence $|x + y| < |x| + |y|$.

A subset $\mathfrak{K}$ of the real numbers is called a *field* if it satisfies the eleven laws in the following list. The set $\mathfrak{R}$ of all real numbers and the set $\mathfrak{F}$ of all rational numbers are examples of fields, since the laws listed are all satisfied if $\mathfrak{K} = \mathfrak{R}$ or if $\mathfrak{K} = \mathfrak{F}$.

LAWS FOR ADDITION.

A1. *If a and b belong to $\mathfrak{K}$, their sum $a + b$ belongs to $\mathfrak{K}$. This is also expressed by saying that $\mathfrak{K}$ is closed under addition.*

A2. *Commutative law. $a + b = b + a$.*

A3. *Associative law. $(a + b) + c = a + (b + c)$.*

A4. *Zero element. There is an element 0 in $\mathfrak{K}$ such that if $a \in \mathfrak{K}$, $a + 0 = a$.*

A5. *If $a \in \mathfrak{K}$, there is a uniquely determined element $-a$ in $\mathfrak{K}$, called the negative of a, such that $a + (-a) = 0$.*

LAWS FOR MULTIPLICATION

M1. *If a, b belong to $\mathfrak{K}$, their product ab belongs to $\mathfrak{K}$, or $\mathfrak{K}$ is closed under multiplication.*

M2. *Commutative law.* $ab = ba$.

M3. *Associative law.* $(ab)c = a(bc)$.

M4. *Unit element.* There is an element 1 in $\mathfrak{K}$ such that $1a = a$ for every element a in $\mathfrak{K}$.

M5. If $a \neq 0$, there is a unique element a^{-1} (or $1/a$) such that $aa^{-1} = 1$.

DISTRIBUTIVE LAW

D1. If a, b, c belong to $\mathfrak{K}$ then $a(b + c) = ab + ac$.

Actually, any set $\mathfrak{K}$ for whose elements operations of addition and multiplication are defined and satisfy the eleven laws above is called a field. That is to say in general the elements of a field *need* not be real numbers. We shall see, for example, in Chapter 10, that the set of all complex numbers is a field. In this book however we are primarily interested in the field $\mathfrak{R}$ of all real numbers.

The eleven laws above are called the *field axioms* or *postulates*. It is possible to prove (see Exercise 1.3) by using only these eleven postulates that for any elements a, b in any field $\mathfrak{K}$, $a0 = 0$, $(-a)(-b) = ab$, $a(-b) = -ab$ and that if $ab = 0$ either $a = 0$ or $b = 0$. These are of course familiar facts for real numbers. Moreover A5 enables us to define subtraction by $a - b = a + (-b)$ and similarly M5 takes care of division if we define a/b to be ab^{-1}.

There is also an order relation $a < b$ or a *is less than* b defined on the real numbers. For convenience we also define the relation $b > a$ (b is greater than a) to mean the same as $a < b$. The order relation satisfies the following laws, called the *postulates of order*.

O1. *For any two real numbers a and b one and only one of the three relations $a < b$, $a = b$ and $a > b$ holds.*

O2. If $a < b$ and $b < c$, then $a < c$.

O3. If $a < b$ and x is any real number, $a + x < b + x$.

O4. If $a < b$ and $x > 0$, then $ax < bx$.

These are the basic rules for operating with inequalities. The student should note especially rule O4. If $a < 7$ it follows that $3a < 21$. That is, each side of an inequality can be multiplied by any *positive* number. If each side is multiplied by a negative number, the direction of the inequality must be reversed. For example, $-3a > -21$ since $3a < 21$ (see Exercise 1.3, Problem 9).

The notation $a \leq b$ is read "a is less than or equal to b." For example the inequality $x \leq 2$ is satisfied by $x = 2$ and also by all real numbers less than 2, whereas $x < 2$ is not satisfied by $x = 2$. Note that the inequality $x^2 \leq 4$ is equivalent to the two inequalities $-2 \leq x \leq 2$ which is read "-2 is less than or equal to x and x is less than or equal to 2." Similarly, $a \geq b$ is read "a is greater than or equal to b."

Example. *Find all values of x for which*

$$|2x - 5| < 3.$$

Solution. If $|2x - 5| < 3$, then

$$-3 < 2x - 5 < 3.$$

By O3 we get, adding 5 to each member,

$$2 < 2x < 8$$

and by O4, multiplying by $\frac{1}{2}$,

$$1 < x < 4.$$

Hence the values of x that satisfy the given inequality are all values of x between 1 and 4.

EXERCISE 1.3

1. Below is a proof that if a is any element of a field $\mathfrak{K}$, then $a0 = 0$. Check that each step follows from the field postulates quoted.

   Proof. For any element b of $\mathfrak{K}$

	$b + 0 = b$	by A4
Hence	$a(b + 0) = ab$	by M1
and	$ab + a0 = ab$	by D1
	$-(ab) + (ab + a0) = -(ab) + ab$	by A1
	$[-(ab) + ab] + a0 = -(ab) + ab$	by A3
	$0 + a0 = 0$	by A2 and A5
whence	$a0 = 0$	by A2 and A4

2. Check each step in the following proof that $a(-b) = -(ab)$ and supply a reason for each step, as was done in Problem 1.

Proof. $\qquad b + (-b) = 0,$

therefore $\qquad a[b + (-b)] = a0 = 0,$

therefore $\qquad ab + a(-b) = 0,$

and $\qquad a(-b) = -(ab).$

3. Prove that if a, b are any elements of a field

$$(-a)(-b) = ab.$$

4. Prove that if a and b are elements of a field and $ab = 0$, then either $a = 0$ or $b = 0$.

5. Prove that if a, b, c are elements of a field and $a \neq 0$, then $ab = ac$ implies $b = c$.

6. Find all values of x that satisfy each of the following inequalities:

(a) $2x > 10,$ $\qquad\qquad$ (e) $x^2 - 4 < 0,$

(b) $|2x| > 10,$ $\qquad\qquad$ (f) $|x^2 - 4| \le 2,$

(c) $|x - 5| < 2,$ $\qquad\qquad$ (g) $(x - 1)(x - 2) \ge 0,$

(d) $|3x - 1| < 4,$ $\qquad\qquad$ (h) $x(3x - 5) < 0.$

7. Prove that for all real values of x:

(a) $x^2 + 2 \ge 2,$ (b) $4 - x^2 \le 4,$ (c) $x^2 + 6x + 12 \ge 3.$

Hint: For every real number x, $x^2 \ge 0$.

8. Prove that for all real values of x and y

$$x^2 + 2xy + 5y^2 \ge 0.$$

9. Using the postulates of order, prove that if $a < b$ and $x < 0$ then $ax > bx$.

10. Find all values of x that satisfy the following:

(a) $0 < 2x - 3 < 5,$ $\qquad\qquad$ (c) $|x - 7| < |x - 5|,$

(b) $0 < |2x - 3| < 5,$ $\qquad\qquad$ (d) $|x - 7| = 2|x - 10|.$

CHAPTER 2

| COORDINATES, FUNCTIONS,
| AND GRAPHS

2.1 Coordinates on a line

Let l be any straight line. We set up a one-to-one correspondence between the points of l and the real numbers by the following device. Choose an arbitrary point O on the line l to correspond to the number 0. Now choose another point E, different from O, to correspond to the number 1. The point O will be called the *origin* and the point E the *unit point*. The point O divides the line l into two *rays* or half-lines. The ray containing the unit point E will be called the positive ray, the other one the negative ray. To any point P on the positive ray we now assign the real number x which measures the distance OP in terms of the unit OE. To any point Q on the negative ray we assign the negative of the real number that measures the length of OQ in terms of the unit OE (see Fig. 2.1). In each case the real number assigned to a point is called the *coordinate* of that point. Thus the coordinate of O is 0, the coordinate of E is 1. The coordinate of any point other than O on the positive ray is a positive real number, on the negative ray, a negative real number.

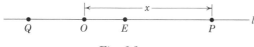

Fig. 2.1

If P_1 and P_2 are points on l with coordinates x_1 and x_2, the length of the segment P_1P_2 is equal to $|x_2 - x_1|$. This always holds, whether x_1 and x_2 are positive, negative, or zero and whether they have like or opposite signs. The student should verify this statement for particular values of x_1, x_2.

The existence of the above one-to-one correspondence between the real numbers and the points of a line is the basic postulate of analytic geometry. We state it formally thus:

Basic Postulate. *There exists a one-to-one correspondence $x \leftrightarrow P_x$ between the real numbers x and the points P_x of the line l such that*

(a) $x < y$ *if and only if P_x is to the left of P_y*
(b) *the length of the segment P_xP_y is $|x - y|$.*

2.2   Coordinates in a plane

Let l_1 and l_2 be any two lines in a plane that intersect in the point O. Choose the origin O and unit points P_1 on l_1 and Q_1 on l_2 and set up coordinates on each line as in the previous section. Now let P be any point in the plane. Through P (see Fig. 2.2) draw a line parallel to l_2 to

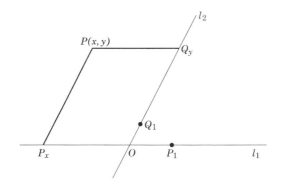

Fig. 2.2

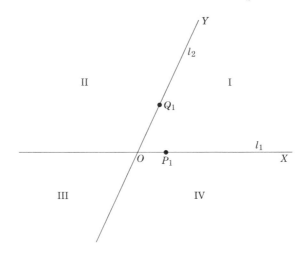

Fig. 2.3

cut l_1 in P_x with coordinate x and a line parallel to l_1 to cut l_2 in the point Q_y with coordinate y. The point P is then uniquely determined by the ordered pair of real numbers (x, y), and these are called *Cartesian coordinates* of P relative to the coordinate axes l_1 and l_2 and the unit points P_1 and Q_1. For most purposes the coordinate axes l_1 and l_2 are chosen at right angles to each other, and the corresponding coordinates are called *rectangular Cartesian coordinates*. In this case, if l_1 is horizontal, the unit point P_1 is usually chosen to the right of the origin and the unit point Q_1 above the origin. For many purposes equal units must be chosen on the two axes so that $OP_1 = OQ_1$, but this is not always assumed. Coordinates on l_1 are designated by x and for this reason l_1 will be called the x-axis. Similarly, coordinates on l_2 are designated by y and l_2 is called the y-axis. It is common usage to refer to x as the *abscissa* and to y as the *ordinate* of the point $P(x, y)$. The unit points P_1 and Q_1 will normally be chosen so that the positive ray on l_1 can be rotated into the positive ray on l_2 by a *counterclockwise* rotation through an angle less than 180°. In the case of rectangular coordinates this angle would be 90°. The coordinate axes divide the plane into four regions or *quadrants*. These are numbered and are referred to as the first, second, third, and fourth quadrants in accordance with the diagram in Fig. 2.3.

2.3 Coordinates in space

Let l_1, l_2, and l_3 be any three lines that intersect in a common point O and do not lie in one plane. Choose unit points P_1 on l_1, Q_1 on l_2, and R_1 on l_3 and set up coordinates on each line with origin O as in Section 2.1. Now let P be any point in space. A plane through P parallel to the plane of l_2 and l_3 will cut l_1 in a point P_x with coordinate x (see Fig. 2.4). Similarly, the plane through P parallel to the plane of l_1 and l_3 will cut l_2 in a point Q_y with coordinate y and a plane through P parallel to the plane of l_1 and l_2 will cut l_3 in R_z with coordinate z. The three numbers (x, y, z) are uniquely determined by P and are called the coordinates of P relative to the axes l_1, l_2, and l_3 and the unit points P_1, Q_1, and R_1. If each of the axes is perpendicular to the other two, these are called *rectangular coordinates*. The unit points on l_1, l_2, and l_3 will be chosen so that to an observer on the positive ray of l_3 the sense of rotation, through an angle less than 180°, of the positive ray on l_1 into the positive ray of l_2 is counterclockwise. Such a system of coordinate axes is called a *right-hand system*, for if l_3 is grasped in the right hand with thumb pointing in the direction of the positive ray, the fingers will then point from the positive ray on l_1 to the positive ray of l_2. The lines l_1, l_2, and l_3 are called the x-axis, the

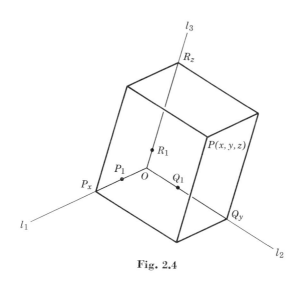

Fig. 2.4

y-axis, and the z-axis respectively. The plane containing the x-axis and the y-axis is called the xy-plane. Similarly, we speak of the yz-plane and the xz-plane. Collectively these are called the three *coordinate planes*, and their three lines of intersection l_1, l_2, and l_3 are the *coordinate axes*.

We call the set of all points in the plane $\mathcal{E}_2$ and the set of all points in space $\mathcal{E}_3$. If $\mathcal{R}$ is the set of all real numbers, then the Cartesian product $\mathcal{R} \times \mathcal{R}$ is the set of all pairs (x, y) in which $x \in \mathcal{R}$ and $y \in \mathcal{R}$. The introduction of coordinates therefore sets up a one-to-one correspondence between the sets $\mathcal{E}_2$ and $\mathcal{R} \times \mathcal{R}$. In practice we shall not distinguish between these two sets but shall identify a point of $\mathcal{E}_2$ with its coordinate symbol (x, y) once the coordinate system has been chosen. Similarly, $\mathcal{E}_3$ will be identified with the Cartesian product $\mathcal{R} \times \mathcal{R} \times \mathcal{R}$. Thus we shall talk about the point (x, y) or the point (x, y, z) rather than the point whose coordinates are (x, y) or (x, y, z).

EXERCISE 2.1

In all the following problems assume rectangular coordinate axes.

1. Draw coordinate axes and locate the following points:

    (*a*) $(0, -6)$, $(0, 0)$, $(0, 1)$, $(0, 7)$.
    (*b*) $(-4, 0)$, $(2, 0)$, $(3.5, 0)$, $(15, 0)$.
    (*c*) $(4, -2)$, $(4, 0)$, $(4, 1)$, $(4, 5)$.
    (*d*) $(-1, -3)$, $(-1, 1)$, $(-1, 3)$, $(-1, 7)$.
    (*e*) $(-3, -3)$, $(-1, -1)$, $(0, 0)$, $(2, 2)$, $(5.3, 5.3)$.

2. Each part of Problem 1 should suggest a general principle to you. State this principle in each case. For example, (*c*) suggests: for all values of y the point $(4, y)$ lies on a line parallel to and 4 units to the right of the y-axis.

3. The *projection* of a point onto a line is the foot of the perpendicular from the point to the line. Find the coordinates of the projection of the point $P(x, y)$:

    (*a*) onto the x-axis,
    (*b*) onto the y-axis.

4. The *projection* of a line segment AB onto a line l is the segment joining the projections of the end points A and B onto l. Find the length of the projections onto the coordinate axes of the line segments joining:

    (*a*) $A(2, 11)$ and $B(8, 6)$,
    (*b*) $A(0, 3)$ and $B(0, -2)$,
    (*c*) $A(-6, -1)$ and $B(5, 18)$.

Draw a figure in each case, showing the projections.

5. Find a formula for the length of the projections onto:

   (a) the x-axis and (b) the y-axis, of the line segment AB joining $A(x_1, y_1)$ and $B(x_2\ y_2)$.

6. Show that the projection of AB onto the x-axis is equal to its projection onto any line parallel to the x-axis.

7. Given the points $A(-7, 2)$ and $B(3, -4)$ find the length of the projection of AB:

   (a) onto the line through $(-2, 6)$ and $(-2, 7)$,
   (b) onto the line through $(0, 8)$ and $(7, 8)$,
   (c) onto the line through $(4, 1.5)$ and $(9, 1.5)$.

8. Assuming rectangular coordinates in space what can be said about the position of the following points:

   (a) $(0, 0, 0)$,   (b) $(x, 0, 0)$,   (c) $(0, 0, z)$,   (d) $(x, 0, z)$,   (e) $(x, y, 0)$,
   (f) $(0, y, 0)$,   (g) $(c, c, 0)$.

9. What common geometric property have the points in each of the following sets?

   (a) $(1, 2, 9)$, $(1, 3, -2)$, $(1, 4, 3)$, $(1, 5, -3)$.
   (b) $(3, 5, -1)$ $(3, 9, -1)$ $(3, -14, -1)$.
   (c) $(0, 1, 2)$, $(0, 3, -4)$, $(0, 2, 5)$.
   (d) $(3, 4, -1)$, $(3, 4, 3)$, $(3, 4, 7.5)$.
   (e) $(x, y, 9)$ for all real values of x and y.
   (f) $(2, y, -3)$ for all real values of y.

10. Prove that if a line is parallel to the xy-plane all points on it have the same z-coordinate.

11. The projection of a point onto a plane is the foot of the perpendicular from the point to the plane. Find the coordinates of the projections:

    (a) of $(2, -1, 4)$ onto the xy-plane, the yz-plane, the xz-plane,
    (b) of $(2, -1, 4)$ onto the planes through $(5, 9, -3)$ parallel to the xy-plane, the yz-plane, the xz-plane.

    Draw figures in each case.

12. Find the projections of $A(4, 5, 8)$ onto each of the coordinate planes and onto each of the coordinate axes. *Hint:* the perpendicular from A to the x-axis is parallel to the yz-plane and hence every point on it has the same x-coordinate.

13. Find the projections of (x, y, z) on each coordinate plane and on each coordinate axis. Draw a figure showing all these projections.

14. Given $A(2, -1, 6)$ and $B(4, 5, -1)$ find the length of the projections of AB onto each coordinate axis.

15. Given $A(x_1, y_1, z_1)$ and $B(x_2, y_2, z_2)$ prove that the lengths of the projections of AB on the x-, y-, and z-axes are $|x_1 - x_2|$, $|y_1 - y_2|$ and $|z_1 - z_2|$.

16. Let x_1 and x_2 be the coordinates on a line of points P_1 and P_2. Prove that the midpoint P of the segment P_1P_2 has coordinate $(x_1 + x_2)/2$.

17. Find the midpoints of the segments joining the following pairs of points:

(a) $(3, 0)$ and $(13, 0)$,   (e) $(0, -2)$ and $(0, 8)$,
(b) $(-7, 0)$ and $(4, 0)$,   (f) $(0, y_1)$ and $(0, y_2)$.
(c) $(-5, 0)$ and $(5, 0)$,   (g) $(x_1, 0)$ and $(x_2, 0)$.
(d) $(-2, 0)$ and $(-18, 0)$,

18. Prove that if A_1 and B_1 are the projections of the points A and B on a line l, then the midpoint of the segment A_1B_1 is the projection of the midpoint of AB.

19. Use the results of Problems 17f, 17g, and 18 to prove that the midpoint of the segment joining (x_1, y_1) and (x_2, y_2) is the point with coordinates

$$[(x_2 + x_2)/2, \ (y_1 + y_2)/2)].$$

20. Prove that if A_p and B_p are the projections of points A and B onto a plane p, then the midpoint of the segment A_pB_p is the projection of the midpoint of AB.

21. Use the results of Problems 18, 19, and 20 to find the coordinates of the midpoint of the segment joining the points (x_1, y_1, z_1) and (x_2, y_2, z_2).

22. Find the midpoints of the segments joining each of the following pairs of points:

(a) $(2, -1)$ and $(4, 9)$ (c) $(7, -8, 4)$ and $(2, 1, 0)$,
(b) $(-5, 2)$ and $(4, 1)$,   (d) $(-7, 4, 3)$ and $(7, 1, 5)$.

23. A quadrilateral is a parallelogram if and only if its diagonals bisect each other. Prove that the four points $(1, -2)$, $(5, 6)$, $(7, 4)$, and $(3, -4)$ are the vertices of a parallelogram.

24. If A and B have coordinates (a_1, a_2) and (b_1, b_2), find the fourth vertex of the parallelogram of which OA and OB are adjacent sides.

25. Prove that $(1, 4, -6)$, $(2, 8, 1)$, $(4, 3, -1)$, and $(5, 7, 6)$ are the vertices of a parallelogram. *Hint:* Show that the midpoints of the diagonals coincide.

26. If A and B have coordinates (x_1, y_1, z_1) and (x_2, y_2, z_2), find the coordinates of the fourth vertex of the parallelogram of which OA and OB are adjacent sides.

27. Given the points $A(2, -4)$, $B(7, 2)$, find C so that B is the midpoint of AC.

28. Given the points $A(3, -1, 6)$ and $B(5, 4, 2)$, if AB is produced its own length to C find the coordinates of C.

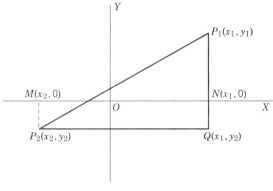

Fig. 2.5

2.4 The distance formula

Let l be a line on which coordinates have been assigned as in Section 2.1. Let P_1 and P_2 be points on l whose coordinates are x_1 and x_2. It has already been pointed out that the length of P_1P_2 or the distance d between P_1 and P_2, in terms of the coordinate unit, is $|x_1 - x_2|$. Another way of writing this is

$$(1) \qquad d = \sqrt{(x_1 - x_2)^2},$$

where the square root sign indicates as usual the positive square root. We introduce the form (1) because it readily generalizes to two and three dimensions. To show this, suppose that rectangular Cartesian coordinates have been chosen in a plane with equal units on the two coordinate axes.

Let $P_1(x_1, y_1)$ and $P_2(x_2, y_2)$ be any two points in the plane. Through P_1 draw a line parallel to the y-axis and through P_2 draw a line parallel to the x-axis. Let these intersect in the point Q as shown in Fig. 2.5. The coordinates of Q are then (x_1, y_2) since it has the same abscissa as P_1 and the same ordinate as P_2. It is now clear that

$$P_2Q = |x_1 - x_2| = \sqrt{(x_1 - x_2)^2}$$

since $P_2Q = MN$, where M and N are the projections of P_2 and P_1 onto the x-axis. Similarly,

$$QP_1 = |y_1 - y_2| = \sqrt{(y_1 - y_2)^2}.$$

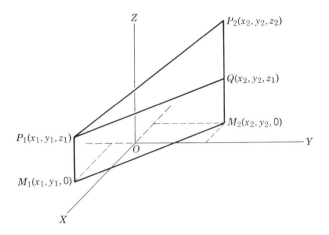

Fig. 2.6

Since by the Pythagorean theorem $P_1P_2{}^2 = P_2Q^2 + QP_1{}^2$, the distance d between P_1 and P_2 is given by

$$(2) \qquad d = \sqrt{(x_1 - x_2)^2 + (y_1 - y_2)^2}.$$

Now let $P_1(x_1, y_1, z_1)$ and $P_2(x_2, y_2, z_2)$ be any two points in space and suppose these coordinates have reference to a rectangular Cartesian system with equal units of length on the three coordinate axes. Through P_1 and P_2 draw lines perpendicular to the xy-plane to meet that plane in M_1 and M_2. The coordinates of M_1 and M_2 are then $(x_1, y_1, 0)$ and $(x_2, y_2, 0)$. From P_1 draw a line perpendicular to M_2P_2 to meet M_2P_2 in Q (see Fig. 2.6). The coordinates of Q are then (x_2, y_2, z_1). Now $M_1M_2QP_1$ is a rectangle and by equation (2)

$$P_1Q = M_1M_2 = \sqrt{(x_1 - x_2)^2 + (y_1 - y_2)^2}.$$

Moreover, P_2Q is parallel to the z-axis and therefore

$$QP_2 = |z_1 - z_2|.$$

Hence if $d = P_1P_2$

$$d^2 = P_1P_2{}^2 = P_1Q^2 + QP_2{}^2 = (x_1 - x_2)^2 + (y_1 - y_2)^2 + (z_1 - z_2)^2$$

or

$$(3) \qquad d = \sqrt{(x_1 - x_2)^2 + (y_1 - y_2)^2 + (z_1 - z_2)^2}.$$

Equations (1), (2), and (3) give the distance between two points in terms of their coordinates in one, two, and three dimensions respectively. These three distance formulas fall into an obvious pattern; thus they may all be viewed as special cases of one general formula. The reader with a good mathematical imagination might well argue as follows: if a point on a line can be represented (in a suitable coordinate system) by a single real number (x), a point in a plane by an ordered pair of real numbers (x, y) and a point in space by an ordered triple of real numbers (x, y, z), then a point in "four-dimensional space" should be represented by four real numbers (x, y, z, w) and a point in "n-dimensional space" by an ordered n-tuple of real numbers of the form

(4) $$(x_1, x_2, \ldots, x_n).$$

If $n > 3$, such a "point" and the "n-dimensional space" in which it lies may have no physical existence but this does not detract from the mathematical significance of such ideas. Actually, the concept of an n-dimensional space consisting of "points" of the form (4) is a very useful one that not only leads to a great deal of interesting mathematics but also to many applications in a variety of fields.

By analogy with equations (1), (2), and (3) it seems reasonable to *define* the distance d between the "points" $P(x_1, x_2, \ldots, x_n)$ and $Q(y_1, y_2, \ldots, y_n)$ by the formula

(5) $$d = \sqrt{(x_1 - y_1)^2 + (x_2 - y_2)^2 + \cdots + (x_n - y_n)^2}.$$

This definition of distance does indeed prove useful. We shall make no immediate use of the concept of a space of dimension greater than three but we shall return to these ideas from time to time, for example, in Chapters 7 and 9. In the meantime, even if values of n greater than 3 are excluded, equation (5) includes all three of the distance formulas (1), (2), and (3). These special formulas are obtained by putting $n = 1$, $n = 2$, and $n = 3$ in the general formula (5).

We draw attention to one important fact. The derivation of the distance formula in $\mathcal{E}_2$ or in $\mathcal{E}_3$ depends on two assumptions: (1) that the coordinates are rectangular and (2) that the same unit of length is used on each of the coordinate axes. Hence whenever the distance formula is used these two assumptions are tacitly made, whether or not they are stated explicitly.

EXERCISE 2.2

1. Find the distance between each of the following pairs of points:

   (a) (2, 5) and (7, 3),   (d) (4, 0) and (0, −2),
   (b) (0, 0) and (4, −6),   (e) (a, b) and (2, 1).
   (c) (−7, 5) and (−2, −4),

2. Show that the three points $(1, 1 + 2\sqrt{3})$, $(2 + \sqrt{3}, 2 + \sqrt{3})$, and $(\sqrt{3}, \sqrt{3})$ are vertices of an equilateral triangle.

3. Show that the four points (4, −2), (10, 8), (−6, 5), and (0, 15) are vertices of a parallelogram.

4. Show that the three points (−2, 2), (5, 1), and (4, −6) lie on a circle with center at (1, −2). What is the radius of this circle?

5. Prove that, if the point (x, y) lies on a circle with center at (3, −2) and radius 4 units, then
$$x^2 + y^2 - 6x + 4y = 3.$$

6. If the point (x, y) is equidistant from the points (3, 7) and (4, −5), prove that $2x - 24y + 17 = 0$.

7. Find the coordinates of a point on the x-axis that is equidistant from (3, −2) and (−7, 4).

8. Find a point on the y-axis that is equidistant from (9, −11) and (5, −15).

9. Find the coordinates of the center of the circle that passes through the three points $A(-1, 1)$, $B(6, 0)$ and $C(5, 1)$. What is the radius of this circle? *Hint:* the center is equidistant from A and B and also from B and C.

10. Find the distance between the following pairs of points:

    (a) $A(2, -1, 4)$, $B(-3, 5, 2)$,
    (b) $A(0, 1, 5)$, $B(2, -2, 4)$,
    (c) $A(\frac{1}{2}, -3, \frac{2}{3})$, $B(2, \frac{1}{2}, 2)$,
    (d) $A(0, 0, 0)$, $B(7, 4, 4)$,
    (e) $A(a, 0, a)$, $B(0, a, 0)$.

11. Given that the four points $A(-1, 2, 7)$, $B(3, 1, 5)$, $C(2, -4, 6)$, and $D(6, -5, 4)$ lie in one plane, show that they are the vertices of a parallelogram.

12. Show that the four points $A(1, 0, 2\sqrt{2})$, $B(0, \sqrt{3}, 0)$, $C(0, -\sqrt{3}, 0)$, and $D(3, 0, 0)$ are vertices of a regular tetrahedron.

13. Prove that if the point $P(x, y, z)$ is 5 units from the point (1, 0, −6), then
$$x^2 + y^2 + z^2 - 2x + 12z + 12 = 0.$$

14. Prove that if $P(x, y, z)$ is equidistant from the two points $A(1, -3, 4)$ and $B(5, 9, 2)$, then
$$2x + 6y - z = 21.$$

15. Find the coordinates of a point on the x-axis that is equidistant from the points $A(2, 1, -5)$ and $B(-1, 7, 3)$. Is there more than one such point?

16. Find the coordinates of a point on the xy-plane that is equidistant from the points $A(3, -1, 4)$ and $B(5, 2, -1)$. Is there more than one such point?

17. Find a point on the x-axis that is distant $2\sqrt{3}$ from the point $(1, -2, 2)$. How many such points are there?

18. Find a point in the xy-plane that is five units distant from the point $(0, 0, 4)$. How many such points are there and where are they located? Illustrate by drawing a figure.

19. If four points do not lie in one plane, is it possible to find a point that is equidistant from each of the four points? Try this for the four points $(0, -5, 3)$, $(4, -6, 2)$, $(4, -5, 5)$, and $(0, -9, 5)$.

2.5   Functions and graphs

A set $\mathcal{A}$ is said to be *mapped into* a set $\mathcal{B}$ if to every element x of $\mathcal{A}$ there is designated a uniquely determined element of $\mathcal{B}$ called the image of x. If every element of $\mathcal{B}$ is the image of some element of $\mathcal{A}$, we say that $\mathcal{A}$ is mapped *onto* $\mathcal{B}$. We give the following three examples:

(a) Let $\mathcal{A}$ be the set of all students in a certain class and $\mathcal{B}$ the set of integers from 0 to 100. An examination assigns a mark out of 100 to each student and hence sets up a mapping of $\mathcal{A}$ into $\mathcal{B}$. Note that two or more elements of $\mathcal{A}$ can well be mapped on the same element of $\mathcal{B}$ (i.e., several students may get the same mark) but that each element of $\mathcal{A}$ has a unique image in $\mathcal{B}$. This is not a mapping of $\mathcal{A}$ *onto* $\mathcal{B}$ unless there are at least 101 students in the class and *every* possible mark from 0 to 100 is achieved by at least one student.

(b) The formula $y = x^2 + 1$ assigns to each real number x a real number y such that $y \geq 1$ (since $x^2 \geq 0$). Hence if $\mathcal{R}$ is the set of all real numbers, the formula defines a mapping of $\mathcal{R}$ into $\mathcal{R}$ or of $\mathcal{R}$ onto the set $\mathcal{D}$ of all real numbers ≥ 1. The student should check the statement that *every* element of $\mathcal{D}$ is the image of at least one element of $\mathcal{R}$.

(c) Let $\mathcal{S}$ be the set of all points of $\mathcal{E}_3$ and $\mathcal{T}$ the set of all points in the xy-plane. The mapping

$$(x, y, z) \rightarrow (x, y, 0)$$

that maps every point of $\mathcal{E}_3$ onto its projection in the xy-plane is a mapping of $\mathcal{S}$ onto $\mathcal{T}$.

Definition. *If $\mathcal{Q}$ and $\mathcal{B}$ are any sets, a mapping of any non-null subset $\mathcal{D}$ of $\mathcal{Q}$ into $\mathcal{B}$ is called a* function *from $\mathcal{Q}$ to $\mathcal{B}$.*

A function is usually denoted by the letter f although any other letter may be used. If $x \in \mathcal{D}$, the image of x in $\mathcal{B}$ under f is denoted by $f(x)$ and is called the *value* of f at x. The notation $f(x)$ is read "f of x." In our first example, x could represent any student who wrote the examination and $f(x)$ would represent his mark out of 100. In the second example x could represent any real number and $f(x)$ would be the real number $x^2 + 1$. In the third example if P were any point in $\mathcal{E}_3$, $f(P)$ would be the projection of P in the xy-plane. The set $\mathcal{D}$ of all elements of $\mathcal{Q}$ mapped by f into $\mathcal{B}$ is called the *domain* of f. The set consisting of all elements of $\mathcal{B}$ that are images under f is called the *range* of f. *Any function, therefore, maps its domain onto its range.*

Example 1. *If for every real number x we define $f(x)$ as $1/(1 + x^2)$, then f is a function whose domain is the set $\mathcal{R}$ of all real numbers and whose range is the set $\mathcal{S}$ of all real numbers y such that $0 < y \leq 1$. For since $x^2 \geq 0$ it follows that $0 < 1/(1 + x^2) \leq 1$ for all x.*

The student should prove that every number y for which $0 < y \leq 1$ is the image of a suitable x under the function f.

Example 2. *If $f(x) = 1/(x - 2)$, then every real number x, with the single exception $x = 2$, is mapped by f onto a real number $y = 1/(x - 2)$. From this we deduce $x = (2y + 1)/y$ and hence y may take any real value different from 0. The domain of f may therefore be taken to be the set of all real numbers different from 2 and the range of f is the set of all non-zero real numbers.*

When a function f from $\mathcal{R}$ to $\mathcal{R}$ is defined by a formula, there may be ambiguity about the domain of f unless it is explicitly specified. If the domain is not so specified, it is assumed to be the largest set of real numbers that can serve as the domain. For example if $f(x) = \sqrt{1 - x^2}$ the domain of f, unless otherwise specified, would be taken to be the set of real numbers x for which $-1 \leq x \leq 1$. Similarly, in Example 2 the domain is taken as the set of all real numbers except $x = 2$.

Example 3. *Let P be any point (x, y, z) in space and let f be the function*

*that maps P onto its projection on the xy-plane. Then f(P) is the point
(x, y, 0). The domain of f is the set of all points in space and the range is
the set of all points in the xy-plane.*

Example 4. *Let P be any point (x, y) in the Cartesian plane $\mathcal{E}_2$ and let
$f(P) = x^2 + y^2$. Then f is a function from the set of points in the plane
to the real numbers. Its domain is the set of all points (x, y) and its range
is the set of all non-negative real numbers.*

Let $\mathfrak{R}$ be the set of real numbers and let f be a function from $\mathfrak{R}$ to $\mathfrak{R}$.
If x is a real number in the domain $\mathfrak{D}$ of f, $f(x)$ is also a real number, and
$(x, f(x))$ are the coordinates of a point in the Cartesian plane. This set of
points $(x, f(x))$ where $x \in \mathfrak{D}$ is called the *graph* of the function f.

Example 5. *Let f be the function defined by $f(x) = 2$ for all real numbers
x. The graph of f is the set of points (x, 2), that is, all points on the line
parallel to the x-axis and two units above it.*

If $f(x)$ has the same value for every x in the domain of f, then f is
called a *constant* function.

Example 6. *Let f be the function that maps every real number x on itself
so that $f(x) = x$ for all x. Its graph is the set of points (x, x), that is, the
line through the first and third quadrants making a 45° angle with the
x-axis.*

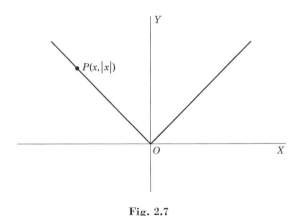

Fig. 2.7

Example 7. *Let f be the function that maps each real number x on its
absolute value $|x|$. The graph of f consists of the set of points $(x, |x|)$, that
is, the two 45° rays bisecting the first and second quadrants (see Fig. 2.7).*

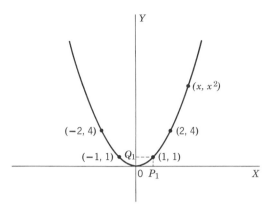

Fig. 2.8

Example 8. *The graph of the function with domain $\Re$ defined by $f(x) = x^2$ is the set of points (x, x^2), that is, the curve shown in Fig. 2.8. Sample points on it are $(0, 0)$, $(\frac{1}{2}, \frac{1}{4})$, $(1, 1)$, $(2, 4)$, $(10, 100)$, $(-1, 1)$, $(-2, 4)$.*

Let f be any function from $\Re \times \Re$ to $\Re$. The domain of f is a subset $\mathcal{D}$ of $\Re \times \Re$ and may be considered either as a set of ordered pairs (x, y) of real numbers or as a set of points in $\mathcal{E}_2$. The function f maps each point (x, y) in $\mathcal{D}$ onto a real number which will be denoted by $f(x, y)$. Such a function is called a function of two real variables x and y, since x and y may be assigned values from $\Re$ independently except for the restriction that $(x, y) \in \mathcal{D}$. An example of such a function is the one defined by $f(x, y) = x^2 + y^2$ which was discussed in Example 4. Here f associates with each point (x, y) in $\mathcal{E}_2$ the square of its distance from the origin. Again, let x and y represent the latitude and longitude of a point on the Earth's surface and let $f(x, y)$ be the height above sea level of the point (x, y). What is the domain of this function? What is its range? Are there any points at which the function is not properly defined?

The graph of a function f of two real variables is the set of points (x, y, z) in $\mathcal{E}_3$ for which $z = f(x, y)$, that is, the set of all points

$$(x, y, f(x, y)).$$

Similarly, a function F may map the points of $\mathcal{E}_3$ into the real numbers. The image of the point (x, y, z) would then be denoted by

$F(x, y, z)$ and F would be called a function of three real variables. Such a function has no graph in three-dimensional space.

The notation here introduced for the value of a function is very flexible. If, for example, f is a function from the real numbers to the real numbers, the value of f at $x = 2$, -7, or 0 is denoted by $f(2)$, $f(-7)$, or $f(0)$ respectively. Thus if

$$f(x) = x + \frac{1}{2x - 1}$$

$f(0) = -1$ and $f(6) = 6 + 1/11 = 67/11$. Similarly, if $F(x, y) = xy + 2$, then $F(0, 0) = 2$ and $F(2, -3) = -4$.

If f and g are two functions from $\Re$ to $\Re$ and $x \in \Re$, then $g(x) \in \Re$. If the real number $g(x)$ is in the domain of f, then $f[g(x)] \in \Re$. Thus if the *range of g is contained in the domain of f* we can construct a new function $f \circ g$ defined by

$$(f \circ g)(x) = f[g(x)],$$

which is called the composite function of f and g.

Example 9. *If $g(x) = 2x + 1$ and $f(x) = x^2 - 1$ and the domains of g and f are both assumed to be $\Re$, then*

$$f[g(x)] = (2x + 1)^2 - 1 = 4x^2 + 4x.$$

On the other hand

$$g[f(x)] = 2(x^2 - 1) + 1 = 2x^2 - 1.$$

Note that domain $f \circ g =$ domain g and that the image of x under $f \circ g$ is found by applying first g to get the image $g(x)$ and then applying f to this image (assumed to be in domain f) to get the image $f[g(x)]$ of x under $f \circ g$.

EXERCISE 2.3

Each of the functions defined in Problems 1 through 10 is a function from the real numbers to the real numbers. In each case specify the largest set that will serve as domain, give the range, and sketch the graph of the function.

1. $f(x) = x$.
2. $f(x) = x + 1$.
3. $f(x) = x - 1$.
4. $f(x) = -x$.

5. $f(x)$ equals the greatest integer less than or equal to x.

6. $f(x) = \sqrt{4 - x^2}$. *Hint:* Let $y = \sqrt{4 - x^2}$, square, and use the distance formula.

7. $f(x) = -2$ for $x < -2$
   $f(x) = x$ \quad for $-2 \le x \le 2$ $\Bigg\}$.
   $f(x) = 2$ \quad for $x > 2$

   (This is a single function whose domain is the set of *all* real numbers.)

8. $f(x) = 1/x$.

9. $f(x) = 1/(x - 5)$.

10. $f(x) = x + 1/x$.

11. If $f(x) = (x^2 - 6)/x$, find $f(-1)$ and $f(10)$.

12. If $f(x, y) = (x^2 + y^2)/xy$ find $f(2, 2)$, $f(3, 3)$, $f(c, c)$. Is $f(0, 0)$ defined? Find $f(1, 3)$, $f(2, 6)$, $f(c, 2c)$.

13. If $f(x, y, z) = \dfrac{x^2 + y^2 + z^2 - 1}{x + y + z}$, find $f(0, 0, 1)$ and $f(-1, -1, 3)$. What is the domain of f.

14. If $f(x) = 1 - 1/(1 - x)$, find $f(1/x)$. Show that $f[f(x)] = x$.

2.6   Relations and graphs

The concept of the graph of a function can be extended to cover more general situations. Let (x, y) be the coordinates of a point P in $\mathcal{E}_2$. If x and y are unrestricted (that is, both x and y may represent any real number and neither one is restricted by the value assigned to the other), then P may represent any point in the plane. If, however, x and y are restricted by requiring them to satisfy some condition, the point P will be restricted to some subset of points in $\mathcal{E}_2$.

Definition. *Any condition on x and y that restricts the point (x, y) to lie in some proper subset of $\mathcal{E}_2$ is called a relation in x and y.*

A relation in x and y will be denoted by the notation $R(x, y)$. The letter R will be used to denote an arbitrary relation just as f is used to represent any function or x to denote any real number. The set of points (x, y) that satisfy the relation $R(x, y)$ is often represented by the notation

$$\{(x, y) \in \mathcal{E}_2 \,|\, R(x, y)\},$$

which is read "the set of all points (x, y) in $\mathcal{E}_2$ such that x and y satisfy the relation R." This set of points is called the *graph* of the relation $R(x, y)$. One of the commonest types of relation is an equation in x and y.

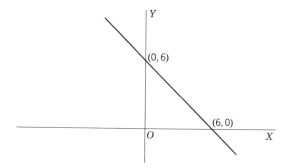

Fig. 2.9. $\{(x, y) \in \mathcal{E}_2 \mid x + y = 6\}$.

Definition. *The graph of an equation in x and y is the set of all points (x, y) in $\mathcal{E}_2$ whose coordinates satisfy the given equation.*

Example 1. *The graph of the equation $x + y = 6$ consists of all points (x, y) in $\mathcal{E}_2$ such that $x + y = 6$. In the notation described above it is the set*

$$\{(x, y) \in \mathcal{E}_2 \mid x + y = 6\}.$$

Sample points of this set are $(3, 3)$, $(2, 4)$, $(\frac{3}{2}, \frac{9}{2})$, $(1, -7)$, $(5, 1)$.

It should not be too difficult for the student to convince himself that all points of this set lie on the line shown in Fig. 2.9.

Example 2. *Discuss the graph of the relation $x^2 + y^2 = 4$.*

Solution. Since $\sqrt{x^2 + y^2}$ is the distance from the point (x, y) to the origin, the set

$$\{(x, y) \in \mathcal{E}_2 \mid x^2 + y^2 = 4\}$$

consists of all points in $\mathcal{E}_2$ that are 2 units from the origin. The graph of the equation $x^2 + y^2 = 4$ is therefore the circle with radius 2 and center at the origin. Similarly, if we require that $x^2 + y^2 < 4$ it is clear that the point (x, y) must be inside this circle and the graph of $x^2 + y^2 < 4$ is the interior of the circle $x^2 + y^2 = 4$ described above.

Example 3. *What is the graph of the relation $x + 2 = 0$?*

Solution. The relation $x + 2 = 0$ restricts the point (x, y) to lie 2 units to the left of the y-axis. Its graph $\{(x, y) \in \mathcal{E}_2 \mid x + 2 = 0\}$ is therefore the straight line parallel to the y-axis and 2 units to the left of it.

Example 4. *If f is any function from $\mathfrak{R}$ to $\mathfrak{R}$ with domain $\mathfrak{D}$, then $y = f(x)$ is a relation in x and y whose graph*

$$\{(x, y) \in \mathcal{E}_2 \,|\, y = f(\mathrm{x})\}$$

is precisely the set of points $(x, f(x))$, $x \in \mathfrak{D}$, and is therefore identical with the graph of the function f.

Example 5. *The graph of the relation $-1 \leq y \leq 3$ is the set of all points in the shaded region of the plane shown in Fig. 2.10.*

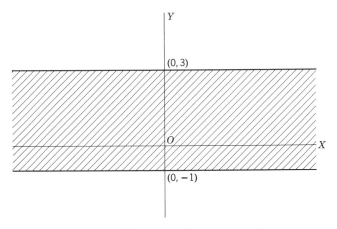

Fig. 2.10. $\{(x, y) \in \mathcal{E}_2 \,|\, -1 \leq y \leq 3\}$.

Theorem 2.1. *Let R_1 and R_2 be two relations in x and y and let $\mathcal{S}_1 = \{(x, y) \in \mathcal{E}_2 \,|\, R_1\}$ and $\mathcal{S}_2 = \{(x, y) \in \mathcal{E}_2 \,|\, R_2\}$. Then*

$$\{(x, y) \in \mathcal{E}_2 \,|\, R_1 \text{ and } R_2\} = \mathcal{S}_1 \cap \mathcal{S}_2$$

and

$$\{(x, y) \in \mathcal{E}_2 \,|\, R_1 \text{ or } R_2\} = \mathcal{S}_1 \cup \mathcal{S}_2.$$

The truth of this theorem is obvious once the notation and the statement of the theorem are understood. For if x and y satisfy both R_1 and R_2, then (x, y) belongs to $\mathcal{S}_1 \cap \mathcal{S}_2$. Similarly, if x and y satisfy either R_1 or R_2, then (x, y) belongs to $\mathcal{S}_1 \cup \mathcal{S}_2$. The converse statements are also true.

Example 6. *Find the points common to the graphs of* $x^2 + y^2 = 25$ *and* $x = 4$.

Solution. We seek the points common to $\{(x, y) \in \mathcal{E}_2 \,|\, x^2 + y^2 = 25\}$ and $\{(x, y) \in \mathcal{E}_2 \,|\, x = 4\}$ that is, the points (x, y) whose coordinates satisfy *both* the relations $x^2 + y^2 = 25$ and $x = 4$. Since for such points $x = 4$ and $x^2 + y^2 = 25$, we get $y^2 = 9$ or $y = \pm 3$. The points common to the two graphs are therefore $(4, 3)$ and $(4, -3)$.

Example 7. *Find the points equidistant from* $(6, -3)$ *and* $(-2, 1)$ *that are also 5 units from the origin.*

Solution. Suppose (x, y) is such a point. Since it is equidistant from $(6, -3)$ and $(-2, 1)$, we have

(7) $$(x - 6)^2 + (y + 3)^2 = (x + 2)^2 + (y - 1)^2$$

or $x^2 - 12x + 36 + y^2 + 6y + 9 = x^2 + 4x + 4 + y^2 - 2y + 1,$

whence $$16x - 8y = 40$$

or

(8) $$2x - y = 5.$$

Similarly, (8) implies (7) and hence the set of points equidistant from $(6, -3)$ and $(-2, 1)$ is

$$\{(x, y) \in \mathcal{E}_2 \,|\, 2x - y = 5\}.$$

Since (x, y) is to be 5 units from the origin, we have also

(9) $$x^2 + y^2 = 25.$$

Solving (8) and (9) simultaneously we get

$$x^2 + 4x^2 - 20x + 25 = 25,$$

$$x = 0 \quad \text{or} \quad 4,$$

$$y = -5 \quad \text{or} \quad 3.$$

The intersection of the two graphs consists therefore of the two points $(0, -5)$ and $(4, 3)$. Figure 2.11 shows the two graphs and the points of intersection.

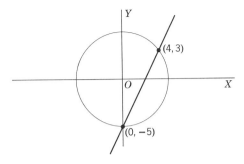

Fig. 2.11

Example 8. *Sketch the graph of the relation*

$$x^2 + y^2 \leq 4 \quad \text{and} \quad y < x.$$

Solution. As in Example 2 the set

$$\{(x, y) \in \mathcal{E}_2 \,|\, x^2 + y^2 \leq 4\}$$

is the interior and circumference of a circle with center at the origin and radius 2. The set $\{(x, y) \in \mathcal{E}_2 \,|\, y < x\}$ is the set of points below the line bisecting the angle between the positive rays of the coordinate axes. The required graph is the intersection of these two sets and is sketched in Fig. 2.12. Note that the points on the boundary line AB

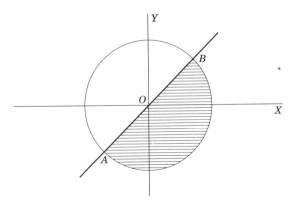

Fig. 2.12. $\{(x, y) \in \mathcal{E}_2 \,|\, x^2 + y^2 \leq 4, \, y < x\}$.

do not belong to this set but that the points on the semicircular boundary do.

Example 9. *Sketch the graph of* $x^2 - y^2 = 0$.

Solution. This relation may be written $(x - y)(x + y) = 0$, and since x and y are real numbers this is (Exercise 1.3, Problem 4) equivalent to the relation $x = y$ or $x = -y$. We have seen that the graph of $x = y$ is the 45° line bisecting the first and third quadrants. Similarly, $x = -y$ is the 45° line bisecting the second and fourth quadrants. The graph of $x^2 - y^2 = 0$ therefore (by Theorem 2.1) consists of both these lines, and is shown in Fig. 2.13.

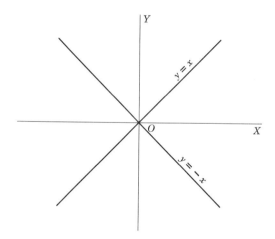

Fig. 2.13. $\{(x, y) \in \mathcal{E}_2 \mid x^2 - y^2 = 0\}$.

If we denote by $\mathcal{E}_3$ the set of all points $P(x, y, z)$ in three-dimensional space, a relation in x, y, z is any condition that restricts the point (x, y, z) to lie in some proper subset of $\mathcal{E}_3$. For example,

$$\{(x, y, z) \in \mathcal{E}_3 \mid z = 0\}$$

is the set of all points in the xy-plane. The set

$$\{(x, y, z) \in \mathcal{E}_3 \mid x = 0, y = 0\}$$

is the set of all points on the z-axis. The set

$$\{(x, y, z) \in \mathcal{E}_3 \mid x^2 + y^2 + z^2 = 1\}$$

is the set of all points one unit distant from the origin and hence on a sphere of radius 1 with center at the origin. In general, the set of points

$$\{(x, y, z) \in \mathcal{E}_3 \,|\, R(x, y, z)\}$$

is called the *graph* of the relation $R(x, y, z)$. The obvious analogue of Theorem 2.1 holds for graphs in three-dimensional space just as it does in the plane.

EXERCISE 2.4

1. Describe and sketch the graphs in $\mathcal{E}_2$ of the following relations. Assume rectangular coordinates with equal units on the axes.

   (a) $y \geq x$,
   (b) $y^2 \geq x^2$,
   (c) $|x - 3| \leq 1$,
   (d) $x^2 + y^2 = 16$,
   (e) $(x - 4)^2 + (y + 3)^2 = 4$,

   (f) $-1 < x < 1$,
   (g) $|x| < 2$ and $|y| < 4$,
   (h) $|x - 2| < 1$ and $|y - 4| < 3$,
   (i) $x^2 + y^2 < 9$ and $y > 2$.

2. Describe and sketch each of the following pairs of graphs:

   (a) $\{(x, y) \in \mathcal{E}_2 \,|\, x = 0\}$, $\{(x, y, z) \in \mathcal{E}_3 \,|\, x = 0\}$.
   (b) $\{(x, y) \in \mathcal{E}_2 \,|\, x^2 + y^2 = 1\}$, $\{(x, y, z) \in \mathcal{E}_3 \,|\, x^2 + y^2 = 1\}$.

   Hint: Because $(x, y, 0)$ is the projection of (x, y, z) onto the xy-plane, the second graph in (b) consists of all points whose projections onto the xy-plane lie on a circle with radius 1 and center at the origin.

3. Reread Problem 14, Exercise 2.2, and describe and sketch the graph $\{(x, y, z) \in \mathcal{E}_3 \,|\, 2x + 6y - z = 21\}$.

4. Describe and sketch

   (a) $\{(x, y, z) \in \mathcal{E}_3 \,|\, x^2 + y^2 + z^2 = 25$ and $z = 4\}$.
   (b) $\{(x, y, z) \in \mathcal{E}_3 \,|\, x^2 + y^2 + z^2 = 25$ and $x^2 + y^2 = 9\}$.

5. Describe and sketch

   (a) $\{(x, y) \in \mathcal{E}_2 \,|\, (x - 1)^2 + (y + 2)^2 = 0\}$.
   (b) $\{(x, y, z) \in \mathcal{E}_3 \,|\, (x - 1)^2 + (y + 2)^2 = 0\}$.

6. Describe the sets $\{(x, y) \in \mathcal{E}_2 \,|\, x^2 + y^2 + 1 = 0\}$
   and $\{(x, y, z) \in \mathcal{E}_3 \,|\, x^2 + y^2 + z^2 + 1 = 0\}$.

7. Describe, and where possible sketch, the graphs in $\mathcal{E}_3$ of each of the relations in Problem 1.

8. Show that the graph of the equation

$$(x - 2)^2 + (y + 1)^2 + (z - 6)^2 = 36$$

is a sphere with center at $(2, -1, 6)$ and radius 6.

9. Write an equation of a sphere with center at (a, b, c) and radius r.

10. What is the graph of the equation $x^2 - 4x + y^2 + z^2 = 0$? *Hint:* Add 4 to each side of the equation.

11. A set $\mathcal{S}$ of points in $\mathcal{E}_2$ is *symmetric with respect to a line l* if for every point P in $\mathcal{S}$, P' is also in $\mathcal{S}$ where P' is the mirror image of P in l. More precisely if (see Fig. 2.14) l' is the line through P perpendicular to l and if M is the

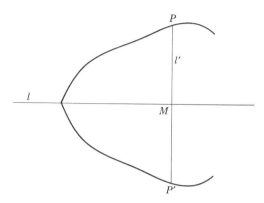

Fig. 2.14

point of intersection of l and l', then P' is the point on l', on the side of l opposite to P, such that $MP = MP'$. Show that a set $\mathcal{S}$ is symmetric with respect to

(a) the x-axis if $(x, y) \in \mathcal{S}$ implies $(x, -y) \in \mathcal{S}$,
(b) the y-axis if $(x, y) \in \mathcal{S}$ implies $(-x, y) \in \mathcal{S}$,
(c) the line $y = x$ if $(x, y) \in \mathcal{S}$ implies $(y, x) \in \mathcal{S}$.

12. Discuss symmetry properties of the graphs in $\mathcal{E}_2$ of the following equations:

(a) $x^2 + 4y^2 = 6$,
(b) $x + y = 6$,
(c) $y = |x|$,

(d) $3x^2 - 2xy + 3y^2 = 10$,
(e) $|x| + |y| = 1$,
(f) $|x - 6| = 4$.

13. A set $\mathcal{S}$ in $\mathcal{E}_3$ is symmetric with respect to a plane p if the mirror image P' (treating p as the mirror) of every point P of $\mathcal{S}$ is also in $\mathcal{S}$. Give criteria for symmetry of $\mathcal{S}$ with respect to the coordinate planes similar to those of Problem 11.

14. Discuss symmetry properties of the graphs in $\mathcal{E}_3$ of the following relations:

(a) $x^2 + 5y^2 + 2z^2 = 10$,
(b) $x + y - 4z = 0$,
(c) $y^2 = 2x$,
(d) $z = x^2 + y^2$,

(e) $|x| < 2$,
(f) $-2 < z \leq 2$,
(g) $|x| + |y| + |z| = 1$.

15. A set $\mathcal{S}$ in $\mathcal{E}_2$ or $\mathcal{E}_3$ is symmetric with respect to a point M if whenever $P \in \mathcal{S}$, then $P' \in \mathcal{S}$ where P' is the point on the line l through P and M such that M is the midpoint of the segment PP'. Show that a set $\mathcal{S}$ in $\mathcal{E}_2$ is symmetric with respect to the origin if $(x, y) \in \mathcal{S}$ implies $(-x, -y) \in \mathcal{S}$. Give a criterion for symmetry with respect to the origin in $\mathcal{E}_3$.

16. Show that the graph in $\mathcal{E}_2$ of the equation $xy = 6$ is symmetric with respect to the origin but not with respect to either coordinate axis.

17. Prove that the graph of the equation $y = x^2 - 4x + 5$ is symmetric about the line parallel to the y-axis and 2 units to the right of it.

18. Prove that symmetry of a set in $\mathcal{E}_2$ with respect to both coordinate axes implies symmetry with respect to the origin.

19. Give a definition of symmetry with respect to a line of a set $\mathcal{S}$ in $\mathcal{E}_3$, and find criteria for symmetry in $\mathcal{E}_3$ with respect to each of the coordinate axes.

| STRAIGHT LINES AND CIRCLES IN THE PLANE

3.1 Slope of a line

Choose rectangular coordinate axes in $\mathcal{E}_2$ and let l be any straight line that is not parallel to the y-axis. Choose two points $A(x_1, y_1)$ and $P(x, y)$ on l and assume $x > x_1$. It is easy to prove that the ratio

$$\frac{y - y_1}{x - x_1}$$

is independent of the particular choice of the points P_1 and P on l. We look first at the right-hand diagram of Fig. 3.1, which illustrates the case in which $y > y_1$, and note that if AQ and QP are drawn parallel to the coordinate axes, then

$$\frac{y - y_1}{x - x_1} = \frac{QP}{AQ}.$$

Now if $A'(x_1', y_1')$ and $P'(x', y')$ are any other points on l and $A'Q'$, $Q'P'$ are drawn parallel to the axes as shown, we have if $x' > x_1'$,

$$\frac{y' - y_1'}{x' - x_1'} = \frac{Q'P'}{A'Q'}.$$

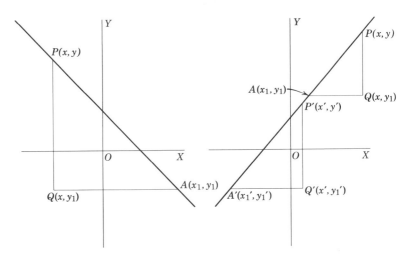

Fig. 3.1

But the triangles AQP and $A'Q'P'$ are clearly similar, and hence

$$\frac{y' - y'_1}{x' - x'_1} = \frac{Q'P'}{A'Q'} = \frac{QP}{AQ} = \frac{y - y_1}{x - x_1}.$$

If $x' < x'_1$, then both $x' - x'_1$ and $y' - y'_1$ are negative and their ratio therefore is unchanged. This completes the proof if $y > y_1$.

The case $y < y_1$ is illustrated in the left-hand diagram of Fig. 3.1. Here the ratio $(y - y_1)/(x - x_1)$ is always negative but its absolute value is independent of the choice of the points P and P_1 for the same reasons as in the preceding case. Finally, if $y_1 = y$ the line l is parallel to the x-axis and the ratio $(y - y_1)/(x - x_1)$ is 0 for all choices of P and P_1. The invariance of this ratio justifies the following.

Definition. *If l is any line not parallel to the y-axis and (x, y) and (x_1, y_1) are any two distinct points on l, the number*

(1)
$$\frac{y - y_1}{x - x_1}$$

is called the slope of the line l.

The slope of the line joining the points $(0, 0)$ and $(1, m)$ is therefore $(m - 0)/(1 - 0) = m$. Hence every real number m is the slope of some line and m is a measure of the steepness of ascent or descent on the line.

If (x, y) and (x_1, y_1) are on l and $x > x_1$, the slope of l is positive if $y > y_1$, negative if $y < y_1$, and 0 if $y = y_1$. Thus if the slope of l is positive, l is directed uphill to the right (Fig. 3.1, right). If its slope is negative, l is directed downhill to the right (Fig. 3.1, left). If its slope is 0, l is parallel to the x-axis.

If l is parallel to the y-axis, its slope is not defined because any two points on it then have the same abscissa and the ratio (1) is not defined.

Theorem 3.1. *Two lines have the same slope if and only if they are parallel to each other but not to the y-axis.*

Proof. Suppose l_1 and l_2 are parallel to each other but not to the y-axis. If we make the constructions indicated in Fig. 3.2, it is clear that the triangles AQB and CRD are similar since corresponding sides are parallel. Hence

$$\frac{y_2 - y_1}{x_2 - x_1} = \frac{QB}{AQ} = \frac{RD}{CR} = \frac{y_2' - y_1'}{x_2' - x_1'}$$

and l_1 and l_2 have equal slopes. The same proof applies when the slope is negative.

Conversely, if l_1 and l_2 have the same slope m, they are not parallel to the y-axis. If they intersect in the point $P(x, y)$, choose points

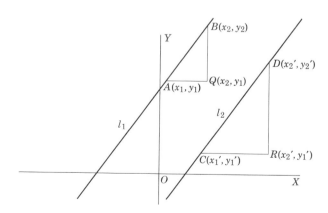

Fig. 3.2

$P_1(x_1, y_1)$ and $P_2(x_1, y_2)$ on l_1 and l_2 respectively, having the same abscissa $x_1 \neq x$. Then $y_1 \neq y_2$ and

$$\frac{y_1 - y}{x_1 - x} \neq \frac{y_2 - y}{x_1 - x}.$$

This contradicts the fact that l_1 and l_2 have the same slope. Hence the two lines do not intersect and must be parallel.

Example 1. *Find the slope of the line joining* $(2, 7)$ *and* $(5, -1)$.

Solution. The slope is $(-1 - 7)/(5 - 2)$ or $-\frac{8}{3}$. Note that the order in which the points are named is immaterial. Thus we have also

$$[7 - (-1)]/(2 - 5) = -\frac{8}{3}.$$

Example 2. *Show that the points* $A(2, 1)$, $B(7, 4)$, $C(2, 6)$, *and* $D(-3, 3)$ *are the vertices of a parallelogram.*

Solution. Slope of $AB = (4 - 1)/(7 - 2) = \frac{3}{5}$. Slope of $CD = (6 - 3)/[2 - (-3)] = \frac{3}{5}$. Hence AB and CD are parallel. Similarly, slope of $BC = (6 - 4)/(2 - 7) = -\frac{2}{5}$, slope of the AD is

$$\frac{(3 - 1)}{(-3 - 2)} = -\frac{2}{5}$$

and hence AC and BD are parallel. Therefore $ABCD$ is a parallelogram.

3.2   Equation of a line in $\mathcal{E}_2$

Let l be any line in $\mathcal{E}_2$. If l is parallel to the y-axis and passes through the point (x_1, y_1), then every point on the line has the same abscissa x_1 and conversely every point with abscissa x_1 is on the line. The line l is thus the graph of the equation $x = x_1$ and we say that $x = x_1$ is an *equation of the line.*

Now suppose l is not parallel to the y-axis and has slope m. If $A(x_1, y_1)$ is a fixed point on l, a point $P(x, y)$ other than A is on l if and only if AP has slope m, that is,

(2) $$\frac{y - y_1}{x - x_1} = m$$

or

(3) $$y - y_1 = m(x - x_1).$$

Since (3) is also satisfied by the coordinates of A, it is satisfied by the coordinates of all points of l and only such points. The line l is therefore the graph of equation (3) and (3) is called an *equation of the line l.*

Example 1. *Find an equation of the line of slope* $-\frac{4}{5}$ *that passes through the point* $A(2, -5)$.

Solution. A point $P(x, y)$ other than A is on this line if and only if AP has slope $-\frac{4}{5}$, or if and only if

$$\frac{y + 5}{x - 2} = -\frac{4}{5}.$$

By simplifying we get

$$4x + 5y + 17 = 0,$$

which is satisfied also by the coordinates of A and hence is an equation of the required line.

Example 2. *Find an equation of the line through the points* $(4, -1)$ *and* $(2, 3)$.

Solution. By definition the slope of this line is $(3 + 1)/(2 - 4) = -2$. Proceeding as in Example 1, we get

$$\frac{y + 1}{x - 4} = -2$$

or

$$2x + y = 7$$

which is an equation of the given line.

We have seen that every straight line l has an equation either of the form

$$x = x_1 \qquad \text{(l parallel to y-axis)}$$

or

$$y - y_1 = m(x - x_1) \qquad \text{(if l has slope m).}$$

Both these equations have the property of being *linear*, i.e., of the first degree in x and y.

Conversely, we can show that every linear equation in x and y is an equation of a straight line, i.e., has a straight line for its graph. Let

$$(4) \qquad\qquad ax + by = c$$

be any linear equation. If $b = 0$, it has the form

$$x = \frac{c}{a}$$

and its graph is a line parallel to the y-axis. If $b \neq 0$, let (x, y) and (x_1, y_1) be two distinct points on the graph of (4). Hence

$$ax + by = c$$

and

$$ax_1 + by_1 = c.$$

Subtracting we get

$$a(x - x_1) + b(y - y_1) = 0$$

or, since $b \neq 0$,

(5) $$y - y_1 = -\frac{a}{b}(x - x_1).$$

By (3) this states that (x, y) is on the line through (x_1, y_1) with slope $-(a/b)$ and this holds for every point (x, y) that satisfies (4). Similarly, every point (x, y) that satisfies (5) satisfies (4). Hence (4) and (5) have the same graph and (4) is an equation of the line through (x_1, y_1) with slope $-(a/b)$. We now state these results formally.

Theorem 3.2. *Relative to a rectangular Cartesian coordinate system every straight line is the graph of a linear equation in x and y. Conversely, the graph of every linear equation in x and y is a straight line.*

Hence to draw the graph of a linear equation such as $2x + 5y = 10$ it is only necessary to find two points on the graph and to draw the straight line through these two points. Usually the points where the line crosses the coordinate axes are most easily found. In this case, for example, the graph is the straight line through the points $(5, 0)$ and $(0, 2)$.

It should be noted that the slope of a line not parallel to the y-axis can immediately be found from an equation of the line. As in the proof of the converse part of Theorem 3.2 if $b \neq 0$, the slope of the line whose equation is $ax + by = c$ is $-(a/b)$. Thus if the equation is written in the form $y = mx + k$, the slope of the line is equal to the coefficient of x.

Finally, we shall usually speak of "the line $2x + y = 7$" rather than "the line whose equation is $2x + y = 7$."

3.3   Linear inequalities

Consider the following three relations in x and y:

(6) $2x + 5y = 10,$

(7) $2x + 5y > 10,$

(8) $2x + 5y < 10.$

We know that the graph of (6) is the straight line l shown in Fig. 3.3.

Moreover, for all real values of x and y, $2x + 5y$ must be either equal to, greater than, or less than 10. Hence every point (x, y) lies in the graph of one and only one of the three relations. Let $P(x, y)$ be any point in the plane and let $Q(x, y_0)$ be the point on the line l that has the same abscissa as P (see Fig. 3.3). We then have

$$2x + 5y_0 = 10$$

and it follows that $y > y_0$ if and only if

$$2x + 5y > 10.$$

This means that (x, y) is above the line l if and only if (7) holds. Similarly (x, y) is below the line l if and only if (8) holds.

The graph of (7) is therefore the set of all points above the line l and the graph of (8) is the set of all points below the line l. These graphs

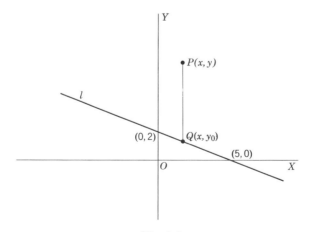

Fig. 3.3

are called *half-planes*. More precisely they are *open* half-planes because they do not include the points of the boundary l. The graph of the relation

$$2x + 5y \geq 10$$

is the set of all points *above* or *on* the line l and is called a *closed* half-plane. Similarly, the graph of $2x + 5y \leq 10$ is a closed half-plane consisting of all points below or on the line l.

The preceding discussion can be carried through in general terms to prove the next theorem.

Theorem 3.3 *If $b > 0$, the graph of the relation*

$$ax + by > c$$

is the open half-plane consisting of all points above the line $ax + by = c$. The graph of

$$ax + by < c$$

is the open half-plane consisting of all points below this line.

Proof. Let $P(x, y)$ be any point and let (x, y_0) be the point on the line $ax + by = c$, which has the same abscissa as P. Then

$$ax + by_0 = c,$$

and if

$$ax + by > c,$$

we get by subtraction,

$$b(y - y_0) > 0.$$

Since $b > 0$ this implies $y > y_0$ and (x, y) is above the line

$$ax + by + c = 0.$$

Conversely, if (x, y) is above this line, $y > y_0$ and since $b > 0$, $by > by_0$ and hence

$$ax + by > ax + by_0 = c.$$

Thus the graph of $ax + by > c$ consists precisely of those points above the line. The proof for the relation $ax + by < c$ is similar.

Note that the graph of $7x - 3y > 6$ is the same as the graph of $-7x + 3y < -6$ and hence consists of all points below the line $7x - 3y = 6$.

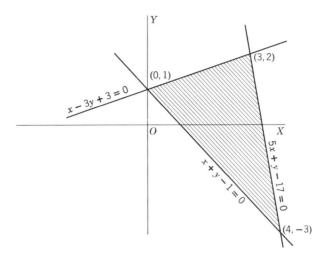

Fig. 3.4

Example. *Draw the graph of the relation*

$$x + y - 1 \geq 0,$$

$$x - 3y + 3 \geq 0,$$

and
$$5x + y - 17 \leq 0,$$

that is, the set of points (x, y) that satisfy all three of these inequalities.

Solution. Replace the inequalities by equalities and draw the corresponding straight lines.

The graph is the shaded triangular area in Fig. 3.4, since each point of it must be above or on the line $x + y - 1 = 0$, below or on the line $x - 3y + 3 = 0$ and below or on the line $5x + y - 17 = 0$. Since in this case the half-planes are closed, the sides and vertices of the triangle are included in the graph.

EXERCISE 3.1

1. Given the points $A(1, 2)$, $B(-5, 3)$, and $C(4, -1)$, find equations of the lines AB, BC and CA.
2. Find an equation of the line joining A to the midpoint of BC.
3. Find an equation of the line joining the midpoints of AB and AC.

4. Find a system of three linear inequalities of which the graph is the interior of the triangle ABC.

5. Draw the graphs of the following systems of inequalities

(a) $x - y \geq 0,$ (b) $x - y + 4 \geq 0,$ (c) $x - y + 4 \geq 0,$

       $x \geq 2.$ $2x + y - 4 \geq 0,$ $2x + y - 4 \geq 0,$

                              $x + 5y - 2 \leq 0.$ $x + 5y - 2 \geq 0.$

6. What is the graph of the following system?

$$x - y + 4 \leq 0,$$
$$2x + y - 4 \geq 0,$$
$$x + 5y - 2 \leq 0.$$

7. Draw the graphs of the three lines

$$x - 2y + 7 = 0,$$
$$2x + 3y - 2 = 0,$$
$$x - 10y + 50 = 0.$$

and show that they divide the plane into seven regions. Write a system of inequalities whose graph is each of these regions by replacing the equals sign by $\geq$ or $\leq$ in each equation. There are eight ways of replacing the three equals signs by inequalities. What is the graph of this eighth system of inequalities?

8. Prove that n straight lines divide a plane into at most $(n^2 + n + 2)/2$ different regions. *Hint:* Let P_n be the number of regions into which the plane is divided by n lines no three of which are concurrent and no two of which are parallel. Show first that $P_n = n + P_{n-1}$. See [6], pp. 49–52.

3.4   Parallel and perpendicular lines

If two lines are parallel, either they are both parallel to the y-axis or they have the same slope. In the first case their equations can be written in the form

$$x = k_1 \quad \text{and} \quad x = k_2$$

and in the second case in the form

$$y = mx + b_1$$
$$y = mx + b_2.$$

Hence equations of two parallel lines can always be written in the form

$$ax + by = c_1,$$

and

$$ax + by = c_2,$$

in which the two equations differ only in their constant terms. For example the two lines $x - 2y = 6$ and $3x - 6y = 19$ are parallel since they both have slope $\frac{1}{2}$. They can be written

$$x - 2y = 6$$

and

$$x - 2y = \tfrac{19}{3}.$$

Let l_1 and l_2 be lines with slopes m_1 and m_2 and suppose l_1 and l_2 are perpendicular to each other. Draw lines l_1' and l_2', parallel to l_1 and l_2, through the origin.

Equations of l_1' and l_2' are then

$$y = m_1 x,$$

and

$$y = m_2 x,$$

and hence (see Fig. 3.5) the point $A(1, m_1)$ lies on l_1' and the point $B(1, m_2)$ lies on l_2'. Since the angle AOB is $90°$, we have $OA^2 + OB^2 =$

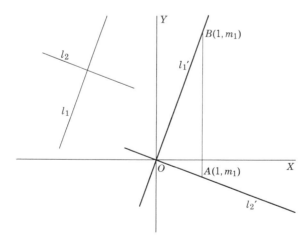

Fig. 3.5

AB^2 and from the distance formula

$$1 + m_1{}^2 + 1 + m_2{}^2 = (1 - 1)^2 + (m_1 - m_2)^2$$

whence

$$2 + m_1{}^2 + m_2{}^2 = m_1{}^2 - 2m_1m_2 + m_2{}^2$$

and

$$m_1m_2 = -1.$$

Conversely, if $m_1m_2 = -1$ it follows on retracing these steps that $OA^2 + OB^2 = AB^2$, and hence angle $AOB = 90°$. Thus we have proved the following:

Theorem 3.4. *Two lines with slopes m_1 and m_2 are perpendicular to each other if and only if $m_1m_2 = -1$, that is, each of these slopes is the negative reciprocal of the other.*

Example 1. *Find an equation of the line through the point $(2, 7)$ parallel to the line $4x - 3y = 1$.*

Solution. Since the line is parallel to $4x - 3y = 1$, its equation can be written in a form that differs from this equation only in the constant term. Hence an equation of the line is

$$4x - 3y = 4(2) - 3(7)$$

or

$$4x - 3y + 13 = 0,$$

where the constant term has been determined so that the equation is satisfied by the coordinates $(2, 7)$.

Example 2. *Find an equation of the line through the point $(5, -1)$ and perpendicular to the line $4x - 3y = 1$.*

Solution. The given line has slope $\frac{4}{3}$; hence a line perpendicular to it has slope $-\frac{3}{4}$. A line with slope $-\frac{3}{4}$ may be written in the form

$$3x + 4y = k.$$

The constant term k must be determined so that the equation is satisfied by the coordinates $(5, -1)$. Hence an equation of the line is

$$3x + 4y = 3(5) + 4(-1)$$

or

$$3x + 4y = 11.$$

Example 3. *Find the coordinates of the point of intersection of the two lines $x - 5y = 7$ and $2x + y = 3$.*

Solution. The coordinates of the point of intersection must satisfy both the equations

$$x - 5y = 7,$$

$$2x + y = 3.$$

Eliminating x we get $11y = -11$ or $y = -1$ and, on substituting, $x = 2$. Hence the point of intersection is $(2, -1)$.

3.5   Lines through the point of intersection of two given lines

If $f(x, y) = 0$ and $g(x, y) = 0$ are any two equations in x and y, then, whatever the value of k, the equation

$$(9) \qquad f(x, y) + kg(x, y) = 0$$

must be satisfied by the coordinates of every point in the intersection of the graphs of $f(x, y) = 0$ and $g(x, y) = 0$. This is obvious since any pair of values of x and y for which $f(x, y) = 0$ and $g(x, y) = 0$ necessarily satisfy (9).

Example 1. *Find an equation of the line of slope $\frac{2}{3}$ that passes through the point of intersection of the lines*

$$x - 5y - 7 = 0, \quad and \quad 2x + y - 3 = 0.$$

Solution. For any value of k the equation

$$(10) \qquad (x - 5y - 7) + k(2x + y - 3) = 0$$

is an equation of a line because it is linear. Moreover, its graph contains the point of intersection of the given lines for the reason already stated. Equation (10) may be written in the form

$$(1 + 2k)x - (5 - k)y - 7 - 3k = 0,$$

whence its slope is seen to be $(1 + 2k)/(5 - k)$, provided $k \neq 5$. We therefore equate this to $\frac{2}{3}$ and solve for k, getting

$$3 + 6k = 10 - 2k$$

or

$$k = \tfrac{7}{8}$$

Substituting this value for k in (10) and simplifying we get

$$8(x - 5y - 7) + 7(2x + y - 3) = 0,$$

or

$$2x - 3y - 7 = 0,$$

which is an equation of the required line.

This problem can also be solved by first finding the point of intersection of the given lines but the preceding method is of some importance.

EXERCISE 3.2

1. Given the three points $A(-1, 5)$, $B(2, -3)$, and $C(5, 7)$, find:

   (a) The slopes of AB, BC, and CA.
   (b) Equations of the three lines determined by the three points.
   (c) An equation of the line through A parallel to BC.
   (d) An equation of the line through A perpendicular to BC.
   (e) Equations of the three medians of the triangle ABC and show that they pass through one point.
   (f) Equations of the perpendicular bisectors of the three sides of the triangle ABC and show that they pass through one point.

2. Find an equation of the line through $(-1, 4)$ that is parallel to the line $5x - 2y = 7$.

3. Find an equation of the line through $(7, 2)$ that is perpendicular to the line $3x - 7y = 20$.

4. Prove that the points $(3, -1)$, $(7, 4)$, $(2, 9)$, and $(6, 14)$ are the vertices of a parallelogram.

5. Prove that the points $(3, -4)$, $(5, 1)$, and $(9, 11)$ are collinear.

6. Prove that for all real values of t and u the points $(2, 3)$, $(2 + 4t, 3 - 5t)$, and $(2 + 4u, 3 - 5u)$ are collinear and find an equation of the line on which they lie.

7. Let $x = 7 - 2t$ and $y = 2 + 3t$. Prove that for all real values of t the points (x, y) lie on a fixed line. Find an equation of this line.

8. If $x = x_0 + at$ and $y = y_0 + bt$, show that for all real values of t the points (x, y) lie on a fixed line and find its equation.

9. Find an equation of the line through the point of intersection of the lines $2x - y = 7$ and $x + 3y = 4$, which:

   (a) passes through the origin,
   (b) has slope -3,
   (c) passes through the point $(7, 2)$.

10. Prove that every line through the point of intersection of $2x - y + 7 = 0$ and $4x + 3y - 8 = 0$ has an equation of the form:

$$k_1(2x - y + 7) + k_2(4x + 3y - 8) = 0$$

for suitable choice of the numbers k_1 and k_2. *Hint:* Show that k_1 and k_2 can be found so that the equation is satisfied by the coordinates of an arbitrary point P other than the point of intersection of the given lines.

11. Prove that with one exception every line that passes through the point of intersection of the lines given in Problem 10 has an equation of the form

$$(2x - y + 7) + k(4x + 3y - 8) = 0$$

for suitable choice of k. What is the exception?

3.6   Circles

A circle is defined as the set of points all of which are a fixed distance r from a fixed point C. Then C is called the center of the circle and r its radius. If $r = 0$, the circle consists of the single point C. From the distance formula it is clear that if C has coordinates (h, k) a point (x, y) is on the circle if and only if

(11) $$(x - h)^2 + (y - k)^2 = r^2.$$

Hence (11) is an equation of the circle with center at (h, k) and radius r. By squaring the terms on the left, (11) can be written in the form

$$x^2 + y^2 - 2hx - 2ky + h^2 + k^2 - r^2 = 0.$$

This is a second degree equation in x and y in which x^2 and y^2 have the same coefficient (in this case 1) and the term in xy is missing. Conversely, if we start with such an equation, we can divide by the coefficient of x^2 and write it in the form

(12) $$x^2 + y^2 + dx + ey + f = 0.$$

We can now by "completing squares" write this

$$x^2 + dx + \frac{d^2}{4} + y^2 + ey + \frac{e^2}{4} = \frac{d^2}{4} + \frac{e^2}{4} - f$$

or

(13) $$\left(x + \frac{d}{2}\right)^2 + \left(y + \frac{e}{2}\right)^2 = \frac{d^2}{4} + \frac{e^2}{4} - f.$$

Comparing (13) with (11) we see that if $\dfrac{d^2}{4} + \dfrac{e^2}{4} - f \geq 0$, then (13) is

an equation of a circle with center at $\left(-\dfrac{d}{2}, -\dfrac{e}{2} \right)$ and radius

$$\sqrt{\dfrac{d^2}{4} + \dfrac{e^2}{4} - f}.$$

Example 1. *Show that* $x^2 + y^2 - 4x + 6y = 4$ *is an equation of a circle and find its center and radius.*

Solution. We can write the equation in the form

$$(x^2 - 4x + 4) + (y^2 + 6y + 9) = 4 + 9 + 4$$

or

$$(x - 4)^2 + (y + 3)^2 = 17.$$

Comparing with (11) we see that this is an equation of a circle with center at $(4, -3)$ and radius $\sqrt{17}$.

Example 2. *What is the graph of the equation*

$$x^2 + y^2 + 3x - 5y + 20 = 0.$$

Solution. Completing squares, we can write the equation in the form

$$(x + \tfrac{3}{2})^2 + (y - \tfrac{5}{2})^2 = \tfrac{9}{4} + \tfrac{25}{4} - 20 = -\tfrac{23}{2}.$$

There are no real values of x and y that satisfy this equation because for x and y real the left-hand side is non-negative. Hence the graph of this equation is the empty set.

Example 3. *Find an equation of the circle that passes through the three points* $A(1, 6)$, $B(-3, 0)$, *and* $C(2, 5)$.

Solution. The center is on the perpendicular bisector of AB and also on that of BC. The midpoint of AB (Exercise 2.1, Problem 19) is $(-1, 3)$. The slope of AB is $(0 - 6)/(-3 - 1)$ or $\tfrac{3}{2}$. The slope of the perpendicular bisector of AB is therefore $-\tfrac{2}{3}$. An equation of the perpendicular bisector is therefore

(14) $$2x + 3y = 2(-1) + 3(3) = 7.$$

Similarly, the perpendicular bisector of BC is the line

(15) $$x + y = 2.$$

Solving (14) and (15) simultaneously we find $x = -1$, $y = 3$. The center of the required circle is therefore $(-1, 3)$ and the radius is the distance from this point to A (or B or C), namely,

$$\sqrt{(-1 - 1)^2 + (3 - 6)^2} = \sqrt{13}.$$

An equation for the circle is therefore

$$(x + 1)^2 + (y - 3)^2 = 13.$$

Alternative solution. Assume an equation of the form (12) for the required circle. Since each of the points A, B, and C is on the circle, their coordinates must satisfy (12). Substituting these coordinates for x and y in (12), we get three equations in d, e, and f. Solve these and substitute in (12) to get the required equation.

Let

(16)
$$x^2 + y^2 + d_1x + e_1y + f_1 = 0$$
$$x^2 + y^2 + d_2x + e_2y + f_2 = 0$$

be equations of any two circles. If we multiply the second of these equations by some real number k and add it to the first, we get

(17) $(1 + k)x^2 + (1 + k)y^2 + (d_1 + kd_2)x + (e_1 + ke_2)y + f_1$
$$+ kf_2 = 0.$$

This equation, for the reasons given in Section 3.5, is satisfied by all common solutions of the two equations (16). Hence if the two circles intersect, the graph of (17) contains their points of intersection and this graph is not the null set. Moreover, if $k \neq -1$, the coefficients of x^2 and y^2 are equal and are not 0. It follows that for every such value of k (17) is an equation of a circle through the points of intersection of the given circles (16). If $k = -1$, then (17) is a linear equation and hence is an equation of a straight line. This straight line is called the *radical axis* of the two circles. If the two circles intersect in two points, it is clear that the radical axis is the line through their points of intersection, since its equation must be satisfied by the coordinates of these points. Any two nonconcentric circles have a radical axis whose equation is obtained by writing equations for each circle in which the coefficients of x^2 and y^2 are 1 and then subtracting one equation from

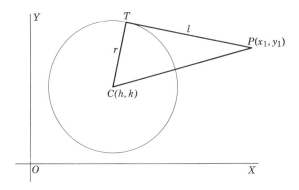

Fig. 3.6

the other. Why does this procedure not define a radical axis for two concentric circles?

Example 4. *Find an equation of the circle that passes through the points of intersection of the circles $x^2 + y^2 = 16$ and $x^2 + y^2 + 3x - 7y = 8$ and also passes through the origin.*

Solution. Since the required circle is to pass through the origin, the constant term in its equation will be zero. The requirements are therefore satisfied by the equation

$$(x^2 + y^2 - 16) - 2(x^2 + y^2 + 3x - 7y - 8) = 0$$

or

$$x^2 + y^2 + 6x - 14y = 0.$$

Example 5. *Prove that if l is the length of the tangent drawn from the point (x_1, y_1) to the circle*

$$(x - h)^2 + (y - k)^2 = r^2,$$

then $l^2 = (x_1 - h)^2 + (y_1 - k)^2 - r^2$.

Solution. Let T be the point of contact of the tangent. The radius CT is therefore perpendicular to the tangent PT and hence (see Fig. 3.6),

$$l^2 = PT^2 = CP^2 - CT^2$$

$$= (x_1 - h)^2 + (y_1 - k)^2 - r^2.$$

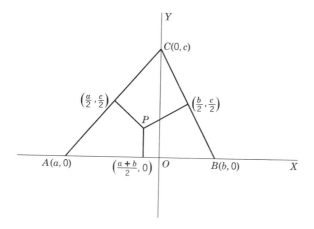

Fig. 3.7

3.7   Analytic proofs of geometric theorems

Many geometric theorems can be proved quite easily by algebraic methods, by using the tools already developed. Proofs are often simplified by a judicious choice of coordinate axes. The following example will illustrate the methods.

Example. *Prove that in any triangle the perpendicular bisectors of the three sides meet in one point.*

Proof. Let ABC be any triangle. Choose the line of AB as x-axis and the line through C perpendicular to AB as y-axis. Let the coordinates of A, B, and C be $(a, 0)$, $(b, 0)$ and $(0, c)$. The midpoint of AC is $(a/2, c/2)$ and the slope of AC is $-c/a$. The perpendicular bisector of AC therefore has slope a/c and equation

$$(18) \qquad ax - cy = \frac{a^2 - c^2}{2}.$$

Similarly, the perpendicular bisector of BC has equation

$$(19) \qquad bx - cy = \frac{b^2 - c^2}{2}.$$

If we subtract (19) from (18), we get

$$(a - b)x = \frac{a^2 - b^2}{2}$$

or, since $a \neq b$,

$$x = \frac{a + b}{2}.$$

Hence the point P in which the lines (18) and (19) intersect has abscissa $(a + b)/2$, and P therefore lies on the perpendicular bisector of AB whose equation is clearly $x = (a + b)/2$.

EXERCISE 3.3

1. Find the center and radius of each of the following circles.

   (a) $x^2 + y^2 = 20$,   (d) $3x^2 + 3y^2 - 6x + 10y = 21$,
   (b) $x^2 + y^2 + 4x = 0$,   (e) $x^2 + y^2 + 10y = 0$,
   (c) $x^2 + y^2 + 5x - 11y = 32$,   (f) $x^2 + y^2 + 10x + 10y = 0$.

2. Write an equation of the circle with center at $(4, -7)$ and radius 3.
3. Find equations for circles satisfying each of the following conditions:

   (a) Passing through the points $(2, 1)$ and $(5, -2)$ and having radius 15.
   (b) Passing through the points $(5, 1)$, $(4, 2)$, and $(-2, -6)$.
   (c) Having the line segment joining $A(3, -1)$ and $B(-2, -4)$ as diameter.
   (d) Having center on the line $x - 2y = 6$ and passing through the points $(1, 4)$ and $(-2, 3)$.

4. Prove that a point P is on the radical axis of two circles if and only if the tangents drawn from P to the two circles have equal length. *Hint:* Use the result of Example 5, Section 3.6.
5. Let A and B be the endpoints of a diameter of a circle and let P be any point on the circle other than A and B. Prove that AP is perpendicular to BP. *Hint:* Choose the x-axis along AB with origin at the center of the circle and let the radius of the circle be r.
6. The circle $x^2 + y^2 = 20$ passes through the two points $A(-2, 4)$ and $B(4, 2)$. The straight line through these two points is $x + 3y - 10 = 0$. Prove that for every real number k,

   (20) $(x^2 + y^2 - 20) + k(x + 3y - 10) = 0$

   is an equation of a circle through A and B. Prove also that an equation of every circle through A and B can be obtained from (20) by assigning a suitable value to k.

7. Prove that all the circles obtained from (20) by assigning different values of k have their centers on the line $3x - y = 0$. How is this line related to the points A and B?

8. Prove analytically that in any triangle the lines drawn from the vertices perpendicular to the opposite sides meet in a point.

9. Prove that the midpoints of the sides of any quadrilateral are the vertices of a parallelogram.

10. Prove that the perpendicular bisector of any chord of a circle passes through the center of the circle.

11. Shade the areas of the xy-plane that represent the graphs of the following systems of inequalities:

    (a) $x^2 + y^2 \le 16$.   (b) $x^2 + y^2 \le 16$,   (c) $x^2 + y^2 \le 16$,

                                   $y \le x$. $x - y \ge 0$,

                                                    $x + y \ge 4$.

12. Let $\mathcal{S}$ be the set of points in $\mathcal{E}_2$ that are twice as far from $(2, -1)$ as from $(6, 6)$. Write an equation whose graph is $\mathcal{S}$, hence showing that $\mathcal{S}$ is a circle. Find the center and radius of the circle $\mathcal{S}$.

CHAPTER 4

| VECTORS

4.1 Translations

Consider a pair of rectangular coordinate axes in the plane $\mathcal{E}_2$, with origin O. If the y-axis were moved 5 units to the right, it is clear that the abscissa of every point would be decreased by 5. Similarly, if the y-axis were moved 3 units to the left, the abscissa of every point would be increased by 3. Both these statements are included in the remark that if a new y-axis is chosen, parallel to OY, through the point $(a, 0)$ where a may be positive or negative, then the point P whose coordinates were (x, y) relative to the original axes will have coordinates $(x - a, y)$ relative to the new axes.

In the same way the effect of moving the x-axis b units upward is to subtract b from the ordinate of every point, whereas to move the x-axis downwards b units is to add b to the ordinate of every point. It is therefore clear (see Fig. 4.1) that if the origin is moved to the point $O'(a, b)$ but the new coordinate axes are parallel to and have the same positive directions as the original axes, the new coordinates of the

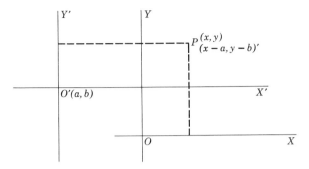

Fig. 4.1

point $P(x, y)$ will be (x', y') where

(1)
$$x' = x - a,$$
$$y' = y - b.$$

The change from the coordinate axes OX, OY to the new axes $O'X'$, $O'Y'$ is called a *translation of axes* and equations (1) are called the equations of this translation. They relate the coordinates relative to the two sets of axes of the arbitrary point P.

There is no difficulty in extending these ideas to three-dimensional space. To move the yz-plane a units to the left or right will add or subtract a from the x-coordinate of every point. To move the xz-plane b units backward or forward will add or subtract b from the y-coordinate of each point. Finally, to move the xy-plane c units downward or upward will add or subtract c from the z-coordinate of each point. From Fig. 4.2 it is clear that if the origin is moved to the point (a, b, c)

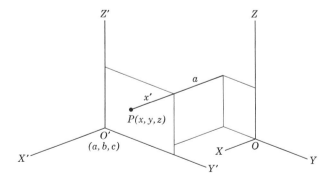

Fig. 4.2

without changing the directions of the positive rays of the axes, the new coordinates of the point $P(x, y, z)$ will be (x', y', z') where

$$x' = x - a,$$
(2)
$$y' = y - b,$$
$$z' = z - c.$$

Equations (2) are called the equations of a translation of axes in $\mathcal{E}_3$.

Example 1. *Find an equation of the sphere*

(3)
$$(x - 2)^2 + (y + 7)^2 + (z - 1)^2 = 9$$

relative to a coordinate system obtained by a translation to the new origin $(2, -7, 1)$.

Solution. Let (x', y', z') be the coordinates of the point (x, y, z) relative to the new axes. Then the equations of the translation are

$$x' = x - 2,$$
$$y' = y + 7,$$
$$z' = z - 1.$$

Substitution in (3) gives $x'^2 + y'^2 + z'^2 = 9$ for the new equation of the sphere. This result was to be expected, of course, since the new origin is at the center of the given sphere.

Example 2. *Transform the equation of the line*

$$y - y_1 = m(x - x_1)$$

by translating to the new origin (x_1, y_1).

Solution. Left as an exercise for the student.

Example 3. *By a suitable translation of axes, simplify the equation*

$$y = x^2 + 7x - 8.$$

Solution. Completing squares, we can write the equation

$$y = (x^2 + 7x + \tfrac{49}{4}) - 8 - \tfrac{49}{4}$$

or
$$y + \tfrac{81}{4} = (x - \tfrac{7}{2})^2.$$

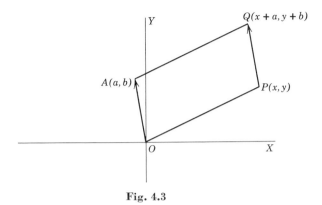

Fig. 4.3

The translation

$$x' = x - \tfrac{7}{2}$$

$$y' = y + \tfrac{81}{4}$$

to the new origin $(\tfrac{7}{2}, -\tfrac{81}{4})$ reduces the equation to

$$y' = x'^2.$$

This example illustrates the fact that an equation of a graph can often be simplified by means of a translation of axes.

Instead of changing the coordinate axes we now adopt another point of view that leads to a different aspect of translation. Suppose we keep the coordinate axes fixed but map every point (x, y) in the plane $\mathcal{E}_2$ onto another point (x', y') where

$$(4) \qquad \begin{aligned} x' &= x + a, \\ y' &= y + b. \end{aligned}$$

The point $(0, 0)$ is therefore mapped onto the point $A(a, b)$ whereas $P(x, y)$ is mapped onto $Q(x + a, y + b)$. It is clear that PQ is parallel to OA since either both have slope b/a or, if $a = 0$, both are parallel to OY (see Fig. 4.3). Moreover, AQ is parallel to OP since either both have slope y/x or both are parallel to OY. It follows that every point P in the plane is mapped on a point that is reached from P by traveling a fixed distance, $\sqrt{a^2 + b^2}$, in the direction parallel to and in the same sense as the shift from O to A. The mapping may therefore be thought of as a rigid motion of the entire plane in a fixed direction. Such a mapping is called a translation of the plane.

To sum up, a translation may mean either of two things. A *translation of axes* (points fixed, coordinate axes move) is called an *alias** translation because in the process every point gets a new name (that is, new coordinates). It is a rigid motion of the coordinate axes, keeping them parallel to their original direction. A *translation of the plane* (coordinate axes fixed, points move) is called an *alibi* translation because in the process each point moves to a different location. (Here we think of the coordinate axes as being superimposed on the plane so that it is possible to move the entire plane without moving the axes.)

Note the difference between equations (1), the alias translation that takes the point (a, b) as the origin for the new coordinates, and equations (4), the alibi translation that maps the point $(0, 0)$ onto the point (a, b).

EXERCISE 4.1

1. Write the equations of the translation of axes that takes the point $(3, -4)$ as new origin.
2. Write the equations of the alibi translation that maps the point $(0, 0)$ onto the point $(3, -4)$.
3. Show that if the equations

$$x' = x + a$$
$$y' = y + b$$

are interpreted as an alibi translation T, then T maps the origin on the point (a, b) but that if they are interpreted as the equations of an alias translation they represent a translation of axes to the new origin $(-a, -b)$.
4. Find the equations of an alibi translation that maps the point $(2, -6)$ onto the point $(7, 3)$. Is there more than one such translation?
5. Show that there is one and only one (alibi) translation that maps the point (a, b) onto the point (c, d). What are its equations?
6. Simplify the following equations by a suitable translation of axes.

(a) $x^2 + y^2 - 6x + 2y = 14$,   (c) $4x^2 + 16x + y^2 - 5y = 4$,
(b) $y^2 + 4y + 2x + 12 = 0$,   (d) $x^2 + y^2 + z^2 - 5x + 8y + 2z = 7$.

---

* The terms *alias* and *alibi* were first used in this context in [3].

4.2   Direction in $\mathcal{E}_3$; vectors

Before considering alibi translations in $\mathcal{E}_3$ it is desirable to devise some way of designating directions in three-dimensional space. A useful tool to this end is a mathematical concept called a vector. For our purposes a *vector* is an ordered pair of points. If A and B are any two points (either in $\mathcal{E}_2$ or in $\mathcal{E}_3$), the vector defined by the ordered pair (A, B) will be written $\overrightarrow{AB}$. A useful geometric representation of this vector is to identify it with the directed line segment drawn from A to B, the direction from A to B being indicated by an arrow as in Fig. 4.4. The first point A in the ordered pair is called the *initial point* and the second point B the *terminal point* of the vector. The length of the segment AB, measured in a suitable unit, is called the *length of the vector* and the *direction* of the vector is the direction from its initial point to its terminal point. If two vectors lie in the same straight line, it is clear what is meant by saying that they have the same direction or the opposite direction. If two vectors $\overrightarrow{AB}$ and $\overrightarrow{CD}$ are parallel to each other, that is, the line segments AB and CD are parallel, then $\overrightarrow{AB}$ and $\overrightarrow{CD}$ have the same direction if the segments AC and BD do not intersect but have the opposite direction if these segments do intersect (see Fig. 4.5). Nonparallel vectors never have the same direction.

Definition of equality. *Two vectors $\overrightarrow{AB}$ and $\overrightarrow{CD}$ are said to be equal if and only if they have the same direction and equal lengths.*

Choose a rectangular coordinate system in $\mathcal{E}_3$ with equal units on the coordinate axes. Let $\overrightarrow{AB}$ be the vector with initial point at $A(x_1, y_1, z_1)$

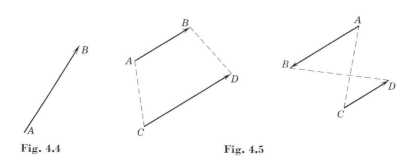

Fig. 4.4   **Fig. 4.5**

and terminal point $B(x_2, y_2, z_2)$. If we now translate axes choosing A as the new origin, the equations of this translation are

$$x' = x - x_1,$$

$$y' = y - y_1,$$

$$z' = z - z_1.$$

In particular the new coordinates of B are $(x_2 - x_1, y_2 - y_1, z_2 - z_1)$. The three angles BAX', BAY' and BAZ' (Fig. 4.6) are called the *direction* angles of AB and are denoted by α, β, and γ, respectively. Two vectors have the same direction in the sense described above if and only if they have the same direction angles. It is clear that

$$0° \leq \alpha \leq 180°$$

and that similar inequalities hold for β and γ. Since an angle in the range $0°$ to $180°$ is uniquely determined by its cosine, the direction of a vector is determined by the cosines of the three direction angles. These are called the *direction cosines* of the vector.

The projection of B onto the x'-axis has coordinates $(x_2 - x_1, 0, 0)$ relative to the translated axes, and $x_2 - x_1$ is positive, zero, or negative according as $\alpha < 90°$, $\alpha = 90°$, or $\alpha > 90°$. Hence if r is the length of $\overrightarrow{AB}$ we have in all cases $x_2 - x_1 = r \cos \alpha$. Similarly, by projecting B

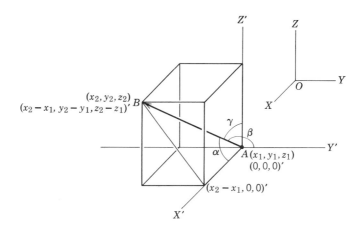

Fig. 4.6

onto the y'-axis and the z'-axis we find

$$x_2 - x_1 = r \cos \alpha,$$

(5) $$y_2 - y_1 = r \cos \beta,$$

$$z_2 - z_1 = r \cos \gamma.$$

Now by the definition of equality any vector $\overrightarrow{CD}$ that is equal to $\overrightarrow{AB}$ has the same length r and the same direction cosines $\cos \alpha$, $\cos \beta$, $\cos \gamma$ as $\overrightarrow{AB}$. Hence equations (5) tell us that the differences $x_2 - x_1$, $y_2 - y_1$, $z_2 - z_1$ obtained by subtracting the coordinates of the initial point from those of the terminal point are the same for any two equal vectors. We state this important result formally as follows.

Theorem   4.1.   *If $A(x_1, y_1, z_1)$, $B(x_2, y_2, z_2)$, $C(u_1, v_1, w_1)$ and $D(u_2, v_2, w_2)$ are four points in $\mathcal{E}_3$, the vectors $\overrightarrow{AB}$ and $\overrightarrow{CD}$ are equal if and only if $x_2 - x_1 = u_2 - u_1, y_2 - y_1 = v_2 - v_1$ and $z_2 - z_1 = w_2 - w_1$.*

Proof. We have seen from equations (5) that $\overrightarrow{AB} = \overrightarrow{CD}$ implies the equality of the coordinate differences. Conversely, by the distance formula, if the coordinate differences are equal, then $CD = AB = r$ and hence by (5) the two vectors also have the same direction cosines and $\overrightarrow{CD} = \overrightarrow{AB}$.

Theorem 4.1 shows that a vector $\overrightarrow{AB}$ is completely determined by the ordered triple of numbers $x_2 - x_1$, $y_2 - y_1$, $z_2 - z_1$ obtained by subtracting the coordinates of its initial point from those of its terminal point. These three numbers are called the *coordinates* of the vector $\overrightarrow{AB}$ and since equal vectors have equal coordinates we shall write

$$\overrightarrow{AB} = [x_2 - x_1, y_2 - y_1, z_2 - z_1].$$

If now (see Fig. 4.7) we let $\overrightarrow{OP}$ be the vector equal to $\overrightarrow{AB}$ with its initial point at the origin and terminal point at $P(x, y, z)$, we have since $\overrightarrow{OP} = \overrightarrow{AB}$,

$$[x - 0, y - 0, z - 0] = [x_2 - x_1, y_2 - y_1, z_2 - z_1],$$

and hence the coordinates of P are $(x_2 - x_1, y_2 - y_1, z_2 - z_1)$. We have therefore proved the following theorem.

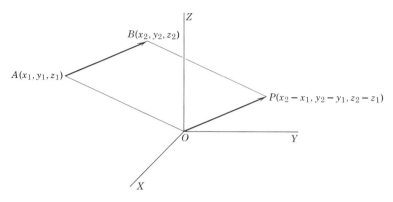

Fig. 4.7

Theorem 4.2. *Every vector $\overrightarrow{AB}$ is equal to a unique vector $\overrightarrow{OP}$ whose initial point is the origin and the coordinates of $\overrightarrow{AB}$ are equal to those of the point P. Thus if P is the point (x, y, z), then $\overrightarrow{AB} = \overrightarrow{OP} = [x, y, z]$.*

Many books use the same symbol (x, y, z) for the point P and for the vector $\overrightarrow{OP}$. Although no real confusion arises from this practice we shall continue to use square brackets for the vector and parentheses for the point.

It should always be remembered that although the coordinates of a vector are unchanged by a translation of axes, they do nevertheless depend on the coordinate system. A rotation of axes, a change in the unit of length, or a change to oblique (that is, nonrectangular) axes will in general change the coordinates of a vector. Thus when we speak of "the vector $[2, 9, -4]$," for example, there must always be a designated coordinate system in the background. And when we use the distance formula, as we shall below, it is assumed that the coordinate system is rectangular, with equal units on the coordinate axes, because these assumptions were made in deriving the distance formula.

We now return to equations (5) which gave the coordinates of the vector $\overrightarrow{AB}$ in terms of its length r and its direction cosines. We see by the distance formula and by (5) that

$$r^2 = (x_2 - x_1)^2 + (y_2 - y_1)^2 + (z_2 - z_1)^2$$
$$= r^2(\cos^2 \alpha + \cos^2 \beta + \cos^2 \gamma),$$

and hence $\cos^2 \alpha + \cos^2 \beta + \cos^2 \gamma = 1$. This proves the next theorem.

Theorem 4.3. *The sum of the squares of the direction cosines of any vector is equal to 1.*

We note also from equations (5) that the direction cosines of a vector are found by dividing its coordinates by its length. For purposes of reference we state this fact formally.

Theorem 4.4. *The length of the vector $[x, y, z]$ is $r = \sqrt{x^2 + y^2 + z^2}$ and its direction cosines are x/r, y/r, and z/r.*

A vector of length 1 is called a *unit vector*. Hence if $[x, y, z]$ has length r, $[x/r, y/r, z/r]$ is a unit vector. Thus we have the following:

Corollary. *The direction cosines of a vector $\overrightarrow{AB}$ are the coordinates of the unit vector that has the same direction as $\overrightarrow{AB}$.*

It is clear (Fig. 4.8) that a vector $\overrightarrow{AB}$ in $\mathcal{E}_2$ with initial point $A(x_1, y_1)$ and terminal point $B(x_2, y_2)$ is equal to the vector $\overrightarrow{OP}$ whose terminal point is $P(x_2 - x_1, y_2 - y_1)$ and that the coordinate differences $x_2 - x_1, y_2 - y_1$ are the same for all vectors equal to $\overrightarrow{AB}$. We therefore write

$$\overrightarrow{AB} = [x_2 - x_1, y_2 - y_1]$$

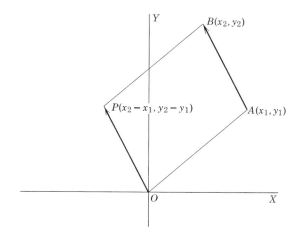

Fig. 4.8

and call the numbers $x_2 - x_1$, $y_2 - y_1$ the coordinates of the vector $\overrightarrow{AB}$ (or of any vector equal to $\overrightarrow{AB}$).

The vectors (and points) in $\mathcal{E}_2$ can be identified with vectors and points in $\mathcal{E}_3$ for which the z-coordinates are all zero and which therefore lie in the xy-plane. In this way theorems valid for $\mathcal{E}_2$ can in general be obtained from theorems for $\mathcal{E}_3$ by replacing the z-coordinates by 0 and identifying the point $(x, y, 0)$ with the point (x, y) in $\mathcal{E}_2$.

EXERCISE 4.2

1. Find the coordinates, length and direction cosines of the following vectors:

   (a) Initial point $(2, -1, 7)$,   terminal point $(9, 4, 2)$.
   (b) Initial point $(9, 4, 2)$ terminal point $(2, -1, 7)$.
   (c) Initial point $(0, 0, 0)$,   terminal point $(2, 2, 1)$.
   (d) Initial point $(2, 2, 1)$,   terminal point $(0, 0, 0)$.
   (e) Initial point $(0, 0, 0)$,   terminal point $(5, -1, 2)$.
   (f) Initial point $(0, 0, 0)$,   terminal point $(15, -3, 6)$.
   (g) Initial point $(0, 0, 0)$,   terminal point $(-5, 1, -2)$.

2. If the vector $\overrightarrow{AB}$ has direction cosines λ, μ, ν show that $\overrightarrow{BA}$ has direction cosines $-\lambda$, $-\mu$, $-\nu$. How are the direction angles of these two vectors related?

3. If the vector $[3, -7, 4]$ has its initial point at $(2, 1, 5)$, find its terminal point.

4. If the vector $[3, -7, 4]$ has its terminal point at $(-4, 2, 6)$ find its initial point.

5. Prove that if a, b, and c are not all 0, the vectors $[a, b, c]$ and $[ka, kb, kc]$ have the same direction if $k > 0$ and opposite direction if $k < 0$.

6. Prove that if the vectors $[a, b, c]$ and $[d, e, f]$ have the same direction, there is a number $k > 0$ such that $d = ka$, $e = kb$, and $f = kc$. *Hint:* If the vectors have the same direction, their direction cosines must be the same.

4.3   Alibi translations in $\mathcal{E}_3$

An (alibi) translation in $\mathcal{E}_3$ is a transformation or mapping that maps each point (x, y, z) on the point (x', y', z') where

$$x' = x + a,$$

(6) $$y' = y + b,$$

$$z' = z + c,$$

in which a, b, c are any three real numbers and do not depend on x, y, z. Now let $\overrightarrow{AB}$ be any vector in $\mathcal{E}_3$ with initial point $A(x_1, y_1, z_1)$ and terminal point $B(x_2, y_2, z_2)$. If the translation (6) maps A onto $A'(x_1', y_1', z_1')$ and B onto $B'(x_2', y_2', z_2')$ we say it maps the vector $\overrightarrow{AB}$ onto the vector $\overrightarrow{A'B'}$. From equations (6) we have

$$x_1' = x_1 + a, \qquad x_2' = x_2 + a,$$

$$y_1' = y_1 + b, \qquad y_2' = y_2 + b,$$

$$z_1' = z_1 + c, \qquad z_2' = z_2 + c,$$

and therefore by subtracting

$$x_2' - x_1' = x_2 - x_1, \; y_2' - y_1' = y_2 - y_1, \; z_2' - z_1' = z_2 - z_1.$$

Hence the vectors $\overrightarrow{AB}$ and $\overrightarrow{A'B'}$ have equal coordinates and we have

$$\overrightarrow{A'B'} = \overrightarrow{AB} = [x_2 - x_1, y_2 - y_1, z_2 - z_1].$$

We have therefore proved the first half of the following.

Theorem 4.5. *A translation in* $\mathcal{E}_3$ *maps every vector onto an equal vector. In other words, translations preserve both length and direction. Conversely, every one-to-one mapping of* $\mathcal{E}_3$ *onto itself that maps every vector onto an equal vector is a translation.*

To prove the converse part of this theorem, suppose the origin O is mapped onto the point $A(a, b, c)$ and let $P(x, y, z)$ be an arbitrary point. If P is mapped onto $Q(x', y', z')$, since $\overrightarrow{OP}$ is mapped on $\overrightarrow{AQ}$ we must have $\overrightarrow{AQ} = \overrightarrow{OP}$ and hence

$$[x' - a, y' - b, z' - c] = [x, y, z].$$

Equating corresponding coordinates we get

$$x' = x + a,$$

$$y' = y + b,$$

$$z' = z + c,$$

and hence the mapping is a translation.

The translations of $\mathcal{E}_3$, therefore, are precisely those one-to-one mappings of $\mathcal{E}_3$ onto $\mathcal{E}_3$ that preserve lengths and directions and hence map vectors onto equal vectors. The same statement holds also in $\mathcal{E}_2$. Hence translations may be thought of as rigid motions of the entire space in which every point moves the same distance parallel to a fixed direction.

4.4   Addition of vectors

From now on we shall usually use either single capital letters X, Y, and so on, or coordinate notation to denote vectors. We shall state our definitions and theorems for vectors in $\mathcal{E}_3$. The corresponding statements for vectors in $\mathcal{E}_2$ are obtained by identifying the vector $[x, y]$ in $\mathcal{E}_2$ with the vector $[x, y, 0]$ in $\mathcal{E}_3$.

Let $X_1 = [x_1, y_1, z_1]$ and $X_2 = [x_2, y_2, z_2]$ be any two vectors. We define the *sum* $X_1 + X_2$ to be the vector

$$X_1 + X_2 = [x_1 + x_2, y_1 + y_2, z_1 + z_2].$$

A vector for which the initial point coincides with the terminal point is called a *zero vector*. It has zero length but no direction. All zero vectors are considered to be equal since they have zero coordinates. We denote the zero vector by O and write

$$O = [0, 0, 0].$$

Thus we have $X + O = O + X = X$ for all vectors X. The vector $[-x_1, -y_1, -z_1]$ is called the *negative* of X_1 and is denoted by $-X_1$. We have

$$X_1 + (-X_1) = -X_1 + X_1 = O$$

for all vectors X_1. We define the difference $X_1 - X_2$ to be the vector $X_1 + (-X_2)$ and hence

$$X_1 - X_2 = [x_1 - x_2, y_1 - y_2, z_1 - z_2].$$

It is clear from these definitions that addition of vectors obeys the same basic rules as addition of real numbers. We list these below, where X, X_1, X_2, X_3 represent arbitrary vectors.

VECTOR ADDITION

A1. *The sum of any two vectors is a uniquely defined vector.*
A2. *Commutative law:* $X_1 + X_2 = X_2 + X_1$.

A3. *Associative law*: $(X_1 + X_2) + X_3 = X_1 + (X_2 + X_3)$.

A4. *Zero vector. There is a vector O such that $X + O = X$ for every vector X.*

A5. *Every vector X has a negative $-X$ such that $X + (-X) = O$. The sum $X + (-Y)$ is written $X - Y$ and is called the difference of X and Y.*

The following theorem supplies a geometric interpretation of vector addition.

Theorem 4.6. *If A, B, and C are any three points, then $\overrightarrow{AC} = \overrightarrow{AB} + \overrightarrow{BC}$.*

Proof. Choose rectangular coordinate axes with origin at A and suppose the coordinates of B and C are then (x_1, y_1, z_1) and (x_2, y_2, z_2). Then

$$\overrightarrow{AB} = [x_1, y_1, z_1],$$
$$\overrightarrow{BC} = [x_2 - x_1, y_2 - y_1, z_2 - z_1],$$

and $\qquad \overrightarrow{AC} = [x_2, y_2, z_2] = \overrightarrow{AB} + \overrightarrow{BC}.$

Corollary 1. *If $\overrightarrow{AB}$ and $\overrightarrow{AC}$ are vectors with the same initial point A, then $\overrightarrow{AB} + \overrightarrow{AC} = \overrightarrow{AD}$ where D is the fourth vertex of the parallelogram of which AB and AC are adjacent sides.*

Proof. Draw the parallelogram $ABDC$ (Fig 4.9). Since $\overrightarrow{AC} = \overrightarrow{BD}$,

$$\overrightarrow{AB} + \overrightarrow{AC} = \overrightarrow{AB} + \overrightarrow{BD} = \overrightarrow{AD}.$$

Corollary 2. *If $\overrightarrow{AB}$, $\overrightarrow{AC}$ are vectors with the same initial point,*

$$\overrightarrow{AC} - \overrightarrow{AB} = \overrightarrow{BC}.$$

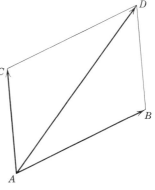

4.5 Multiplication by scalars

Fig. 4.9

In the algebra of vectors a real number has traditionally been called a *scalar* to distinguish it from a vector. We shall use the term scalar in this way to mean a real number.

Let $X = [x, y, z]$ be any vector and k any real number. The vector $[kx, ky, kz]$ is called a *scalar multiple* of X or the *product* of the vector X by the scalar k. We denote it by kX and write

$$kX = [kx, ky, kz].$$

It is easy to verify that the following rules hold.

SCALAR MULTIPLICATION

If X, Y are any vectors and k, k_1, k_2 any scalars, then

S1. kX *is a uniquely determined vector.*
S2. $k(X + Y) = kX + kY.$
S3. $(k_1 + k_2)X = k_1X + k_2X.$
S4. $k_1(k_2X) = (k_1k_2)X.$
S5. $1X = X$, $(-1)X = -X$ *and* $0X = O.$

We shall use the notation $||X||$ for the length of the vector X. By Theorem 4.4 we then have

$$||kX|| = \sqrt{k^2x^2 + k^2y^2 + k^2z^2} = |k|\sqrt{x^2 + y^2 + z^2} = |k|\,||X||.$$

Hence if $k > 0$ it follows, again by Theorem 4.4, that the direction cosines of kX are kx/kr, ky/kr, kz/kr, or x/r, y/r, z/r, where $r = ||X||$. Thus if $k > 0$, kX has the same direction as X. If, on the other hand, $k < 0$ the direction cosines of kX are $\dfrac{kx}{|k|r}$, $\dfrac{ky}{|k|r}$, $\dfrac{kz}{|k|r}$ or $-x/r$, $-y/r$, $-z/r$. Hence if $k < 0$ the direction of kX is opposite to that of X (see Problem 2, Exercise 4.2). If $k = 0$, $kX = O$. This completes the proof of the following.

Theorem 4.7. *If k is any scalar and X any vector the length of kX is $|k|$ times the length of X. The direction of kX is the same as or opposite to the direction of X according as k is positive or negative.*

Corollary. *Two nonzero vectors X and Y are parallel if and only if $Y = kX$, k a scalar. They are parallel and similarly directed if and only if $Y = kX$ where $k > 0$.*

4.6   Inner products and the angle between two vectors

If $\overrightarrow{AB}$ and $\overrightarrow{AC}$ are any two vectors with the same initial point the angle BAC is called the angle between the two vectors. If we denote

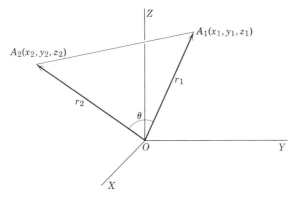

Fig. 4.10

this angle by θ it is clear that $0 \leq \theta \leq 180°$. If the vectors X and Y do not have the same initial point, we choose vectors X' and Y' equal to X and Y such that X' and Y' do have the same initial point. The angle between X and Y is then defined to be the angle between X' and Y'.

Choose a rectangular coordinate system with equal units on the coordinate axes and let $X_1 = [x_1, y_1, z_1]$ and $X_2 = [x_2, y_2, z_2]$ be any two vectors. In finding the angle between X_1 and X_2 there is no loss of generality in assuming that their initial points are at the origin so that their terminal points are $A_1(x_1, y_1, z_1)$ and $A_2(x_2, y_2, z_2)$ (see Fig. 4.10). Let $||X_1|| = r_1$ and $||X_2|| = r_2$. By the distance formula and by the law of cosines

$$(A_1A_2)^2 = (x_1 - x_2)^2 + (y_1 - y_2)^2 + (z_1 - z_2)^2$$
$$= r_1{}^2 + r_2{}^2 - 2r_1r_2 \cos \theta.$$

Expanding, and using the fact that $x_1{}^2 + y_1{}^2 + z_1{}^2 = r_1{}^2$ and $x_2{}^2 + y_2{}^2 + z_2{}^2 = r_2{}^2$, we get

(7) $$x_1x_2 + y_1y_2 + z_1z_2 = r_1r_2 \cos \theta.$$

The expression on the left-hand side of (7) is called the *inner product* of the vectors X_1 and X_2. It is denoted by $X_1 \cdot X_2$ and thus

(8) $$X_1 \cdot X_2 = x_1x_2 + y_1y_2 + z_1z_2.$$

It might appear from (8) that since $X_1 \cdot X_2$ is defined in terms of the coordinates of X_1 and X_2 it must depend on the choice of rectangular coordinate axes. But equation (7) tells us that $X_1 \cdot X_2 = r_1r_2 \cos \theta$

and therefore depends only on the lengths of X_1, X_2 and on the angle θ between them. Thus if the coordinate axes were rotated, for example, leaving the origin fixed, the coordinates of the vectors X_1 and X_2 would change, say, to $[x'_1, y'_1, z'_1]$ and $[x'_2, y'_2, z'_2]$, but only in such a way that

$$x'_1 x'_2 + y'_1 y'_2 + z'_1 z'_2 = x_1 x_2 + y_1 y_2 + z_1 z_2.$$

The basic rules for operating with inner products are listed below.

INNER PRODUCTS

For any vectors X, Y, Z, and any scalar c,

I1. $X \cdot (Y + Z) = X \cdot Y + X \cdot Z$.
I2. $(cX) \cdot Y = c(X \cdot Y)$.
I3. $X \cdot Y = Y \cdot X$.
I4. $X \cdot X \geq 0$, and $X \cdot X = 0$ only if $X = 0$.

These laws follow immediately from the definition of $X \cdot Y$ and should be verified by the student. Note that I1 and I2 imply a general distributive law for inner products. For example,

$$X \cdot (c_1 Y_1 + c_2 Y_2) = c_1 (X \cdot Y_1) + c_2 (X \cdot Y_2).$$

Similarly, using I1 and I3,

$$
\begin{aligned}
(X_1 + X_2) \cdot (Y_1 + Y_2) &= (X_1 + X_2) \cdot Y_1 + (X_1 + X_2) \cdot Y_2 \\
&= Y_1 \cdot (X_1 + X_2) + Y_2 \cdot (X_1 + X_2) \\
&= Y_1 \cdot X_1 + Y_1 \cdot X_2 + Y_2 \cdot X_1 + Y_2 \cdot X_2 \\
&= X_1 \cdot Y_1 + X_2 \cdot Y_1 + X_1 \cdot Y_2 + X_2 \cdot Y_2
\end{aligned}
$$

Note also that if $X = [x_1, x_2, x_3]$ then

$$X \cdot X = x_1{}^2 + x_2{}^2 + x_3{}^2 = ||X||^2.$$

This proves I4 and also shows that the length of a vector may be defined in terms of the inner product by

$$||X|| = \sqrt{X \cdot X}.$$

Equation (7) also yields

$$(9) \qquad \cos \theta = \frac{x_1 x_2 + y_1 y_2 + z_1 z_2}{r_1 r_2} = \frac{X \cdot Y}{||X||\,||Y||},$$

a formula for the cosine of the angle between the vectors X and Y in terms of their coordinates.

Two nonzero vectors are said to be *orthogonal* or perpendicular to each other if the angle between them is a right angle. Since $\cos 90° = 0$ it follows that two nonzero vectors X, Y are orthogonal if and only if $X \cdot Y = 0$. If we adopt the convention that the zero vector is orthogonal to every vector we have the following result.

Theorem 4.8. *The vectors X and Y are orthogonal if and only if $X \cdot Y = 0$.*

For vectors $X = [x_1, y_1]$, $Y = [x_2, y_2]$ in $\mathcal{E}_2$ we have the analogous formulas

$$X \cdot Y = x_1 x_2 + y_1 y_2 = r_1 r_2 \cos \theta$$

and

(10) $$\cos \theta = \frac{X \cdot Y}{r_1 r_2} = \frac{x_1 x_2 + y_1 y_2}{\sqrt{x_1^2 + y_1^2}\sqrt{x_2^2 + y_2^2}}.$$

The condition that X and Y be orthogonal is similarly

$$X \cdot Y = x_1 x_2 + y_1 y_2 = 0.$$

EXERCISE 4.3

1. Find the equations of a translation in $\mathcal{E}_3$ that maps $(0, 0, 0)$ onto $(2, -1, 7)$. Into what point does this translation map $(3, 4, -1)$?
2. Find the equations of a translation that maps $(2, 1, 5)$ onto $(-1, 4, -6)$.
3. Show that there is one and only one translation that maps the point (a, b, c) onto (d, e, f) and write its equations.
4. Show that the following sets of four points are the vertices of a parallelogram:

   (a) $(0, 0, 0)$, $(1, 5, 2)$, $(6, -2, 4)$, $(7, 3, 6)$,
   (b) $(1, 2, -3)$, $(5, 7, 2)$ $(-3, 12, 4)$, $(1, 17, 9)$.

5. The points $(1, -5, 8)$, $(5, 2, 4)$ and $(3, 9, 1)$ are three vertices of a parallelogram. Find three points each of which will serve as the fourth vertex.
6. If AB, AD are adjacent sides of a parallelogram $ABCD$, show that the lengths of the diagonals of the parallelogram are $\|\overrightarrow{AB} + \overrightarrow{AD}\|$ and $\|\overrightarrow{AB} - \overrightarrow{AD}\|$.
7. Given two points $A(x_1, y_1, z_1)$ and $B(x_2, y_2, z_2)$ use the parallelogram law for vector addition and the fact that the diagonals of a parallelogram

bisect each other to show that the midpoint of the segment AB is

$$\left(\frac{x_1 + x_2}{2}, \frac{y_1 + y_2}{2}, \frac{z_1 + z_2}{2}\right).$$

8. Show that if X, Y are two vectors such that $X + Y$ is orthogonal to $X - Y$, then $\|X\| = \|Y\|$. Using Problem 6, interpret this as a geometric theorem about parallelograms.

9. Write out a complete proof of the formula

$$\cos \theta = \frac{x_1 x_2 + y_1 y_2}{r_1 r_2}$$

for the cosine of the angle between the vectors $[x_1, y_1]$ and $[x_2, y_2]$ in $\mathcal{E}_2$.

10. Find unit vectors perpendicular to each of the following vectors:

(a) $[3, 4]$,   (b) $[2, 2, -1]$,   (c) $[2, 5, -3]$,   (d) $[2, -3, 6]$.

11. Find the angle between each of the following pairs of vectors:

(a) $[1, 2]$ and $[2, 1]$,
(b) $[3, 5]$ and $[-5, 3]$
(c) $[1, 3, 2]$ and $[2, -6, 5]$.

12. Show that for any two vectors X and Y

$$\|X + Y\|^2 = \|X\|^2 + 2(X \cdot Y) + \|Y\|^2.$$

13. Show that for any two vectors X and Y,

$$\|X + Y\|^2 + \|X - Y\|^2 = 2(\|X\|^2 + \|Y\|^2)$$

and interpret this geometrically if X and Y are adjacent sides of a parallelogram.

14. Show that for any two vectors X, Y in $\mathcal{E}_3$

$$|X \cdot Y| \leq \|X\| \, \|Y\|.$$

15. Show that if $|X \cdot Y| = \|X\| \, \|Y\|$ for two nonzero vectors X, Y then $Y = kX$ for some scalar k.

16. If X, Y, Z are three vectors in $\mathcal{E}_3$ such that X is orthogonal to Y and also to Z, show that for any scalars a and b, X is orthogonal to $aY + bZ$. Interpret this geometrically.

4.7 Applications to geometry in $\mathcal{E}_2$

A *normal* to a line l is a line perpendicular to l. Similarly, a vector perpendicular to l is called a vector normal to l.

Theorem 4.9. *The vector $[a, b]$ is normal to the line $ax + by = c$.*

Proof. Let (x_1, y_1) and (x_2, y_2) be any two points on this line. Then

$$ax_1 + by_1 = c,$$

$$ax_2 + by_2 = c,$$

and by subtracting we get

(11) $$a(x_1 - x_2) + b(y_1 - y_2) = 0.$$

Now the vector $[x_1 - x_2, y_1 - y_2]$ lies in the given line and equation (11) states that this vector is perpendicular to $[a, b]$. Hence the line $ax + by = c$ is perpendicular to $[a, b]$.

Example 1. *Find the perpendicular distance from the point* (9, 5) *to the line* $2x + 3y = 7$.

Solution 1. Let A be the point (9, 5) and P the point in which the normal from A meets the given line. Since $\overrightarrow{AP}$ is normal to

$$2x + 3y = 7$$

it follows, by Theorem 4.9 and the Corollary to Theorem 4.7, that $\overrightarrow{AP} = [2k, 3k]$, and since $\overrightarrow{OP} = \overrightarrow{OA} + \overrightarrow{AP}$, the coordinates of P are $(9 + 2k, 5 + 3k)$. Since P lies on the given line, (see Fig. 4.11)

$$2(9 + 2k) + 3(5 + 3k) = 7$$

whence $13k = -26$ or $k = -2$. Hence $\overrightarrow{AP} = [-4, -6]$ and $AP = \sqrt{16 + 36} = 2\sqrt{13}$. Since $\overrightarrow{OP} = \overrightarrow{OA} + \overrightarrow{AP} = [5, -1]$, P is the point (5, −1).

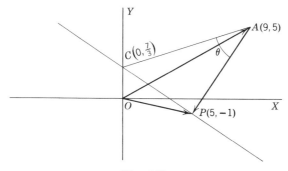

Fig. 4.11

Solution 2. The point $C(0, \frac{7}{3})$ lies on the given line and $\overrightarrow{AC} =$ $[-9, -\frac{8}{3}]$. Let θ be the angle between $\overrightarrow{AC}$ and the normal vector $N = [2, 3]$. Then (see Fig. 4.11)

$$AP = |AC \cos \theta| = (AC) \left| \frac{\overrightarrow{AC} \cdot N}{(AC)||N||} \right| = \frac{18 + 8}{\sqrt{13}} = 2\sqrt{13}.$$

Example 2. *Given the points $A(2, -3)$ and $B(6, 5)$, find the point of trisection of AB that is closer to A.*

Solution. If the required point is $P(x, y)$, (see Fig. 4.12) then $\overrightarrow{AP} = \frac{1}{3}\overrightarrow{AB}$ and

$$\overrightarrow{OP} = \overrightarrow{OA} + \frac{1}{3}\overrightarrow{AB}.$$

Hence

$$[x, y] = [2, -3] + \tfrac{1}{3}[6 - 2, 5 + 3] = [2, -3] + [\tfrac{4}{3}, \tfrac{8}{3}] = [\tfrac{10}{3}, -\tfrac{1}{3}]$$

and the coordinates of P are $(\frac{10}{3}, -\frac{1}{3})$.

Example 3. *Let l be the line through the point $(2, 5)$ parallel to the vector $[-7, 4]$. Show that the coordinates of every point on l have the form*

(12)
$$x = 2 - 7t,$$
$$y = 5 + 4t,$$

where t is a real number and that every point (x, y) defined by (12) is on l.

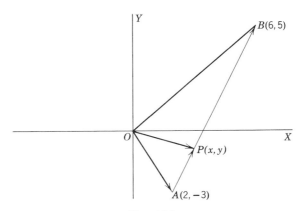

Fig. 4.12

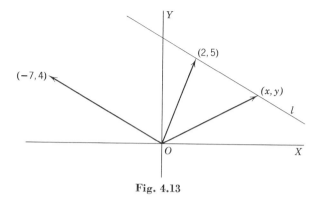

Fig. 4.13

Solution. From Fig. 4.13 we see that the point (x, y) is on l if and only if the vector $[x - 2, y - 5]$ is parallel to $[-7, 4]$ or, by the corollary to Theorem 4.7, $[x - 2, y - 5] = t[-7, 4]$, t a scalar. Hence $x = 2 - 7t$ and $y = 5 + 4t$ as required.

Equations (12) are called *parametric equations* of the line l. They give the coordinates of an arbitrary point on l in terms of the *parameter* t. Every real value of t corresponds to a unique point on the line and every point on l to a unique value of t. An ordinary x, y-equation of l, namely, $4x + 7y = 43$, is found by eliminating t from (12).

Example 4. *Let A, B, and X be three nonzero vectors in $\mathcal{E}_2$ with initial points at the origin and A not a scalar multiple of B. Prove that the terminal points of A, B, and X are collinear if and only if $X = sA + tB$ where s and t are scalars such that $s + t = 1$.*

Solution. From Fig. 4.14 the terminal points are collinear if and only if $X = A + t(B - A) = (1 - t)A + tB$, or, $X = sA + tB$ where $s + t = 1$.

Example 5. *If P and Q have coordinates $(2, 4)$ and $(8, -6)$, find the coordinates of the point R on the segment PQ such that $PR = \frac{3}{5}(PQ)$.*

Solution. As in Example 4, $\overrightarrow{OR} = \overrightarrow{OP} + \frac{3}{5}(\overrightarrow{OQ} - \overrightarrow{OP}) = \frac{2}{5}\overrightarrow{OP} + \frac{3}{5}(\overrightarrow{OQ})$. Thus if R has coordinates (x, y)

$$[x, y] = \tfrac{2}{5}[2, 4] + \tfrac{3}{5}[8, -6] = [\tfrac{28}{5}, -2]$$

and R is the point $(\frac{28}{5}, -2)$.

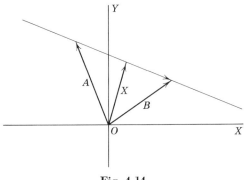

Fig. 4.14

Example 6. *Given the points $A(2, -1)$, $B(5, 4)$, and $C(-7, 8)$ find an equation of the line that bisects the angle BAC.*

Solution. Let $P(x, y)$ be any point on the bisector. Then the angles PAB and PAC are equal. The first is the angle between the vectors $\overrightarrow{AP} = [x - 2, y + 1]$ and $\overrightarrow{AB} = [3, 5]$ and the second the angle between $\overrightarrow{AP}$ and $\overrightarrow{AC} = [-9, 9]$. Letting $AP = r$ and equating the cosines of these two angles obtained from (10), we get

$$\frac{3(x - 2) + 5(y + 1)}{r \sqrt{9 + 25}} = \frac{-9(x - 2) + 9(y + 1)}{r \sqrt{81 + 81}}.$$

This simplifies to

$$\frac{3x + 5y - 1}{\sqrt{34}} = \frac{-x + y + 3}{\sqrt{2}}$$

or $(3 + \sqrt{17})x + (5 - \sqrt{17})y = 1 + 3\sqrt{17}$

which is an equation of the bisector of the angle.

EXERCISE 4.4

1. Find three vectors normal to the line $3x - 2y = 7$.
2. Find two unit vectors normal to the line $12x + 5y = 25$.
3. Find the terminal point of a vector X normal to $2x - y = 6$ if the initial point of X is the origin and $\|X\| = \sqrt{15}$.

4. Solve Problem 3 if the initial point of X is $(4, 7)$.
5. Find the acute angle between the lines $x - 2y = 6$ and $3x + 5y = 4$. *Hint:* Find the angle between normals to the two lines.
6. Given the two points $A(3, -1)$ and $B(5, 7)$, find the lengths of the projections of the segment AB

   (a) on the line $x + 2y = 6$,
   (b) on a line perpendicular to the line $x + 2y = 6$.

7. Find the perpendicular distance from the origin to the line $4x - 3y = 15$.
8. Find the perpendicular distance from the point $(1, -7)$ to the line $3x + 5y = 10$.
9. Find the perpendicular distance from the point $(2, 4)$ to the line $5x - 12y = 10$.
10. Find a formula for the perpendicular distance from the point (x_1, y_1) to the line $ax + by + c = 0$.
11. Given the points $A(-2, 5)$, $B(1, -3)$, and $C(6, 7)$, let P be the midpoint of BC. Find the point of trisection of the median AP of the triangle ABC that is closer to P and show that it is also a point of trisection of the other medians of the triangle.
12. Find the coordinates of the centroid (point of intersection of the medians) of the triangle whose vertices are (x_1, y_1), (x_2, y_2) and (x_3, y_3).
13. Find the angles of the triangle whose vertices are $A(7, -1, 4)$, $B(5, 2, -6)$, and $C(1, 4, 3)$.
14. Find the angle that the diagonal of a cube makes with an edge of the cube.
15. Find the angle that a diagonal of a cube makes with the diagonal of one face of the cube.
16. Find an equation of the bisector of the angle ABC where A, B, C are the points given in Problem 11.
17. Find parametric equations for the line through the points $A(2, -7)$ and $B(5, 5)$.
18. (a) Show that $x = 3 + 2t$, $y = 7 - 5t$ are parametric equations of the line through $A(3, 7)$ and $B(5, 2)$.
    (b) What value of t gives the point A? And the point B?
    (c) What values of t give points between A and B.
    (d) Where are the points on the line for which $t > 1$?
    (e) What values of t give points of the line that are on the opposite side of A from B.
19. Let $P(x_1, y_1, z_1)$ and $Q(x_2, y_2, z_2)$ be any two distinct points in $\mathcal{E}_3$. Show that if r and s are two real numbers such that $r + s = 1$, the point

$$(rx_1 + sx_2, ry_1 + sy_2, rz_1 + sz_2)$$

is on the line PQ and lies between P and Q on this line if and only if r and s are both positive. *Hint:* See Example 4.
20. Let $P_i(x_i, y_i, z_i)$, $i = 1, 2, 3$, be any three points of $\mathcal{E}_3$ that do not lie in the same straight line. Show that a point P is in the same plane as P_1,

P_2, and P_3 if and only if its coordinates have the form

$$(rx_1 + sx_2 + tx_3, ry_1 + sy_2 + ty_3, rz_1 + sz_2 + tz_3)$$

where r, s, t are real numbers such that $r + s + t = 1$. Show also that the point P in the plane of P_1, P_2, P_3 is inside the triangle $P_1P_2P_3$ if and only if r, s, and t are all positive. *Hint:* Let the line P_1P cut the line P_2P_3 in Q and use the result of Problem 19 to write the coordinates of Q in terms of those of P_2 and P_3. Then apply this result again to write the coordinates of P in terms of those of P_1 and Q.

21. Find the coordinates of the centroid of the triangle whose vertices are $P_i(x_i, y_i, z_i)$, $i = 1, 2, 3$.

22. The projection of the vector $\overrightarrow{AB}$ on the line l is defined to be the vector $\overrightarrow{A'B'}$ where A' and B' are the projections on l of the points A and B. Prove that the projections of $\overrightarrow{AB}$ on parallel lines are equal.

23. The projection of a vector X on a vector Y is the projection of X on a line parallel to Y. Find the projection of the vector $[2, -1, 6]$ onto $[3, 4, -2]$; onto $[1, 1, 1]$; onto $[1, 0, 0]$.

24. Prove that the projection of X on Y is $\left(\dfrac{X \cdot Y}{Y \cdot Y}\right) Y$ and check your answers to Problem 23 by using this formula.

25. Find the perpendicular distance between the parallel planes $2x - y + 8z = 6$ and $2x - y + 8z + 10 = 0$. *Hint:* Let P, Q be points on the first and second plane respectively—say, on the y-axis—and find the length of the projection of PQ onto the normal vector to the two planes.

26. Write the vector $[7, -1, 2]$ as the sum of two vectors, one of which is parallel to and the other perpendicular to the vector $[1, -1, 2]$.

CHAPTER 5

PLANES, LINES, AND SPHERES IN $\mathcal{E}_3$

5.1 Equation of a plane

A plane is uniquely determined when one point on it and the direction of a nonzero vector perpendicular to the plane are known. Such a vector, or a line perpendicular to the plane, is called a normal to the plane. A vector is said to lie in a plane if its initial and terminal points are both in the plane. Similarly, a line lies in a plane if two points of the line lie in the plane. The basic geometric fact that we shall assume is that if N is a normal to the plane every vector lying in the plane is orthogonal to N.

Suppose now that a plane has a normal vector $N = [a, b, c]$ and passes through the point $P_0(x_0, y_0, z_0)$. It is clear that a point $P(x, y, z)$ lies in this plane if and only if the vector

$$\overrightarrow{P_0P} = [x - x_0, y - y_0, z - z_0]$$

is orthogonal to N and therefore if and only if

$$a(x - x_0) + b(y - y_0) + c(z - z_0) = 0.$$

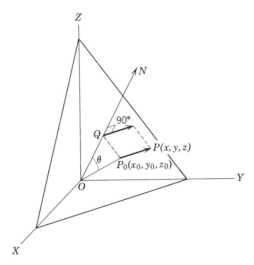

Fig. 5.1

Hence this is an equation of the plane. It can also be written in the form

(1) $$ax + by + cz = ax_0 + by_0 + cz_0.$$

Now let θ be the angle between the vectors N and $\overrightarrow{OP}_0$ and assume that the direction of N has been chosen so that $\theta \leq 90°$, that is, N is directed from the origin toward the plane if the plane does not pass through the origin (see Fig. 5.1). Then

$$ax_0 + by_0 + cz_0 = N \cdot \overrightarrow{OP}_0 = ||N|| \ (OP_0) \cos \theta,$$
$$= p \sqrt{a^2 + b^2 + c^2}$$

where $p = OQ = OP_0 \cos \theta$ is the perpendicular distance from the origin to the plane. Hence dividing by $\sqrt{a^2 + b^2 + c^2}$, equation (1) may be written in the form

(2) $$lx + my + nz = p,$$

where

$$[l, m, n] = \left[\frac{a}{||N||}, \frac{b}{||N||}, \frac{c}{||N||} \right]$$

is the unit vector having the same direction as N, that is the unit normal vector to the plane drawn from the origin towards the plane. Equation (2) is called the *normal form* of the equation of the plane. It is characterized by the two conditions $p \geq 0$ and $l^2 + m^2 + n^2 = 1$ and its constant term p is the perpendicular distance from the origin to the plane.

Every first-degree equation

$$ax + by + cz = d$$

can be reduced to the form (2) by dividing its coefficients by

$$\sqrt{a^2 + b^2 + c^2}$$

and changing their signs if necessary so that the constant term is non-negative. Hence we have the following.

Theorem 5.1. *The graph of the first-degree equation*

$$ax + by + cz = d, \qquad d \geq 0$$

is a plane, perpendicular to the vector $[a, b, c]$, *whose perpendicular distance from the origin is*

$$\frac{d}{\sqrt{a^2 + b^2 + c^2}}.$$

Example 1. *Find an equation of the plane that passes through the point* $P(1, 7, -3)$ *and is perpendicular to the line joining P to $Q(3, 5, 2)$.*

Solution. The vector $\overrightarrow{PQ} = [2, -2, 5]$ is normal to the plane. Hence an equation for the plane is

$$2x - 2y + 5z = 2(1) - 2(7) + 5(-3)$$

or

$$2x - 2y + 5z + 27 = 0.$$

Example 2. *Find the length of the perpendicular from* $P(2, -3, 5)$ *to the plane* $3x + 2y + 6z = 2$.

Solution. Apply the translation of axes $x = x' + 2$, $y = y' - 3$, $z = z' + 5$ which moves the origin to the point $(2, -3, 5)$ and changes the given equation of the plane to

$$3(x' + 2) + 2(y' - 3) + 6(z' + 5) = 2$$

or

$$3x + 2y + 6z = -28$$

on dropping the primes. The normal form of this equation is found by dividing by $\sqrt{3^2 + 2^2 + 6^2} = 7$ and changing signs to get a positive constant term on the right. This yields

$$-\tfrac{3}{7}x + \tfrac{2}{7}y - \tfrac{6}{7}z = 4$$

and by Theorem 5.1 the length of the perpendicular is 4.

Example 3. *Find the point of intersection of the three planes*

$$(A) \quad x + 2y - z = 4,$$
$$(B) \quad 3x + 8y + z = 2,$$
$$(C) \quad x - 5y + 3z = 15.$$

Solution. The coordinates of any point that lies on all three planes must satisfy all three equations. We therefore seek the simultaneous solutions of these equations. These are usually found by successive elimination as follows. Assuming that there exist numbers x, y, z that satisfy these equations, they must also satisfy the equations

$$(D) \quad x + 2y - z = 4,$$
$$(E) \quad y + 2z = -5,$$
$$(F) \quad -7y + 4z = 11,$$

where (E) is obtained by multiplying (A) by 3, subtracting from (B), and dividing through by 2, and (F) by subtracting (A) from (C). Finally, x, y, z must satisfy

$$(G) \quad 18z = -24$$

obtained by multiplying (E) by 7 and adding to (F). Now (G) yields $z = -\tfrac{4}{3}$. Substitution of this value for z in (E) gives $y = -\tfrac{7}{3}$ and finally (D) gives $x = \tfrac{14}{3} - \tfrac{4}{3} + 4 = \tfrac{22}{3}$. Since the values $x = \tfrac{22}{3}$, $y = -\tfrac{7}{3}$, and $z = -\tfrac{4}{3}$ satisfy (A) (B) and (C), the point of intersection of these three planes is $(\tfrac{22}{3}, -\tfrac{7}{3}, -\tfrac{4}{3})$.

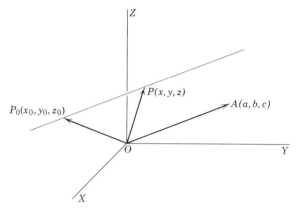

Fig. 5.2

5.2 Parametric equations of a line

A line is uniquely determined when a point on the line and a vector parallel to the line are known. Consider the line through the point $P_0(x_0,\ y_0,\ z_0)$ and parallel to the vector $[a,\ b,\ c]$. A point $P(x,\ y,\ z)$ is on this line if and only if the vector $\overrightarrow{P_0P} = [x - x_0,\ y - y_0,\ z - z_0]$ is parallel to $[a,\ b,\ c]$ and hence, by the corollary to Theorem 4.7, equal to $t[a,\ b,\ c]$ for some scalar t. Equating corresponding coordinates of these two vectors, we see that $P(x,\ y,\ z)$ is on the line if and only if, for some real number t,

$$
\begin{aligned}
x &= x_0 + at, \\
y &= y_0 + bt, \\
z &= z_0 + ct.
\end{aligned}
$$

(3)

These are called *parametric equations* of the line. They express the coordinates of an arbitrary point on the line in terms of the *parameter t*. There is one and only one point on the line for each real value assigned to t.

Example 1. *Find the point in which the line through the two points* $A(3,\ -1,\ 7)$ *and* $B(4,\ 2,\ -3)$ *pierces the plane* $6x + 4y + z = 25$.

Solution. Since the line is parallel to $\overrightarrow{AB} = [1, 3, -10]$, its parametric equations may be written

(4)
$$x = \quad 3 + \quad t,$$
$$y = -1 + \quad 3t,$$
$$z = \quad 7 - 10t.$$

To find t so that the corresponding point (x, y, z) is on the given plane we must have

$$6(3 + t) + 4(-1 + 3t) + (7 - 10t) = 25$$

or
$$8t = 4$$

and $t = \frac{1}{2}$. Substituting in (4) we get $(\frac{7}{2}, \frac{1}{2}, 2)$ for the coordinates of the required point.

Example 2. *Prove that the line*

$$x = -4 + \quad t,$$
$$y = \quad 2 - 3t,$$
$$z = \quad 4 + 5t,$$

lies in the plane $x + 2y + z = 4$.

Solution. Every point on the line has coordinates of the form

$$(-4 + t, 2 - 3t, 4 + 5t).$$

Substituting these in the equation of the plane we find

$$-4 + t + 4 - 6t + 4 + 5t = 4$$

which is satisfied, whatever the value of t. Every point on the line therefore lies in the given plane.

Example 3. *Find equations of the line through $(2, -1, 7)$ perpendicular to each of the vectors $[2, 1, -3]$ and $[4, -2, 1]$.*

Solution. Let $[u, v, w]$ be a vector perpendicular to each of the given vectors. Hence

$$2u + \quad v - 3w = 0$$
$$4u - 2v + \quad w = 0.$$

Subtracting 2 times the first equation from the second yields

$$-4v + 7w = 0$$

of which a solution is clearly $v = 7$, $w = 4$. Substituting these in the first equation gives $u = \frac{5}{2}$. Hence the vector $[\frac{5}{2}, 7, 4]$ is perpendicular to each of the given vectors and equations of the required line are $x = 2 + \frac{5}{2}t$, $y = -1 + 7t$, $z = 7 + 4t$.

EXERCISE 5.1

1. Find equations for the following planes:

   (a) Perpendicular to the vector $[3, -1, 4]$ and passing through the point $(5, 2, -1)$.

   (b) Perpendicular to the vector $[4, 2, -4]$ and perpendicular distance from the origin equal to 9.

   (c) Parallel to the plane $3x - 7y + z = 2$ and passing through the point $(2, -1, 5)$.

   (d) Parallel to each of the vectors $[2, 1, 9]$ and $[4, 3, 1]$ and passing through the point $(0, 0, 10)$. *Hint:* The normal to the plane must be orthogonal to each of the given vectors.

   (e) Passing through the points $(1, 5, 2)$, $(-1, 9, -3)$, and $(7, -1, 2)$.

   (f) Containing the point $(3, -1, 6)$ and the line of intersection of the planes $x + y + z = 1$ and $4x - y + 2z = 7$. *Hint:* See Section 3.5.

2. Find the perpendicular distance from the point $(2, -1, 4)$ to the plane $2x + 5y + 4z = 30$.

3. Find a formula for the perpendicular distance from the point (x_1, y_1, z_1) to the plane $ax + by + cz = d$.

4. Find the acute angle between the planes $x - 3y + z = 4$ and $2x + y + 7z = 1$. (The angle between two planes is the angle between their normals.)

5. Find the acute angle between the two lines

   $$x = 3 - 7t, \quad y = 2 + t, \quad z = 3 + 2t$$

   $$x = 5 - t, \quad y = 3 + 2t, \quad z = -2 - 6t.$$

6. Find the point in which the line through $(2, -1, 7)$ and $(4, 3, 2)$ pierces the plane $x + y - 5z = 10$.

7. Find the acute angle that the given line makes with the given plane in Problem 6. *Hint:* This is the complement of the angle that the line makes with a normal to the plane.

8. Find parametric equations of the line through $(0, -1, 5)$ perpendicular to the plane $3x - y + 9y = 6$.

9. Find two points that lie on both the planes

$$x - 2y + z = 8$$
$$3x + y - 2z = 6$$

and hence find parametric equations of the line of intersection of these two planes.

10. Show that the points $(2, 1, 5)$, $(8, -2, 0)$, and $(14, -5, -5)$ are collinear.

5.3   The line of intersection of two planes

Let

(5)
$$a_1x + b_1y + c_1z = d_1$$
$$a_2x + b_2y + c_2z = d_2$$

be equations of two planes. Vectors normal to these two planes are $N_1 = [a_1, b_1, c_1]$ and $N_2 = [a_2, b_2, c_2]$. Since two planes are parallel if and only if their normal vectors are parallel, we see that equations (5) represent parallel planes if and only if $N_2 = kN_1$ or

(6)
$$[a_2, b_2, c_2] = [ka_1, kb_1, kc_1]$$

for some scalar k. If in addition to (6) we have $d_2 = kd_1$, the two equations in (5) represent the same plane. We then say that the two planes are coincident and consider this as a special case of parallel planes. With this understanding we may state the following.

Theorem 5.2. *The two planes represented by equations* (5) *are parallel if and only if there exists a real number k such that*

$$a_2 = ka_1, \qquad b_2 = kb_1, \qquad c_2 = kc_1.$$

If the planes (5) are not parallel their points of intersection lie on a line and we consider now the problem of finding the direction of this line. We first solve two numerical examples that will illustrate the general method.

Example 1. *Find a vector parallel to the line of intersection of the planes.*

$$2x - 3y + 7z = 2$$
$$3x - 8y + 2z = 5.$$

Solution. Let $[u, v, w]$ be such a vector. The normal vectors to the two planes are $[2, -3, 7]$ and $[3, -8, 2]$. Since the line of intersection lies in each plane it is orthogonal to the normal to each plane and hence

$$2u - 3v + 7w = 0,$$

$$3u - 8v + 2w = 0.$$

If we multiply the first of these equations by 3 and the second by 2 and subtract, we get

$$7v + 17w = 0,$$

of which an obvious solution is $v = -17$, $w = 7$. Substituting these in the first (or second) equation we get $u = -50$. The vector

$$[-50, -17, 7],$$

or any scalar multiple of it, is therefore parallel to the given line.

Example 2. *Find a vector parallel to the line of intersection of the planes* $2y - z = 14$ *and* $3y + 4z = 10$.

Solution. Normals to these planes are $[0, 2, -1]$ and $[0, 3, 4]$. The vector $[1, 0, 0]$ is obviously orthogonal to both of these and is therefore parallel to the line of intersection.

We now consider the line of intersection of the planes (5) whose normal vectors are N_1 and N_2. It is assumed that these planes are not parallel, and therefore N_2 is not a scalar multiple of N_1. The line of intersection lies in each plane and is therefore orthogonal both to N_1 and N_2. Hence a nonzero vector $[u, v, w]$ is parallel to the line of intersection if and only if its coordinates satisfy the equations

(7)
$$a_1 u + b_1 v + c_1 w = 0,$$

$$a_2 u + b_2 v + c_2 w = 0.$$

To find a solution of (7) we first assume a_1 and a_2 are not both zero and later remove this restriction. If a_1 and a_2 are not both zero, we may assume $a_1 \neq 0$ since the order in which the two equations are written is immaterial. We now eliminate u from equations (7) by multiplying the first equation by a_2 and the second by a_1 and subtracting. This yields

$$(a_2 b_1 - a_1 b_2)v + (a_2 c_1 - a_1 c_2)w = 0$$

of which a solution is $v = a_2c_1 - a_1c_2$ and $w = -(a_2b_1 - a_1b_2)$. Substituting these in the first equation of (7) we get

$$a_1u + b_1a_2c_1 - b_1a_1c_2 + c_1a_1b_2 - c_1a_2b_1 = 0$$

or

$$a_1u = a_1(b_1c_2 - b_2c_1),$$

and since $a_1 \neq 0$, $u = b_1c_2 - b_2c_1$. A solution of equations (7) is therefore given by

$$u = b_1c_2 - b_2c_1,$$

(8)
$$v = -(a_1c_2 - a_2c_1),$$

$$w = a_1b_2 - a_2b_1.$$

Although this solution was obtained by using the assumption that a_1 and a_2 were not both zero, it is actually a solution even if a_1 and a_2 are both zero, for it then becomes $u = b_1c_2 - b_2c_1$, $v = 0$, $w = 0$ which is a solution of (7) if $a_1 = a_2 = 0$. Thus in all cases the coordinates of the vector

(9) $$[(b_1c_2 - b_2c_1), -(a_1c_2 - a_2c_1), (a_1b_2 - a_2b_1)]$$

provide a solution of equations (7). It remains to be shown that (9) is not the zero vector. Suppose the contrary, namely, that

$$b_1c_2 - b_2c_1 = 0,$$

$$a_1c_2 - a_2c_1 = 0,$$

$$a_1b_2 - a_2b_1 = 0.$$

Since not all the coefficients a_1, b_1, c_1 can be zero, suppose $c_1 \neq 0$ and let $(c_2/c_1) = k$, so that $c_2 = kc_1$. Then the first equation yields $b_2 = kb_1$ and the second, $a_2 = ka_1$, and we have $N_2 = kN_1$. But by Theorem 5.2 this would mean that the planes (5) are parallel contrary to the supposition that they intersect. We have now proved the following.

Theorem 5.3. *If the planes* (5) *are not parallel, the vector* (9) *is a non-zero vector parallel to their line of intersection.*

The vector (9) is called the *vector product* or *cross product* of the vectors N_1 and N_2 and is denoted by $N_1 \times N_2$. It is orthogonal both to N_1 and to N_2. The apparently difficult feat of learning formula (9) for the coordinates of $N_1 \times N_2$ is greatly simplified by introducing determinants.* The expression $b_1c_2 - b_2c_1$ is called a *determinant of order* 2 and is denoted by the symbol

$$\begin{vmatrix} b_1 & c_1 \\ b_2 & c_2 \end{vmatrix}$$

whose value $b_1c_2 - b_2c_1$ is obtained by subtracting the product of the numbers in the lower left- and upper right-hand corners from the product of those in the upper left- and lower right-hand corners. The three coordinates of $N_1 \times N_2$, where

$$N_1 = [a_1, b_1, c_1]$$

$$N_2 = [a_2, b_2, c_2],$$

are then

$$\begin{vmatrix} b_1 & c_1 \\ b_2 & c_2 \end{vmatrix}, \quad - \begin{vmatrix} a_1 & c_1 \\ a_2 & c_2 \end{vmatrix}, \quad \begin{vmatrix} a_1 & b_1 \\ a_2 & b_2 \end{vmatrix}.$$

Note that a minus sign precedes the second determinant.

We have seen that a line in space is determined by two points on it from which parametric equations of the line may be written. A line is also determined by any two nonparallel planes, namely, the line of intersection of these planes. Let l be any line and let (5) be equations of two planes that intersect in the line l. We say that equations (5) are *equations of the line l.* The line l consists precisely of those points (x, y, z) whose coordinates satisfy *both* equations (5).

Example 3. *Find a vector orthogonal to each of the vectors*

$$A = [2, 7, -1]$$

$$B = [5, 3, 4].$$

Solution. The vector product $A \times B$ has coordinates

$$\begin{vmatrix} 7 & -1 \\ 3 & 4 \end{vmatrix} = 31, \quad - \begin{vmatrix} 2 & -1 \\ 5 & 4 \end{vmatrix} = -13, \quad \begin{vmatrix} 2 & 7 \\ 5 & 3 \end{vmatrix} = -29,$$

and hence $[31, -13, -29]$ is orthogonal to both A and B.

Example 4. *Find an equation of the plane through the points* $A(3, 4, 6)$, $B(-1, 2, 5)$, $C(7, -1, 4)$.

---

* Determinants are discussed in detail in Chapter 8.

Solution. The vectors $\overrightarrow{BA} = [4, 2, 1]$ and $\overrightarrow{BC} = [8, -3, -1]$ lie in the plane and therefore

$$\overrightarrow{BA} \times \overrightarrow{BC} = [1, 12, -28]$$

is normal to the plane. An equation of the plane is therefore

$$x + 12y - 28z = 3 + 12(4) - 28(6)$$

or

$$x + 12y - 28z + 117 = 0.$$

Example 5. *Find an equation of the plane that contains the line*

(10)
$$3x - y + z + 7 = 0,$$
$$x + 2y - z - 4 = 0,$$

and also the point $(0, 3, 1)$.

Solution. We use the method described in Section 3.5 for lines in $\mathcal{E}_2$. For any real number k the equation

(11) $$(3x - y + z + 7) + k(x + 2y - z - 4) = 0$$

represents a plane because it is a first-degree equation in x, y, and z. It is clearly satisfied by all values of x, y, and z that satisfy *both* equations (10). Hence (11) is an equation of a plane containing the line (10). If this plane also contains the point $(0, 3, 1)$, we must have

$$-3 + 1 + 7 + k(6 - 1 - 4) = 0$$

or $k = -5$. Substituting this value for k, (11) becomes

$$2x + 11y - 6z = 27,$$

which is an equation of the required plane.

EXERCISE 5.2

Find equations of planes satisfying the following conditions:

1. Parallel to the plane $3x - y + 6z = 7$ and passing through the point $(1, 5, 2)$.
2. Parallel to the plane $2x + 3y - 6z = 10$ and perpendicular distance from the origin equal to 5.

3. Perpendicular to the vector $[1, -6, 2]$ and passing through the origin.
4. Perpendicular to the line $x = 2 - t$, $y = 3 + 4t$, $z = 1 + t$ and passing through the point $(2, 3, 1)$.
5. Perpendicular to the line

$$x - y + 3z = 6,$$

$$4x + 3y - z = 8,$$

and passing through the point $(1, 1, 1)$.
6. Parallel to each of the lines

$$x - y = 7, \qquad x + y + z = 3,$$
$$\text{and}$$
$$y + z = 4, \qquad y - z = 0,$$

and passing through the point $(1, 2, 3)$.
7. Containing the first line and parallel to the second line in Problem 6.
8. Passing through the three points $(1, 1, 1)$, $(7, -2, 0)$, and $(4, 3, -5)$.
9. Let A, B, C be any three vectors and prove the following properties of the cross product:

(a) $A \times B = -(B \times A)$.
(b) $A \times (B + C) = (A \times B) + (A \times C)$.
(c) $A \times (kB) = (kA) \times B = k(A \times B)$.
(d) $(A \times B) \times C$ lies in the plane determined by A and B.
(e) $A \times (B \times C)$ lies in the plane determined by B and C.

10. Pove that

$$\|A \times B\|^2 = \|A\|^2 \|B\|^2 - (A \cdot B)^2.$$

11. Use the result of Problem 10 to prove that

$$\|A \times B\| = \|A\| \, \|B\| \sin \theta$$

where θ is the angle between A and B.
12. Prove that $|A \cdot (B \times C)|$ is equal to the volume of the parallelepiped of which A, B, and C are the three edges.

5.4   Linear inequalities and linear programming problems

A relation of the form $ax + by \geq c$ or $ax + by > c$ is called a linear inequality in x and y. In Section 3.3 we pointed out that the set

$$\{(x, y) \in \mathcal{E}_2 \mid ax + by \geq c\},$$

which we shall call the *solution set* or *graph* of the linear inequality $ax + by \geq c$, is the closed half-plane consisting, if $b > 0$, of all points of $\mathcal{E}_2$ that lie on or above the line $ax + by = c$. This line is called the

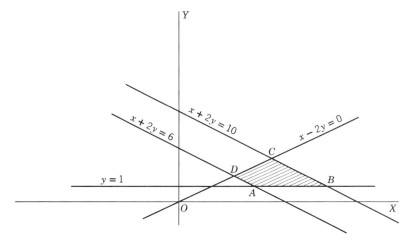

Fig. 5.3

boundary of the half-plane. By the solution set or graph of a system of inequalities we shall understand the set of all points whose coordinates satisfy all the inequalities of the system. For example, the graph of the system

$$x \geq 0$$

$$y \geq 1$$

(12) $$x + 2y \geq 6$$

$$x + 2y \leq 10$$

$$x - 2y \geq 0$$

consists of the points on or to the right of the y-axis, on or above the line $y = 1$, on or above the line $x + 2y = 6$, on or below the line $x + 2y = 10$ and on or below the line $x - 2y = 0$. The graph of this system is therefore the shaded area shown in Fig. 5.3. It is the intersection of four closed half-planes since $x \geq 0$ is a consequence of the other four inequalities.

The graph of any system of linear inequalities has an important property called *convexity*. A set $\mathcal{S}$ of points is said to be *convex*[2] if

---

* The empty set is also considered to be convex and so also is a set consisting of a single point.

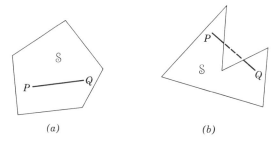

Fig. 5.4. (a) A convex set. (b) A nonconvex set.

when P and Q belong to $\mathcal{S}$ every point of the line segment PQ belongs to $\mathcal{S}$ (see Fig. 5.4).

To show that the solution set of a system of linear inequalities is convex we use the following theorem.

Theorem 5.4. *If $P(x_1, y_1, z_1)$ and $Q(x_2, y_2, z_2)$ are two points in $\mathcal{E}_3$, every point of the line segment PQ has coordinates of the form*

$$(sx_1 + tx_2, sy_1 + ty_2, sz_1 + tz_2)$$

where $0 \le s \le 1$, $0 \le t \le 1$, and $s + t = 1$.

Proof. Let $M(x, y, z)$ be any point of the segment PQ. From Fig. 5.5 we have

$$\overrightarrow{OM} = \overrightarrow{OP} + \overrightarrow{PM} = \overrightarrow{OP} + t\overrightarrow{PQ}, \qquad 0 \le t \le 1$$

$$= \overrightarrow{OP} + t(\overrightarrow{OQ} - \overrightarrow{OP})$$

$$= (1 - t)\overrightarrow{OP} + t\overrightarrow{OQ}$$

$$= s\overrightarrow{OP} + t\overrightarrow{OQ}$$

where $0 \le s \le 1$ and $s + t = 1 - t + t = 1$.

Writing these vectors in coordinate form

$$\overrightarrow{OM} = [x, y, z] = s[x_1, y_1, z_1] + t[x_2, y_2, z_2]$$

$$= [sx_1 + tx_2, sy_1 + ty_2, sz_1 + tz_2],$$

and hence M has coordinates of the form stated.

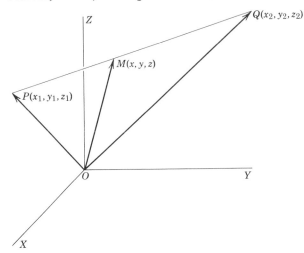

Fig. 5.5

Corollary. *The two-dimensional form of this theorem holds. That is, if* $P(x, y_1)$ *and* $Q(x_2, y_2)$ *are two points of* $\mathcal{E}_2$, *every point of the line segment* PQ *has coordinates of the form* $(sx_1 + tx_2, sy_1 + ty_2)$, *where* $0 \le s \le 1$, $0 \le t \le 1$, *and* $s + t = 1$.

We use this result to prove the following.

Theorem 5.5. *The graph in* $\mathcal{E}_2$ *of any linear inequality in* x *and* y *is a convex set.*

Proof. Let $\mathcal{S}$ be the graph of the inequality

(13) $$ax + by \ge c$$

and let $P(x_1, y_1)$ and $Q(x_2, y_2)$ be any two points of $\mathcal{S}$. Hence

(14)
$$ax_1 + by_1 \ge c,$$
$$ax_2 + by_2 \ge c.$$

Now if M is any point of the segment PQ, the coordinates of M can be written $(sx_1 + tx_2, sy_1 + ty_2)$, where $0 \le s \le 1$, $0 \le t \le 1$, and $s + t = 1$. Since s and t are non-negative, we have from (14)

$$asx_1 + bsy_1 \ge sc,$$
$$atx_2 + bty_2 \ge tc,$$

and on adding these

$$a(sx_1 + tx_2) + b(sy_1 + ty_2) \geq (s + t)c = c,$$

because $s + t = 1$. This result states that the coordinates of M satisfy (13) and hence M is in the set $\mathcal{S}$. Since M was an arbitrary point of the segment PQ, it is proved that $\mathcal{S}$ is convex. This result may be stated: *a closed half-plane is a convex set.* With minor adjustments the same proof holds for an open half-plane.

Theorem 5.6. *The intersection of two or more* convex sets is a convex set.*

Proof. Let $\mathcal{S}_1, \mathcal{S}_2, \ldots, \mathcal{S}_n$ be convex sets and let

$$\mathcal{S} = \mathcal{S}_1 \cap \mathcal{S}_2 \cap \ldots \cap \mathcal{S}_n$$

be their intersection. If $\mathcal{S}$ is the null set, or consists of a single point, it is convex by definition. If P and Q are distinct points of $\mathcal{S}$, they are points of each $\mathcal{S}_i$ $(i = 1, 2, \ldots, n)$. Since each $\mathcal{S}_i$ is convex every point M of the segment PQ lies in each set $\mathcal{S}_i$ and hence in $\mathcal{S}$. Therefore $\mathcal{S}$ is convex.

Corollary. *The graph of any system of linear inequalities in x and y is a convex set.*

Proof. The graph of the system is the intersection of the graphs of the individual inequalities of the system. The latter are half-planes and therefore are convex by Theorem 5.5. Hence the graph of the system is convex by Theorem 5.6.

The graph of a system of inequalities may be *bounded* as in system (12) (see Fig. 5.3) or it may be *unbounded* as in the system

$$x - y \geq 0,$$

$$x - 2y \leq 0,$$

$$x + 2y \geq 6,$$

whose graph is shown in Fig. 5.6. A set of points in $\mathcal{E}_2$ is said to be *bounded* if all points of $\mathcal{S}$ are less than some fixed distance r from the origin. Let $\mathcal{S}$ be the intersection of a finite number of closed half-planes.

---

* Although this theorem remains true for the intersection of an infinite number of convex sets, we use it only for a finite number of such sets and the proof is given for this case.

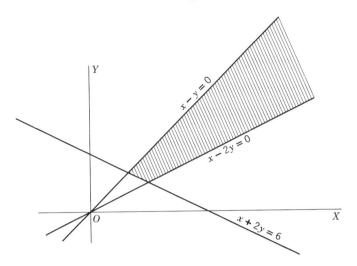

Fig. 5.6

If $\mathcal{S}$ is bounded, it is called a convex *polygon*. Such a set consists of a polygon together with the set of points enclosed by it as, for example, in Fig. 5.4a.

We now consider a class of problems known as *linear programming problems*. The essence of such problems is, given a convex polygon $\mathcal{S}$, defined by a system of linear inequalities, to find the points of $\mathcal{S}$ at which a given linear expression $px + qy$ takes its greatest and least values. We illustrate by the following.

Example 1. *Mr. X decides to give a party at which he will serve a punch. He finds a recipe that calls for equal parts of brandy and fruit juice plus claret according to taste. This suits his purpose well for he has been given a quart bottle of brandy which he does not like, and which he therefore decides to use in the punch. He invites so many guests that at least 6 quarts of punch will be required. On the other hand his available containers restrict him to not more than 10 quarts. He also feels that the alcoholic content of the punch should not exceed 25%. The brandy is 60% alcohol and costs $5 per quart and he chooses a claret that is 20% alcohol and costs $3.50 per quart. If the fruit juice costs $0.50 per quart, find the recipes for (a) the cheapest punch and (b) the punch with the greatest alcoholic content.*

Mathematical statement of the problem. Let x be the number of quarts of claret and y the number of quarts of brandy. Since the recipe then calls for y quarts of fruit juice, there will be $x + 2y$ quarts of punch, of which the alcoholic content will be $(x/5) + (3y/5)$ quarts. Since this must not exceed 25% of the total, we have

$$\frac{x}{5} + \frac{3y}{5} \leq \frac{1}{4}(x + 2y)$$

which simplifies to

$$x - 2y \geq 0.$$

Moreover, since Mr. X.'s quart of brandy must be used, $y \geq 1$, and since the amount of punch must be at least 6 quarts but not more than 10 quarts we have $6 \leq x + 2y \leq 10$. The conditions imposed on x and y are therefore exactly those stated in the system of inequalities (12). The graph of this system is the convex polygon $ABCD$ shown in Fig. 5.3.

Now the total cost C of the punch is given by

$$C = 3.5x + 5y + 0.5y = \frac{7x + 11y}{2}$$

and the total alcoholic content is given by

$$A = \frac{x}{5} + \frac{3y}{5}.$$

Our problem may now be stated as follows:

(a) Find the point (x, y) in the convex polygon defined by (12) at which the expression $\frac{7}{2}x + \frac{11}{2}y$ takes its least value.

(b) Find the point (x, y) in the convex polygon defined by (12) at which the expression $\frac{1}{5}x + \frac{3}{5}y$ takes its greatest value.

This is a typical two-dimensional linear programming problem. Abstractly stated it is this: given a system of linear inequalities in x and y find the point in its solution set that maximizes (or minimizes) the value of a given linear expression $ax + by$. When the solution set of the relevant linear inequalities is a closed convex polygon, the problem can be solved by applying the following theorem.

Theorem 5.7. *If the point (x, y) is restricted to lie in a closed convex polygon S, the linear expression $ax + by$ assumes both its greatest and least values at corner points of the polygon S.*

To simplify the proof of this theorem we first prove the following.

Lemma 5.1. *Let $P_1(x_1, y_1)$ and $P_2(x_2, y_2)$ be any two points in $\mathcal{E}_2$ and let $Q(x', y')$ be any point on the line segment P_1P_2. If $m_1 = ax_1 + by_1$, $m_2 = ax_2 + by_2$, and $m_1 \leq m_2$ then $m_1 \leq ax' + by' \leq m_2$. In other words the value of the expression $ax + by$ at Q lies between its values at P_1 and P_2.*

Proof. By the corollary to Theorem 5.4

$$x' = sx_1 + tx_2,$$

$$y' = sy_1 + ty_2,$$

where $0 \leq s \leq 1$ and $s + t = 1$.

Hence

$$\begin{aligned}
ax' + by' &= s(ax_1 + by_1) + t(ax_2 + by_2) \\
&= sm_1 + tm_2 \\
&= m_1 + t(m_2 - m_1) \qquad \text{since } s = 1 - t \\
&= m_2 - s(m_2 - m_1) \qquad \text{since } t = 1 - s.
\end{aligned}$$

Since s, t, and $m_2 - m_1$ are all non-negative, this result shows that $m_1 \leq ax' + by' \leq m_2$ as required.

Proof of Theorem 5.7. Suppose the convex polygon $\mathcal{S}$ has n corner points $A_1, A_2, \ldots, A_n$. The case $n = 5$ is illustrated in Fig. 5.7. Suppose $m_1, m_2, \ldots, m_n$ are the values assumed by the linear expression $ax + by$ at these corner points. Let m be the least and M the greatest

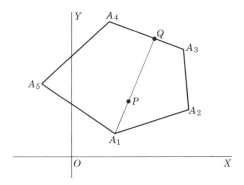

Fig. 5.7

of these n values and suppose the value m occurs at A_1. Let P be any point of $\mathcal{S}$ other than A_1 and join AP. The convexity of $\mathcal{S}$ ensures that if AP is produced it will cut the boundary of $\mathcal{S}$ again at one and only one point Q. If P is on the boundary, then $Q = P$. Since Q lies on the line segment joining two corner points (A_3 and A_4 in Fig. 5.7), it follows from Lemma 5.1 that the value of $ax + by$ at Q lies between its values at these two corner points and hence between m and M. Again by Lemma 5.1 the value of $ax + by$ at P lies between its value at A_1 and its value at Q and hence between m and M. Since P was an arbitrary point of $\mathcal{S}$ the theorem is proved and m is the least and M the greatest value that $ax + by$ can take at any point of $\mathcal{S}$.

We can now complete the solution of Example 1. Referring to Fig. 5.3 and solving the necessary linear equations, we find that the corner points of the convex polygon defined by (12) are $A(4, 1)$, $B(8, 1)$, $C(5, \frac{5}{2})$, and $D(3, \frac{3}{2})$. We compute the values of the cost, $\frac{1}{2}(7x + 11y)$, and the alcoholic content, $\frac{1}{5}(x + 3y)$, at these points. The results are as follows:

	$A(4, 1)$	$B(8, 1)$	$C(5, \frac{5}{2})$	$D(3, \frac{3}{2})$
$\frac{1}{2}(7x + 11y)$	19.50	33.50	31.25	18.75
$\frac{1}{5}(x + 3y)$	1.4	2.2	2.5	1.5

Thus the cheapest punch that fulfills all the conditions is obtained at D by using 3 quarts of claret and $1\frac{1}{2}$ quarts of brandy. The highest alcoholic content is obtained at C by using 5 quarts of claret and $2\frac{1}{2}$ quarts of brandy.

It is not hard to see how the ideas just discussed can be extended to three-dimensional problems. The solution set or graph of the inequality

$$(15) \qquad ax + by + cz \geq d$$

is called a *closed half-space*. If $c > 0$, this set consists of all the points of $\mathcal{E}_3$ that lie on or above the plane

$$(16) \qquad ax + by + cz = d.$$

For, in that case, if $P_0(x_0, y_0, z_0)$ satisfies (16), then $P(x_0, y_0, z)$ satisfies (15) if and only if $z \geq z_0$, that is, if and only if P is above the plane (16) (see Fig. 5.8).

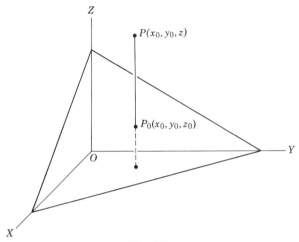

Fig. 5.8

The plane (16) is called the boundary either of the closed half-space

$$\{(x, y, z) \in \mathcal{E}_3 \mid ax + by + cz \geq d\}$$

or of the open half-space

$$\{(x, y, z) \in \mathcal{E}_3 \mid ax + by + cz > d\}.$$

A half space is *closed* if it includes all points of its boundary and *open* if it excludes all these points.

Using Theorem 5.4, we can prove the following.

Theorem 5.8. *A closed (or open) half-space is a convex set.*

The proof is the obvious three-dimensional analogue of the proof of Theorem 5.5.

It then follows from Theorem 5.6 that the intersection of any finite number of closed half-spaces is a convex set and hence the graph of any finite system of inequalities of the form (15) is a convex set. The graph of such a system may be *bounded* (all its points less than some fixed distance from the origin) or *unbounded* (for every real number r the set contains points whose distance from the origin is greater than r). If the solution set $\mathcal{S}$ of a finite system of inequalities of the form (15) is bounded, it is called a *closed convex polyhedron*. It is then the intersection of four or more closed half-spaces and is therefore bounded by four or more plane faces. An example is shown in Fig. 5.9. It is the convex polyhedron defined by the system

$$x \geq 0,$$
$$z \geq 0,$$
$$z \leq 6,$$
$$y \leq 6,$$
$$x - y \leq 0,$$
$$x + z \leq 10.$$

The three-dimensional linear programming problem for a closed convex polyhedron is solved by the following three-dimensional analogue of Theorem 5.7.

Theorem 5.9. *If the point* (x, y, z) *is restricted to lie in a closed convex polyhedron* $\mathcal{S}$, *then the linear expression* $ax + by + cz$ *assumes both its greatest and least values at corner points of* $\mathcal{S}$.

The proof is analogous to that of Theorem 5.7 and depends on the following.

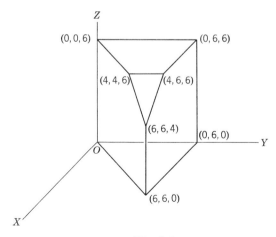

Fig. 5.9

Lemma 5.2. *Let* $P_1(x_1, y_1, z_1)$ *and* $P_2(x_2, y_2, z_2)$ *be any two points of* $\mathcal{E}_3$ *and let* $Q(x', y', z')$ *be any point of the line segment* P_1P_2. *If* $m_1 = ax_1 + by_1 + cz_1$ *and* $m_2 = ax_2 + by_2 + cz_2$ *and* $m_1 \le m_2$, *then* $m_1 \le ax' + by' + cz' \le m_2$. *In other words the value of the expression* $ax + by + cz$ *at* Q *lies between its values at* P_1 *and* P_2.

The proofs of Lemma 5.2 and Theorem 5.9 are so like those of their two-dimensional counterparts given above that they will be left as an exercise (see Exercise 5.3, Problem 8).

Example 2. *A specialist in dietary science, some years hence, discovers that there are only three basic nutrients that are essential to human life. These he calls minavites A, B, and C. They are contained in varying amounts in three basic synthetic foods: beefex, cerelina, and vegetone. The following table gives the number of calories and the number of units of minavites A, B, and C in each unit of the three foods and also their cost per unit.*

	Beefex	Cerelina	Vegetone
Minavite A	60	160	230
Minavite B	80	70	20
Minavite C	10	170	110
Calories	100	300	150
Cost	$1.00	0.60	0.40

An adequate daily diet requires at least 1000 units of minavite A, 330 units of minavite B, and 740 units of minavite C and should contain not more than 3000 calories. Find the amounts of the three foods that should be included in each day's diet in order to meet these requirements at minimum cost.

Solution. Let x, y, and z be the number of units of beefex, cerelina, and vegetone in a daily diet. The requirement of at least 1000 units of minavite A can then be expressed in the form

$$60x + 160y + 230z \ge 1000,$$

or

(17) $$6x + 16y + 23z \ge 100.$$

Similarly, the other minimum minavite requirements yield

(18) $$8x + 7y + 2z \ge 33,$$

(19) $$x + 17y + 11z \ge 74.$$

Since x, y, and z must be non-negative, we have also

(20) $$x \geq 0,$$

(21) $$y \geq 0,$$

(22) $$z \geq 0.$$

Finally, the restriction to not more than 3000 calories implies that

$$100x + 300y + 150z \leq 3000$$

or

(23) $$2x + 6y + 3z \leq 60.$$

The cost per day of this diet in dollars is $x + 0.6y + 0.4z$ or

(24) $$C = \frac{10x + 6y + 4z}{10}.$$

Our problem is therefore to find the point of the convex set $\mathcal{S}$ defined by the inequalities (17) through (23) at which C takes its minimum value. It is easy to see that the set $\mathcal{S}$ is bounded because the graph of the inequalities (20) through (23) is the tetrahedron bounded by the three coordinate planes and the plane $2x + 6y + 3z = 60$, and the graph of the whole set of seven inequalities is therefore contained in this tetrahedron. Moreover, $\mathcal{S}$ is not the null set since the point $(0, 10, 0)$ satisfies all seven inequalities. Hence $\mathcal{S}$ is a closed convex polyhedron and by Theorem 5.9 the expression C takes its minimum at a corner point of this polyhedron.

The polyhedron $\mathcal{S}$ has seven faces that lie in the seven planes (17') through (23') obtained from (17) through (23) by replacing the inequality signs by equals signs. Every corner point of $\mathcal{S}$ is therefore the point of intersection of three of these seven planes. There are $\binom{7}{3}$ or 35 sets of three equations chosen from these seven which give rise to 35 such points of intersection. Each of these 35 points must be checked to see if it is a point of $\mathcal{S}$. If it is, it is a corner point, and all corner points of $\mathcal{S}$ are found in this way. We shall not show all the details but illustrate with two examples. The three equations

$$6x + 16y + 23z = 100$$
$$8x + 7y + 2z = 33$$
$$x + 17y + 11z = 74$$

yield the solution $(1, 3, 2)$, which is the point of intersection of the three corresponding planes. Since $(1, 3, 2)$ satisfies each of the seven inequalities it is necessarily a corner point of $\mathcal{S}$. On the other hand, the three planes

$$6x + 16y + 23z = 100$$

$$8x + 7y + 2z = 33$$

$$y = 0$$

yield the solution $(\frac{13}{4}, 0, \frac{7}{2})$, which does not belong to $\mathcal{S}$ since it fails to satisfy (19). Hence this point is not a corner point of $\mathcal{S}$.

By this method it is found that $\mathcal{S}$ has ten corner points which are listed below:

$$A(1, 3, 2), \qquad F(0, 0, \tfrac{33}{2}),$$

$$B(0, \tfrac{13}{3}, \tfrac{4}{3}), \qquad G(0, 0, 20),$$

$$C(6, 4, 0), \qquad H(0, 10, 0),$$

$$D(\tfrac{5}{2}, 0, \tfrac{13}{2}), \qquad K(\tfrac{438}{19}, 0, \tfrac{88}{19}),$$

$$E(0, \tfrac{25}{4}, 0), \qquad M(\tfrac{144}{7}, \tfrac{22}{7}, 0).$$

We now compute the value of the expression (24) at each of these points. The results are as follows.

Corner point of $\mathcal{S}$	A	B	C	D	E	F	G	H	K	M
Cost in dollars	3.60	3.13	8.40	5.10	3.75	6.60	8.00	6.00	24.90	22.46

Since by Theorem 5.8 the minimum cost occurs at one of the corner points, the minimum cost diet is represented by the point B. It consists of $4\frac{1}{3}$ units of cerelina and $1\frac{1}{3}$ units of vegetone.

EXERCISE 5.3

1. A farmer has 360 acres of land on which he plans to grow wheat, oats, and corn. His expected yields are 15 bu. per acre for wheat, 20 bu. per acre for oats, and 18 bu. per acre for corn. To fulfill the requirements of his own livestock he must plant at least 20 acres of wheat, 30 acres of oats, and 40 acres of corn. He expects to have to store all his grain on the farm and he has storage space for at most 6700 bu. If his expected returns are $2 per bu. for wheat, $1.75 for oats, and $1.25 for corn, find how many acres of each he should plant for maximum total return. *Hint:* Reduce this to a two-

dimensional problem by taking x, y, and 360-x-y for the number of acres of wheat, oats, and corn, respectively.

2. Could the maximum return in Problem 1 be increased if the farmer's storage space were increased? How much additional storage space could he use to advantage?

3. If his returns per bushel were $2 for wheat, $1.50 for oats, and $1.25 for corn, show that he could plant from 84 to 290 acres in wheat without changing his total return.

4. If his returns were as in Problem 3 and, in addition, the government offered a subsidy of 30¢ per bushel on wheat, how should he now plant? Can he now increase his total return by increasing his storage capacity?

5. Referring to the data in Example 2, find the best reducing diet, i.e., the diet that will satisfy all the daily minavite requirements with the least number of calories. What is the daily intake of calories and the daily cost of this diet?

6. What diet will satisfy all the requirements of Example 2 and supply the greatest intake of minavite A? of minavite B? of minavite C?

7. If the per unit salt content of the three foods are beefex 10 mg., cerelina 8 mg., and vegetone 12 mg., find the diet that supplies all the requirements of Example 2 (*a*) with the minimum salt intake and (*b*) with the maximum salt intake.

8. Write out proofs of Lemma 5.2 and Theorem 5.9.

5.5 Spheres

The set of all points in $\mathcal{E}_3$ each of which is the same distance r from a fixed point C is called a sphere with center C and radius r. If the center C has coordinates (a, b, c), it follows from the distance formula that (x, y, z) is a point of the sphere if and only if

(25)
$$(x - a)^2 + (y - b)^2 + (z - c)^2 = r^2.$$

Hence (25) is called an equation of this sphere.

Example 1. *Find an equation of the sphere with center at $C(3, -1, 0)$ and radius 4.*

Solution. A point $P(x, y, z)$ is on this sphere if and only if $PC = 4$ or $(PC)^2 = 16$. Hence

$$(x - 3)^2 + (y + 1)^2 + z^2 = 16$$

or

$$x^2 + y^2 + z^2 - 6x + 2y = 6$$

is an equation of the sphere.

Example 2. *Show that the graph of the equation*

$$x^2 + y^2 + z^2 + 8x - y + 5z = 2$$

is a sphere and find its center and radius.

Solution. We write the given equation in the form (25) by completing squares. Thus

$$(x^2 + 8x + 16) + (y^2 - y + \tfrac{1}{4}) + (z^2 + 5z + \tfrac{25}{4}) = 18 + \tfrac{1}{4} + \tfrac{25}{4}$$

or

$$(x + 4)^2 + (y - \tfrac{1}{2})^2 + (z + \tfrac{5}{2})^2 = \tfrac{49}{2}.$$

Comparing with (25) we see that this is an equation of a sphere with center at $(-4, \tfrac{1}{2}, -\tfrac{5}{2})$ and radius $7/\sqrt{2}$.

Example 3. *What is the graph of the equation*

$$x^2 + y^2 + z^2 - 2x - 4y + 10 = 0.$$

Solution. Completing squares as in Example 2 we get

$$(x - 1)^2 + (y - 2)^2 + z^2 = -5.$$

Since this equation cannot be satisfied by real values of x, y, and z the graph is the null set.

Consider two spheres whose equations are

$$(26) \qquad \begin{aligned} x^2 + y^2 + z^2 + d_1x + e_1y + f_1z &= c_1, \\ x^2 + y^2 + z^2 + d_2x + e_2y &= f_2z = c_2. \end{aligned}$$

If these spheres intersect, the coordinates of the points of intersection must satisfy both equations (26) and hence must also satisfy the equation

$$(27) \qquad (d_1 - d_2)x + (e_1 - e_2)y + (f_1 - f_2)z = c_1 - c_2$$

obtained by subtracting the second equation from the first. Since (27) is an equation of a plane, the points of intersection of two spheres, if there are any, must lie in a plane. It is easy to show that a plane section of a sphere is a circle and hence the intersection of two spheres is either the empty set or a circle, which may, however, have zero radius if the two spheres touch at a single point.

Example 4. *Find the center and radius of the circle of intersection of the two spheres*

(28) $$x^2 + y^2 + z^2 = 35,$$

(29) $$x^2 + y^2 + z^2 - 2x + y - 5z = 11.$$

Solution. The circle of intersection must lie in the plane

(30) $$2x - y + 5z = 24$$

whose equation is obtained by subtraction of equation (29) from (28). This circle is therefore the intersection of the sphere (28) and the plane (30). The radius of this sphere drawn perpendicular to the plane will pass through the center of the circle of intersection. Since the normal vector to the plane is $[2, -1, 5]$, parametric equations of this radius are $x = 2t$, $y = -t$, $z = 5t$. Substituting these in (30), we get

$$4t + t + 25t = 24$$

or $t = \frac{4}{5}$. Hence the normal radius cuts the plane (30) in the point $C(\frac{8}{5}, -\frac{4}{5}, 4)$ which is the center of the circle of intersection. To find the radius let O be the origin (the center of the sphere (28)) and P any point on the circle of intersection. Then OCP is a right triangle with hypotenuse OP = radius of the sphere = $\sqrt{35}$. Hence

$$CP^2 = OP^2 - OC^2 = 35 - \frac{480}{25} = \frac{395}{25}.$$

Hence the radius CP of the circle of intersection is $\sqrt{395}/5$.

Example 5. *Find an equation of the tangent plane to the sphere*

(31) $$(x - 1)^2 + (y + 4)^2 + (z - 2)^2 = 9$$

at the point $P(3, -2, 3)$.

Solution. The center of the sphere is $C(1, -4, 2)$. The tangent plane at P is perpendicular to the vector

$$\overrightarrow{CP} = [2, 2, 1].$$

Hence its equation is

$$2x + 2y + z = 2(3) + 2(-2) + 1(3)$$

or

$$2x + 2y + z = 5.$$

Example 6. *Find the two tangent planes to the sphere* (31) *that are perpendicular to the vector* $[1, -5, 2]$.

Solution. Each of the required planes must touch the sphere at one of the points of intersection of the sphere with the line through its center parallel to $[1, -5, 2]$. This line has parametric equations

$$x = 1 + t,$$
(32)
$$y = -4 - 5t,$$
$$z = 2 + 2t.$$

Substituting these in (31) we get

$$t^2 + (-5t)^2 + (2t)^2 = 9$$

or $t = \pm\sqrt{\frac{3}{10}}$. The points of contact of the two tangent planes are therefore obtained by substituting these values of t in (32). They are $(1 \pm \sqrt{\frac{3}{10}}, -4 \mp 5\sqrt{\frac{3}{10}}, 2 \pm 2\sqrt{\frac{3}{10}})$ and the corresponding tangent planes are

$$x - 5y + 2z = 25 \pm 3\sqrt{30}.$$

Example 7. *Find the maximum value assumed by the expression* $3x + y + 7z$ *on the sphere* $x^2 + y^2 + z^2 = 25$.

Solution. The problem may be restated thus: Find the greatest value of k such that the plane

(33) $3x + y + 7z = k$

intersects the given sphere. By Theorem 5.1 the perpendicular distance from the origin to the plane (33) is $|k|/\sqrt{59}$, and hence this plane intersects the sphere if and only if this distance is less than or equal to the radius of the sphere, i.e., if and only if $|k| \leq 5\sqrt{59}$. The maximum value of the expression $3x + y + 7z$ on the surface of the sphere is therefore $5\sqrt{59}$ and this occurs at the point of tangency of the plane $3x + y + 7z = 5\sqrt{59}$ and the sphere. This point is determined by finding the point of intersection with the sphere of the line through the center perpendicular to the tangent plane. This line has equations

$$x = 3t,$$
$$y = \ t,$$
$$z = 7t.$$

Substitution of these in the equation of the tangent plane gives $t = 5/\sqrt{59}$, and hence the point at which the maximum occurs is $(15/\sqrt{59}, 5/\sqrt{59}, 35/\sqrt{59})$.

EXERCISE 5.4

1. Write equations of the following spheres

   (a) center $(3, 0, 0)$, radius 3,
   (b) center $(1, -1, -4)$, radius 7,
   (c) center $(2, -1, 0)$, radius $\sqrt{5}$.

2. Find the center and radius of each of the following spheres

   (a) $x^2 + y^2 + z^2 - 7x + 4z = 20$,
   (b) $x^2 + y^2 + z^2 + 2x + 8y + 10z = 7$,
   (c) $2x^2 + 2y^2 + 2z^2 + 10x - 3y + 7z = 0$.

3. Show that the set of points in $\mathcal{E}_3$ that are twice as far from the point $(2, -1, 3)$ as they are from the point $(-4, 2, 1)$ is a sphere. Find its center and radius.

4. Find the center and radius of the circle of intersection of the sphere $x^2 + y^2 + z^2 = 36$ and the plane $2x - y + z = 10$.

5. The point P $(2, 3, 6)$ lies on the sphere $x^2 + y^2 + z^2 = 49$. Find an equation of the tangent plane to this sphere at P. Show that every line through P cuts the sphere in another point Q unless it lies entirely in the tangent plane. *Hint:* Use parametric equations for a line through P parallel to the vector $[a, b, c]$.

6. Find the greatest value assumed by the expression $5x - y - 2z$ on the sphere $x^2 + y^2 + z^2 = 90$ and the point at which this greatest value is assumed.

7. Sketch the graphs of the following systems of inequalities:

   (a) $x^2 + y^2 + z^2 \leq 25$.

   (b) $x^2 + y^2 + z^2 \leq 25$,
   $\quad z \geq 4$,
   $\quad x \geq 0$,
   $\quad y \geq 0$.

   (c) $x^2 + y^2 + z^2 \leq 25$,
   $\quad z \geq 4$.

   (d) $x^2 + y^2 + z^2 \leq 25$,
   $\quad x \geq 0$,
   $\quad z \geq 2x$.

CHAPTER **6**

| CONICS AND QUADRICS

6.1 The conics

We have seen that the graph in $\mathcal{E}_2$ of a linear equation $ax + by + c = 0$ is a straight line and that the graph of a quadratic equation of the form

$$x^2 + y^2 + dx + ey + f = 0$$

is either a circle or the empty set. A natural next step would be to investigate the graphs of more general second-degree equations. When this is done, it is found that three new types of curves appear as possible graphs of such equations. These curves, the ellipse, hyperbola, and parabola, have been known and studied by mathematicians since ancient times—long before they were identified as graphs of second-degree equations. Collectively, along with circles and certain combinations of two straight lines, they are called the *conics* or conic sections, because they were first studied by the ancient Greeks as the curves of intersection of a plane with a cone. Figure 6.1 shows from this point of view how these curves arise. The cone may be thought of

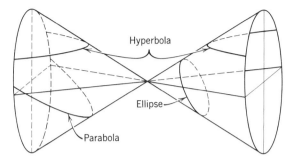

Fig. 6.1

as the surface generated by rotating a line l about a fixed line l' called
the axis of the cone, in such a way that the angle between l and l'
remains constant and is not zero. The point V in which the lines
intersect is called the vertex of the cone. Any line through V lying in
the surface is called a generating line or a *generator* of the cone. The
cone consists of two parts or *nappes* having only the vertex in common.
If a plane, not containing the vertex and not parallel to a generator,
intersects both nappes of the cone, the curve of intersection is a hyperbola, a curve consisting of two disconnected branches. If such a plane
intersects only one nappe, the curve of intersection is an ellipse. If the
plane is perpendicular to the axis of the cone, the ellipse becomes a
circle. If the plane is parallel to a generator, the curve of intersection
is a parabola. It is clear that a plane through the vertex can intersect
the cone either in the single point V, in two intersecting straight lines
through V, or in a single generating line if the plane is tangent to the
cone.

We shall not adopt this historic point of view in discussing the
conics. Instead we give geometric definitions of the ellipse, hyperbola,
and parabola as plane curves, derive equations of these curves when
suitable coordinate axes are chosen, and use these equations to derive
certain geometric properties of the curves.

6.2   The ellipse

We assume that all points considered lie in the plane $\mathcal{E}_2$. Let F_1 and
F_2 be two fixed points and let the length of the segment F_1F_2 be

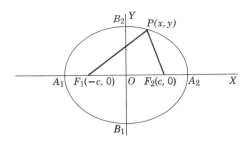

Fig. 6.2

denoted by $2c$. If a is any number greater than c, the set of points P such that $F_1P + F_2P = 2a$ is called an ellipse. We state this formally.

Definition. *An ellipse is a set of points P in the plane such that the sum of the distances of P from two fixed points F_1 and F_2 is constant. Each of the points F_1 and F_2 is called a* focus *of the ellipse. The plural of focus is* foci.

Choose a coordinate system with the line through F_1 and F_2 as x-axis and the perpendicular bisector of the segment F_1F_2 as y-axis (see Fig. 6.2). If $F_1F_2 = 2c$, the coordinates of the foci are $F_1(-c, 0)$ and $F_2(c, 0)$. If $P(x, y)$ is any point on the ellipse, the defining property

$$F_1P + F_2P = 2a$$

can be written in the form

(1) $$\sqrt{(x + c)^2 + y^2} + \sqrt{(x - c)^2 + y^2} = 2a.$$

It is clear that $F_1P + PF_2 \geq F_1F_2$ and hence we must have $2a \geq 2c$. If $a = c$, P could lie only on the line segment F_1F_2. This case is not interesting and will be excluded. We assume therefore that $a > c$.

Equation (1) may be written

$$\sqrt{(x + c)^2 + y^2} = 2a - \sqrt{(x - c)^2 + y^2}.$$

Squaring each side and simplifying yields

(2) $$a\sqrt{(x - c)^2 + y^2} = a^2 - cx.$$

Squaring again and simplifying we get

$$(a^2 - c^2)x^2 + a^2y^2 = a^2(a^2 - c^2).$$

Since $a > c$, $a^2 - c^2$ is positive and there is a positive real number b such that $b^2 = a^2 - c^2$. Our equation therefore takes the form

$$b^2 x^2 + a^2 y^2 = a^2 b^2$$

or, as it is often written,

(3)
$$\frac{x^2}{a^2} + \frac{y^2}{b^2} = 1.$$

By retracing steps and equating positive square roots when indicated, it can be shown that any point (x, y) that satisfies (3) also satisfies (1). Hence (3) is an equation of the given ellipse.

The graph of equation (3) is shown in Fig. 6.2. From the form of this equation it is clear that the graph is symmetric with respect to both coordinate axes, cuts the axes in the points $(\pm a, 0)$ and $(0, \pm b)$, and is contained in the closed rectangle $-a \leq x \leq a$, $-b \leq y \leq b$. The point midway between the foci, which has been chosen as origin, is a center of symmetry and is called the *center* of the ellipse. The points $A_1(-a, 0)$ and $A_2(a, 0)$ are called vertices of the ellipse. The segment $A_1 A_2$, of length $2a$, is called the major axis and the segment $B_1 B_2$, of length $2b$, is called the minor axis of the ellipse.

The defining property of the ellipse suggests a simple device for drawing it. If thumbtacks are inserted at the two foci F_1 and F_2, a distance $2c$ apart, and a loop of string of total length $2c + 2a$ is looped around the two tacks and pulled tight with a pencil at P (Fig. 6.2), the pencil can be moved, keeping the string tight so that $F_1 P + P F_2$ remains constant and equal to $2a$. Hence the pencil will trace the ellipse (3) with foci at F_1 and F_2.

From equation (2) it follows that if $P(x, y)$ is on the ellipse (3), then

$$\sqrt{(x - c)^2 + y^2} = a - \frac{cx}{a}.$$

Since the left-hand side of this equation is the distance $F_2 P$ we have

(4)
$$F_2 P = a - ex,$$

where $e = c/a$ is (since $c < a$) a positive number less than 1 called the *eccentricity* of the ellipse. Because $F_1 P = 2a - F_2 P$ we have also

(5)
$$F_1 P = a + ex.$$

Equations (4) and (5) give the lengths of the two *focal radii* F_1P and F_2P at the point $P(x, y)$ on the ellipse.

EXERCISE 6.1

1. Using the definition in Section 6.2, derive equations for the following ellipses:

   (*a*) Foci at $(0, -c)$ and $(0, c)$ and sum of the focal radii $2a$.
   (*b*) Foci at $(-3, 4)$ and $(5, 4)$ and sum of the focal radii 12.
   (*c*) Foci at $(1, 1)$ and $(-1, -1)$ and sum of the focal radii equal to 4.

2. Show by a translation of axes that the equation

   $$\frac{(x - h)^2}{a^2} + \frac{(y - k)^2}{b^2} = 1$$

   represents an ellipse with center at (h, k)

3. By a suitable translation of axes show that the equation

   $$x^2 + 4y^2 + 4x - 12y = 51$$

   represents an ellipse and find the distance between its foci.

4. If e is the eccentricity and $2c$ the distance between the foci of the ellipse (3), show that $c = ae$, $b^2 = a^2(1 - e^2)$

   and

   $$e^2 = \frac{a^2 - b^2}{a^2}.$$

   Show that $0 < e < 1$ and that the closer e is to 0 the more nearly circular is the ellipse.

5. Show that if any two of the numbers a, b, c, e are given, the size and shape of the corresponding ellipse is determined. Using the method described in Section 6.2, draw several ellipses with the same foci but different eccentricities. Draw also several ellipses with eccentricity $\frac{1}{2}$.

6. In drawing an ellipse with eccentricity $\frac{1}{3}$ and major axis 10 inches, how far apart must the foci be taken?

7. If the ellipse (3) has eccentricity e, the line $x = -(a/e)$ is called the *directrix* corresponding to the focus $F_1(-ae, 0)$. Similarly, the line $x = a/e$ is the directrix corresponding to the focus $(ae, 0)$. Prove that if P is any point on the ellipse and PD is the perpendicular distance from P to a directrix, then $FP = e(PD)$ where F is the corresponding focus.

8. The property proved in Problem 7 may be used to define an ellipse as the set of points P whose distance from a fixed line (the directrix) is a constant e (less than 1) times its distance from a fixed point (the focus). Choose the directrix as y-axis and the perpendicular to it through the focus F as x-axis. Assign coordinates $(p, 0)$ to F and use this definition to derive an

equation of the ellipse. Apply a translation of axes that will move the origin to the center of the ellipse, that is, reduce it to form (3).

9. Draw the ellipse (3) and the circle $x^2 + y^2 = a^2$ on the same axes so that the circle has the major axis of the ellipse as diameter. Show that for any x between $-a$ and a the corresponding ordinate of the ellipse is b/a times that of the circle.

10. Prove that each of the lines

$$y = mx \pm \sqrt{m^2a^2 + b^2}$$

has only one point in common with the ellipse (3) and is therefore a tangent to the ellipse.

11. Using the result of Problem 10 prove that if two tangents to the ellipse (3) are perpendicular to each other, they intersect in a point of the circle

$$x^2 + y^2 = a^2 + b^2.$$

12. It can be shown, using calculus, that the slope of the tangent to the ellipse (3) at the point (x_1, y_1) on the ellipse is $-(b^2x_1)/(a^2y_1)$. Assume this result and prove that the normal (i.e., the perpendicular to the tangent) at any point P on the ellipse bisects the angle between the focal radii at P.

13. If p_1, p_2 are the lengths of the perpendiculars drawn from the foci to any tangent of the ellipse (3), prove that $p_1p_2 = b^2$.

14. Suppose we are given a right circular cone. Let a plane p not perpendicular to the axis of the cone intersect the cone in a closed curve C. Then there exist two spheres tangent both to the cone and the plane, one on each side of the plane. Let F_1 and F_2 be the points of contact of these spheres with the plane p and let P be any point on the curve C. Show that $F_1P + F_2P$ is constant and hence C is an ellipse with foci at F_1 and F_2. *Hint:* The spheres touch the cone along two circles that lie in parallel planes. Show that $F_1P + F_2P$ is equal to the distance between these planes. See [1], p. 300.

6.3   The hyperbola

The definition and many of the properties of the hyperbola are so closely analogous to those of the ellipse that we give them only in outline and leave the details to be worked out by the student in Exercise 6.2.

Let two points F_1 and F_2 be given and let their distance apart be denoted by $2c$. If $0 < a < c$, the set of points P for which

(6) $$|F_1P - F_2P| = 2a$$

is called a *hyperbola*.

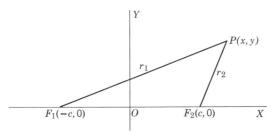

Fig. 6.3

Choose coordinate axes as for the ellipse with the line through F_1F_2 for x-axis and the perpendicular bisector of F_1F_2 for y-axis (see Fig. 6.3). Then if $P(x, y)$ is any point on the hyperbola equation (6) may be written

(7) $$\sqrt{(x + c)^2 + y^2} - \sqrt{(x - c)^2 + y^2} = \pm 2a.$$

By transposing one radical, squaring, simplifying, and squaring again we arrive at the equation

$$(c^2 - a^2)x^2 - a^2y^2 = a^2(c^2 - a^2),$$

which can be shown to be equivalent to (7) in the sense that the two equations have the same graph (see Exercise 6.2, Problem 1). Since $a < c$ we can replace $c^2 - a^2$ by b^2 and this equation becomes

(8) $$\frac{x^2}{a^2} - \frac{y^2}{b^2} = 1.$$

Examination of this equation yields the following information about its graph.

(a) The graph is symmetric with respect to both coordinate axes.

(b) It cuts the x-axis in the points $(\pm a, 0)$. It does not cut the y-axis. In fact, since $(x^2/a^2) = 1 + (y^2/b^2) \geq 1$ it follows that $x^2 \geq a^2$ and there are no points on the graph in the region $-a < x < a$.

(c) Since (8) yields $y^2/b^2 = (x^2/a^2) - 1 < (x^2/a^2)$ we have for every point (x, y) on the graph of (8).

$$-\frac{x}{a} < \frac{y}{b} < \frac{x}{a} \qquad \text{if } x > 0,$$

$$-\frac{x}{a} > \frac{y}{b} > \frac{x}{a} \qquad \text{if } x < 0.$$

Thus for $x > 0$ the entire graph lies below the line $y = (b/a)x$ and above the line $y = -(b/a)x$. For $x < 0$ it lies above $y = (b/a)x$ and below $y = -(b/a)x$.

(d) Since (8) may be written in the form

$$y = \pm \frac{bx}{a} \sqrt{1 - \frac{a^2}{x^2}}.$$

It follows that the larger $|x|$ is, the closer the point (x, y) on the graph of (8) is to the corresponding point $\left(x, \dfrac{bx}{a}\right)$ or $\left(x, -\dfrac{bx}{a}\right)$ on one of the two lines

$$y = \pm \frac{bx}{a}.$$

These lines are called the *asymptotes* of the hyperbola. They are shown with the hyperbola itself in Fig. 6.4. The points $(\pm a, 0)$ are called the *vertices* of the hyperbola. They are the points where the hyperbola cuts its *transverse axis*, the line through the foci. The transverse axis is an axis of symmetry. The perpendicular bisector of F_1F_2 is also an axis of symmetry and is called the *conjugate axis* of the hyperbola.

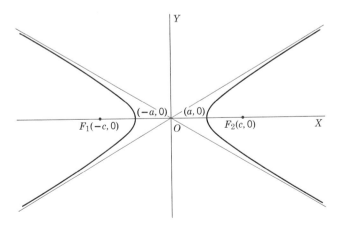

Fig. 6.4

EXERCISE 6.2

1. Give the details of the derivation of equation (8) from equation (7), and show that the two equations have the same graph.

2. Using the definition of a hyperbola in Section 6.3, find equations of each of the following hyperbolas:

   (a) Foci at $(0, c)$ and $(0, -c)$ and difference of focal radii equal to $2a$.
   (b) Foci at $(2, -1)$ and $(2, 5)$ and difference of focal radii equal to 4.
   (c) Foci at $(1, 1)$ and $(-1, -1)$ and difference of focal radii equal to 2.

3. Show by a translation of axes that the equation

$$\frac{(x - h)^2}{a^2} - \frac{(y - k)^2}{b^2} = 1$$

   represents a hyperbola with center at (h, k) and foci at $(h \pm c, k)$ where $c^2 = a^2 + b^2$.

4. Define the eccentricity of the hyperbola (8) to be the ratio c/a and denote it by e. Since $c > a$, it follows that $e > 1$. Show that $c = ae$ and $e^2 = \dfrac{a^2 + b^2}{a^2}$. If $P(x, y)$ is any point on the hyperbola, prove that the focal

   radii at P are given by

$$F_1 P = |ex + a|,$$
$$F_2 P = |ex - a|.$$

5. By a suitable translation of axes show that the equation

$$x^2 - 9y^2 + 6x + 18y = 18$$

   represents a hyperbola. Find its center, its eccentricity, and the distance between its foci. Find also the equations of its asymptotes.

6. Draw the graph of the equation

$$\frac{y^2}{9} - \frac{x^2}{4} = 1.$$

   Show that the graph is a hyperbola. What are the equations of its asymptotes? Locate its foci. *Hint:* Use the result of Problem 2a.

7. Draw on a single sheet, using the same coordinate axes, the graphs of the two hyperbolas

$$\frac{x^2}{4} - \frac{y^2}{9} = 1 \quad \text{and} \quad \frac{x^2}{4} - \frac{y^2}{9} = -1.$$

   These are called *conjugate hyperbolas*. Show that they have the same asymptotes.

8. Prove that for the hyperbola $(x^2/a^2) - (y^2/b^2) = 1$ the length of the perpendicular drawn from a focus to an asymptote is equal to b.

9. Prove that for any hyperbola the product of the lengths of the perpendiculars from a point P on the hyperbola to the two asymptotes is constant, i.e., is independent of the point P chosen.

10. If the hyperbola (8) has eccentricity e, the line $x = a/e$ is called the directrix corresponding to the focus $(ae, 0)$. Similarly, the line $x = -(a/e)$ is the directrix corresponding to the focus $(-ae, 0)$. Prove that if P is any point on the hyperbola and PD is the perpendicular distance from P to a directrix, then $FP = e(PD)$ where F is the corresponding focus.

11. The property proved in Problem 9 may be used to define a hyperbola as the set of points P whose distance from a fixed line (the directrix) is a constant e (greater than 1) times its distance from a fixed point (the focus). Choose the directrix as y-axis and the line perpendicular to it through the focus F as x-axis. Assign coordinates $(p, 0)$ to F and use this definition to derive an equation for the hyperbola. Apply a translation of axes that will move the origin to the center of the hyperbola.

12. It can be shown by using calculus that the slope of the tangent to the hyperbola (8) at the point (x_1, y_1) on the hyperbola is $(b^2 x_1/a^2 y_1)$. Assume this result and prove that the tangent to the hyperbola at $P(x_1, y_1)$ bisects the angle between the focal radii.

13. Prove that if $a^2 m^2 > b^2$ each of the lines

$$y = mx \pm \sqrt{a^2 m^2 - b^2}$$

has only one point in common with the hypberola (8) and is therefore a tangent to the hyperbola.

14. Use the result of Problem 13 to prove that two perpendicular tangents to the hyperbola (8) intersect in a point on the circle

$$x^2 + y^2 = a^2 - b^2.$$

Discuss the case in which $b > a$.

15. If p_1, p_2 are the lengths of the perpendiculars drawn from the foci to any tangent to the hyperbola (8), prove that $p_1 p_2 = b^2$.

6.4 The parabola

The set of points P for which the distance from a fixed line (the directrix) is equal to the distance from a fixed point (the focus) is called a *parabola*. The student should compare this definition with that of the ellipse given in Exercise 6.1, Problem 8, and that of the hyperbola in Exercise 6.2, Problem 11.

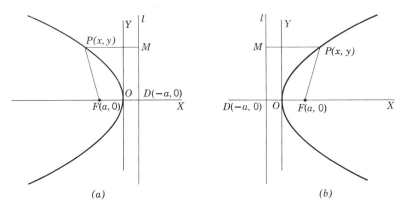

Fig. 6.5. (*a*) *a* < **0,** (*b*) *a* > **0.**

Given a directrix *l* and focus *F*, we choose for *x*-axis the line through *F* perpendicular to *l*. If this line cuts *l* in the point *D*, we find the simplest equation for the parabola results from choosing for origin the midpoint of the segment *DF*.

If we assume that the coordinates of *F* are $(a, 0)$, the equation of the directrix *l* is then $x = -a$. The point $P(x, y)$ is then on the parabola if and only if $FP = MP$ where *M* is the projection of *P* on *l*. This yields

(9) $$\sqrt{(x - a)^2 + y^2} = |x + a|$$

or, squaring* and simplifying,

(10) $$y^2 = 4ax$$

for an equation of the parabola relative to the chosen coordinate system.

It should be noted that if the focus is to the right of the directrix, then $a > 0$ and from equation (10) $x \geq 0$ for all points on the parabola. The entire curve therefore lies to the right of the *y*-axis as in Fig. 6.5*b*. On the other hand, if the focus is to the left of the directrix, $a < 0$ and the entire parabola lies to the left of the *y*-axis as in Fig. 6.5*a*.

---

* Algebraically, the squared equation (10) is equivalent to

$$\pm \sqrt{(x - a)^2 + y^2} = |x + a|.$$

Since, however, no real values of *x*, *y* satisfy this equation if the minus sign is used, equations (9) and (10) have the same graph.

EXERCISE 6.3

1. Given a directrix l and focus F choose the line through F perpendicular to l to be the y-axis and choose the origin half way between the focus and its projection D on l. Let the coordinates of the focus be $(0, a)$ and the equation of the directrix $y = -a$. Show that the parabola now has an equation $x^2 = 4ay$ and sketch its graph for both $a > 0$ and $a < 0$.
2. Derive equations for the following parabolas directly from the definition.

   (a) Focus at $(0, 4)$, directrix $y = -4$,
   (b) Focus at $(0, 4)$, directrix $x = -8$,
   (c) Focus at $(0, -3)$, directrix $y = 3$,
   (d) Focus at $(3, 5)$, directrix $y = 1$,
   (e) Focus at $(0, 0)$, directrix $x + y = 4$. (Use Problem 10, Exercise 4.4.)

3. The line through the focus perpendicular to the directrix is called the *axis* of the parabola. The point in which the parabola cuts its axis is called the *vertex*. Show that the vertex is midway between the focus and directrix. Show that the parabola is symmetric about its axis. Prove that the length of the chord through the focus perpendicular to the axis is twice the distance from the focus to the directrix.
4. Prove by translation of axes that

$$(y - k)^2 = 4a(x - h)$$

is an equation of a parabola with vertex at (h, k), focus at $(h + a, k)$, and directrix $x = h - a$.
5. Show that the graph of the equation

$$6y = x^2 - 8x + 14$$

is a parabola and find its vertex and focus. *Hint:* Completing the square of terms in x, write the equation

$$6y + 2 = x^2 - 8x + 16,$$

or $\qquad\qquad (x - 4)^2 = 6(y + \tfrac{1}{3}).$

Now apply the translation $x' = x - 4$, $y' = y + \tfrac{1}{3}$ to new origin $(4, -\tfrac{1}{3})$, show that the resulting equation represents a parabola, and find its vertex and focus. Show that the original equation represents a parabola with vertex at $(4, -\tfrac{1}{3})$ and focus at $(4, \tfrac{7}{6})$.
6. Find the vertex and focus and sketch the graph of each of the following parabolas.

   (a) $x^2 = -10y$,   (c) $y = 4x - x^2$,
   (b) $x^2 = 12(y - 6)$,   (d) $8x = 10 - 6y + y^2$.

7. Prove that the graph of any equation of the form

$$y = ax^2 + bx + c \qquad a \neq 0$$

is a parabola with axis parallel to the y-axis. Find the vertex and focus and sketch sample graphs for both $a > 0$ and $a < 0$.

8. Discuss the graph of an equation of the form

$$x = ay^2 + by + c$$

for both $a > 0$, $a < 0$.

9. It can be shown using calculus that the tangent to the parabola $y^2 = 4ax$ at the point (x_1, y_1) has an equation

$$2ax - y_1 y + 2ax_1 = 0.$$

Use this result to prove that the normal to the parabola at $P(x_1, y_1)$ bisects the angle between the focal radius at P and the line through P parallel to the axis of the parabola (see Fig. 6.6). (This is the *reflector property* of the parabola since it implies that a parabolic mirror will reflect a parallel beam of light if a light source is placed at the focus. Compare Exercise 6.1, Problem 12, and Exercise 6.2, Problem 12.)

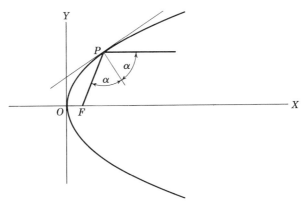

Fig. 6.6

10. Prove that the line $y = mx + a/m$ has only one point in common with the parabola $y^2 = 4ax$ and deduce that since $m \neq 0$ (and hence the line is not parallel to the axis of the parabola), the line is tangent to the parabola.

11. Using the result of Problem 10 prove that if two tangents to a parabola are perpendicular to each other, they intersect on the directrix and the line through their points of contact passes through the focus.

12. Prove that for the parabola $y^2 = 4ax$ the length of any chord through the focus is $4a \csc^2\theta$ where θ is the angle the chord makes with the positive direction on the x-axis. *Hint:* Work directly from the definition of the parabola.

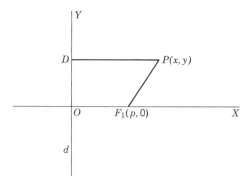

Fig. 6.7

6.5   The conics; an alternative approach

In Problems 7 and 8, Exercise 6.1, and Problems 10 and 11, Exercise 6.2, alternative definitions of the ellipse and hyperbola were suggested that make possible a unified derivation of the equations of the three curves from a single definition. We now outline this procedure.

Definition. *Assume we are given a straight line d, a point F_1 (not on d) in $\mathcal{E}_2$, and a positive real number e. A conic with directrix d, focus F_1, and eccentricity e is defined to be the set of all points P in $\mathcal{E}_2$ such that*

$$PF_1 = e(PD)$$

where PD is the perpendicular distance from P to the directrix d. If $e = 1$, the conic is called a parabola, if $e < 1$ it is called an ellipse, and if $e > 1$ it is called a hyperbola.

Choose the directrix d to be the y-axis and the line through the focus perpendicular to the directrix to be the x-axis. Let the perpendicular distance from the focus to the directrix be p, so that the focus is the point $F(p, 0)$ and $p > 0$. Let $P(x, y)$ be any point on the conic. The definition states (see Fig. 6.7) that

$$PF_1 = e(PD) \qquad \text{or} \qquad \sqrt{(x - p)^2 + y^2} = e|x|$$

which is equivalent to

$$x^2 - 2px + p^2 + y^2 = e^2 x^2$$

or

(11) $(1 - e^2)x^2 - 2px + y^2 + p^2 = 0.$

Thus (11) is an equation of a conic as defined above. We now discuss the three cases mentioned in the definition.

1. The Parabola. If $e = 1$, equation (11) becomes

$$y^2 = 2p\left(x - \frac{p}{2}\right).$$

A translation of axes to a new system with origin at $\left(\frac{p}{2}, 0\right)$ transforms this to the standard form

$$y^2 = 2px,$$

which is the same as (10) if we put $p = 2a$.

2. The Ellipse. If $e < 1$, then $1 - e^2 > 0$ and (11) can be written

$$x^2 - \left(\frac{2p}{1 - e^2}\right)x + \frac{y^2}{1 - e^2} = \frac{-p^2}{1 - e^2}.$$

Completing squares, we get

$$x^2 - \frac{2p}{1 - e^2}x + \frac{p^2}{(1 - e^2)^2} + \frac{y^2}{1 - e^2} = \frac{p^2}{(1 - e^2)^2} - \frac{p^2}{1 - e^2}$$

or

$$\left(x - \frac{p}{1 - e^2}\right)^2 + \frac{y^2}{1 - e^2} = \frac{p^2 e^2}{(1 - e^2)^2}.$$

If we now let $a = pe/(1 - e^2)$ and $b^2 = a^2(1 - e^2)$ and translate to the new origin $\left(\frac{p}{1 - e^2}, 0\right)$ this equation becomes

(12) $$\frac{x^2}{a^2} + \frac{y^2}{b^2} = 1,$$

the standard equation of an ellipse derived in (3).

Note that the coordinates of the focus F_1 after translation are $(p - p/(1 - e^2), 0)$. Since $p - p/(1 - e^2) = -pe^2/(1 - e^2) = -ae$, the focus F_1 has coordinates $(-ae, 0)$. Furthermore, the equation of the directrix after translation is

$$x = -\frac{p}{1 - e^2} = -\frac{a}{e}.$$

The symmetry of the curve about the new coordinate axes, deduced from (12), implies the existence of a second focus $F_2(ae, 0)$ and a second directrix $x = a/e$.

Now if $r_1 = F_1P$ and $r_2 = F_2P$ are the focal radii drawn to a point P on the ellipse, the definition of the ellipse tells us that

$$r_1 = e\left(\frac{a}{e} + x\right) = a + ex$$

and

$$r_2 = e\left(\frac{a}{e} - x\right) = a - ex.$$

Hence $r_1 + r_2 = 2a$ and the constant sum of the focal radii is established.

3. The Hyperbola. If $e > 1$, $1 - e^2 < 0$ and (11) can be written

$$x^2 + \left(\frac{2p}{e^2 - 1}\right)x + \frac{p^2}{(e^2 - 1)^2} - \frac{y^2}{e^2 - 1} = \frac{p^2}{e^2 - 1} + \frac{p^2}{(e^2 - 1)^2}$$

or

$$\left(x + \frac{p}{e^2 - 1}\right)^2 - \frac{y^2}{e^2 - 1} = \frac{p^2 e^2}{(e^2 - 1)^2}.$$

We now let $pe/(e^2 - 1) = a$, let $a^2(e^2 - 1) = b^2$ and translate to the new origin $(-p/(e^2 - 1), 0)$. The equation becomes

$$\frac{x^2}{a^2} - \frac{y^2}{b^2} = 1,$$

the standard equation of a hyperbola obtained in (8). The coordinates of the foci, equations of the directrices, the formulas for the focal radii, and the property $|r_1 - r_2| = 2a$ can be obtained as for the ellipse.

6.6   The quadric surfaces

In Chapter 5 we have studied simple examples of surfaces in $\mathcal{E}_3$, namely, planes, which arise as graphs of linear equations in x, y, and z, and spheres which arise as graphs of quadratic equations of the form

$$(x - a)^2 + (y - b)^2 + (z - c)^2 = r^2.$$

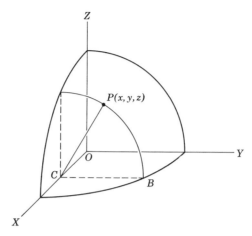

Fig. 6.8

Just as the conics arise as graphs in $\mathcal{E}_2$ of more general quadratic equations in x and y so the study of the graphs in $\mathcal{E}_3$ of more general quadratic equations in x, y, and z leads to new surfaces known as the *quadric surfaces* or *quadrics*. In this section we discuss these surfaces by examining certain standard equations of the second degree. Before doing this, however, we discuss a few examples that will illustrate some of the surfaces so obtained.

Example 1. *Find an equation for the surface generated by rotating the ellipse*

(13)
$$\frac{x^2}{a^2} + \frac{y^2}{b^2} = 1$$

about the x-axis.

Solution. Let $P(x, y, z)$ be any point on the surface. Suppose the plane through P perpendicular to the x-axis cuts the x-axis in C and the given ellipse in B (see Fig. 6.8). The coordinates of C are $(x, 0, 0)$ and of B, $(x, y, 0)$ where from (13) $y = \pm \dfrac{b}{a} \sqrt{a^2 - x^2}$. The definition of the surface requires that $CP = CB$ and therefore

$$y^2 + z^2 = \frac{b^2}{a^2}(a^2 - x^2)$$

or

$$\frac{x^2}{a^2} + \frac{y^2}{b^2} + \frac{z^2}{b^2} = 1,$$

which is an equation of the surface, a segment of which is shown in Fig. 6.8.

Example 2. *A straight line through the origin is rotated about the z-axis so that the angle it makes with the z-axis is constant and equal to α. Find an equation of the surface (a cone) so generated.*

Solution. Let $P(x, y, z)$ be any point on the surface. Then the plane through P perpendicular to the z-axis cuts the z-axis in $C(0, 0, z)$. Since angle $OCP = 90°$ we have (see Fig. 6.9), whether P is above or below the xy-plane,

$$CP^2 = OC^2 \tan^2 \alpha,$$

or

$$x^2 + y^2 = k^2 z^2,$$

where $k = \tan \alpha$. An equation of the given cone is therefore $x^2 + y^2 - k^2 z^2 = 0$. A segment of the cone is shown in Fig. 6.9.

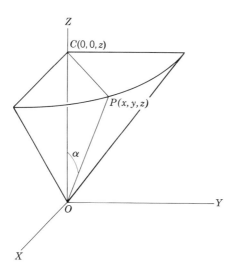

Fig. 6.9

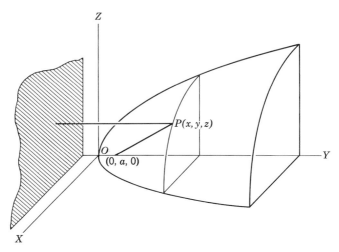

Fig. 6.10

Example 3. *Find an equation for the set of points $P(x, y, z)$ such that the distance of P from the point $(0, a, 0)$ is equal to its distance from the plane $y = -a$.*

Solution. If $P(x, y, z)$ is any such point, then, referring to Fig. 6.10, we see that

$$|y + a| = \sqrt{x^2 + (y - a)^2 + z^2}$$

or

$$x^2 + z^2 = 4ay.$$

The student should show that this is identical with the surface obtained by rotating the parabola $x^2 = 4ay$ about the y-axis.

Example 4. *Investigate the graph of the equation $z^2 = 4ay$.*

Solution. In the yz-plane the points satisfying this equation constitute a parabola with the y-axis as axis of symmetry. The coordinates (x, y, z) satisfy this equation if and only if the coordinates $(0, y, z)$ do, that is, if and only if the projection of the point (x, y, z) onto the yz-plane lies on the parabola. The surface thus contains every line perpendicular to the yz-plane that intersects the parabola $z^2 = 4ay$, $x = 0$. It is called a parabolic cylinder and is shown in Fig. 6.11.

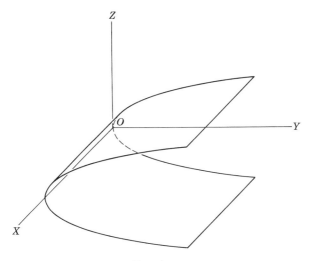

Fig. 6.11

The surfaces just described are examples of quadric surfaces. There are five true quadrics: the ellipsoid, two hyperboloids, and two paraboloids. In addition, there are the quadric cones and cylinders illustrated in Examples 2 and 4. We shall describe these surfaces by deriving their principal features from certain standard second-degree equations. The method used will be to sketch the surface from its equation by finding the curves in which it cuts the coordinate planes and other planes parallel to them. The curve of intersection of a surface and a plane is called the *trace* of the surface in that plane. It is represented by two equations, that of the surface and that of the plane, and consists of all points whose coordinates satisfy both these equations.

The Ellipsoid. Consider the surface whose equation is

$$\frac{x^2}{a^2} + \frac{y^2}{b^2} + \frac{z^2}{c^2} = 1.$$

In this equation, and in what follows, a, b, and c are assumed to be positive. Directly from its equation we can draw several conclusions about this surface. It is symmetric with respect to each of the three coordinate planes since, if (x, y, z) is on the surface, so also are $(-x, y, z)$, $(x, -y, z)$, and $(x, y, -z)$. If (x, y, z) is a point on the surface, then $|x| \leq a$, $|y| \leq b$, and $|z| \leq c$. The surface

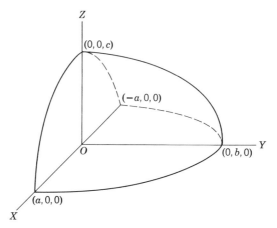

Fig. 6.12. Ellipsoid.

is therefore bounded, lying inside the box bounded by the planes $x = \pm a$, $y = \pm b$, and $z = \pm c$ and touching the faces of this box at the points $(\pm a, 0, 0)$, $(0, \pm b, 0)$, and $(0, 0, \pm c)$. The trace of the surface in the xy-plane is the ellipse

$$\frac{x^2}{a^2} + \frac{y^2}{b^2} = 1,$$

$$z = 0.$$

If $|k| < c$, the trace in the plane $z = k$ is the ellipse

$$\frac{x^2}{a^2\left(1 - \dfrac{k^2}{c^2}\right)} + \frac{y^2}{b^2\left(1 - \dfrac{k^2}{c^2}\right)} = 1,$$

$$z = k,$$

whose semi-axes decrease as $|k|$ increases. Similarly, the traces in the planes $x = k$, where $|k| < a$, and $y = k$, where $|k| < b$, are also ellipses. It is now possible to sketch the surface a segment of which is shown in Fig. 6.12. This surface is called an *ellipsoid*. If two of the numbers a, b, and c are equal, the ellipsoid is an *ellipsoid of revolution*, the surface generated by revolving an ellipse about its major or minor axis. If $a = b = c$, the surface is a sphere with center at the origin.

The Hyperboloid of One Sheet. Consider the surface whose equation is

$$\frac{x^2}{a^2} + \frac{y^2}{b^2} - \frac{z^2}{c^2} = 1.$$

Its trace in the xy-plane is the ellipse

$$\frac{x^2}{a^2} + \frac{y^2}{b^2} = 1,$$

$$z = 0,$$

and in the plane $z = k$, the ellipse

$$\frac{x^2}{a^2\left(1 + \dfrac{k^2}{c^2}\right)} + \frac{y^2}{b^2\left(1 + \dfrac{k^2}{c^2}\right)} = 1,$$

$$z = k.$$

The semi-axes of the ellipse in which the surface cuts the plane $z = k$ therefore increase as $|k|$ increases.

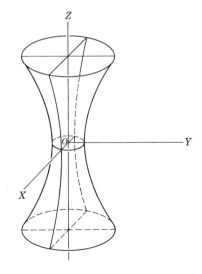

Fig. 6.13. Hyperboloid of one sheet.

The trace in the xz-plane is the hyperbola

$$\frac{x^2}{a^2} - \frac{z^2}{c^2} = 1,$$

$$y = 0,$$

and the trace in the yz-plane is the hyperbola

$$\frac{y^2}{b^2} - \frac{z^2}{c^2} = 1,$$

$$x = 0.$$

A sketch of the surface, which is called a *hyperboloid of one sheet*, is shown in Fig. 6.13. If $a = b$, the trace in any plane $z = k$ is a circle and the surface is a hyperboloid of revolution generated by revolving a hyperbola about its conjugate axis.

The Hyperboloid of Two Sheets. The surface whose equation is

$$-\frac{x^2}{a^2} + \frac{y^2}{b^2} - \frac{z^2}{c^2} = 1$$

does not cut the xz-plane nor indeed any plane $y = k$, where $|k| < b$. However, if $|k| > b$, its trace in the plane $y = k$ is the ellipse

$$\frac{x^2}{a^2} + \frac{z^2}{b^2} = \frac{k^2}{b^2} - 1,$$

$$y = k.$$

In the xy- and yz-planes the traces are, respectively, the hyperbolas

$$\frac{x^2}{a^2} - \frac{y^2}{b^2} = -1, \qquad z = 0,$$

and

$$\frac{y^2}{b^2} - \frac{z^2}{c^2} = 1, \qquad x = 0.$$

The surface is symmetrical with respect to each of the coordinate planes and consists of two parts or *sheets*, one in the region $y \geq b$ and one in the region $y \leq -b$. A sketch of the surface, a *hyperboloid of two sheets*, is shown in Fig. 6.14. If $a = b$, the surface has circular cross sections in planes perpendicular to the y-axis. It is then a hyperboloid of revolution generated by revolving a hyperbola about its transverse axis.

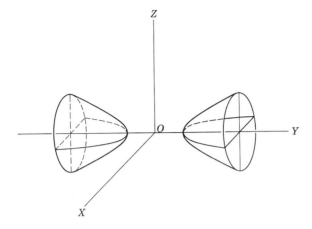

Fig. 6.14. Hyperboloid of two sheets.

The Elliptic Paraboloid. The equation

$$\frac{x^2}{a^2} + \frac{y^2}{b^2} = cz$$

represents an *elliptic paraboloid,* a sketch of which for $c > 0$ is shown in Fig. 6.15. If $k > 0$, its trace in the plane $z = k$ is the ellipse

$$\frac{x^2}{cka^2} + \frac{y^2}{ckb^2} = 1,$$

$$z = k.$$

The surface does not extend below the xy-plane. Its traces in the xz- and yz-planes are the parabolas

$$x^2 = a^2 cz, \qquad y = 0$$

and

$$y^2 = b^2 cz, \qquad x = 0.$$

The surface is symmetric with respect to the xz- and yz-planes. If $a = b$, it is paraboloid of revolution.

The Hyperbolic Paraboloid. The surface whose equation is

$$\frac{y^2}{b^2} - \frac{x^2}{a^2} = cz$$

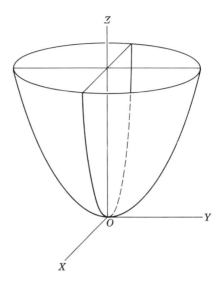

Fig. 6.15. Elliptic paraboloid.

is called a *hyperbolic paraboloid*. Its trace in the xz-plane is the parabola $x^2 = -a^2cz$, $y = 0$, which opens downward if $c > 0$ and has the z-axis as axis of symmetry. Its trace in the yz-plane is the parabola $y^2 = b^2cz$, $x = 0$, which opens upward if $c > 0$ and has the z-axis as axis of symmetry. Its trace in the plane $z = k$, $k \neq 0$, is the hyperbola

$$\frac{x^2}{a^2ck} - \frac{y^2}{b^2ck} = -1,$$

$$z = k.$$

If $k > 0$, the transverse axis of the hyperbola is parallel to the y-axis, but, if $k < 0$, its transverse axis is parallel to the x-axis. The trace in the plane $z = 0$ is the two straight lines

$$\frac{x^2}{a^2} - \frac{y^2}{b^2} = 0,$$

$$z = 0.$$

A sketch of this surface for $c > 0$ is shown in Fig. 6.16.

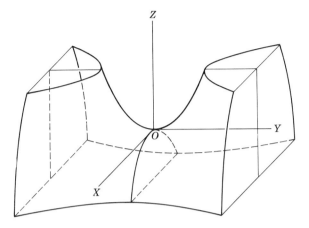

Fig. 6.16. Hyperbolic paraboloid.

The Quadric Cone. The graph of an equation of the form

$$\frac{x^2}{a^2} + \frac{y^2}{b^2} = z^2$$

is called a *quadric cone*. Its trace in the plane $z = k$ is the ellipse

$$\frac{x^2}{k^2 a^2} + \frac{y^2}{k^2 b^2} = 1,$$

$$z = k,$$

whose axes increase as $|k|$ increases. The trace in the plane $z = 0$ is the single point $(0, 0, 0)$ called the *vertex* of the cone. The traces in the xz- and yz-planes are the pairs of lines

$$z = \pm \frac{x}{a}, \quad y = 0, \quad \text{and} \quad z = \pm \frac{y}{b}, \quad x = 0,$$

which intersect in the vertex. The graph is shown in Fig. 6.17.

Quadric Cylinders. If the equation $f(x, y) = 0$ represents a curve in $\mathcal{E}_2$, the graph in $\mathcal{E}_3$ of this same equation consists of all points (x, y, z)

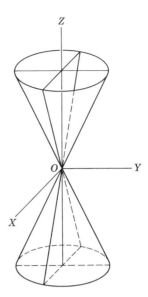

Fig. 6.17. Quadric cone.

in $\mathcal{E}_3$ whose projections $(x, y, 0)$ in the xy-plane lie on the curve

(14)
$$f(x, y) = 0,$$
$$z = 0.$$

Such a surface is called a cylinder. It is generated by a line that moves so that it always intersects the curve (14) and remains perpendicular to the plane in which this curve lies. All cross sections perpendicular to the generating lines are congruent to the original curve. If the curve $f(x, y) = 0$ is a conic, the corresponding cylinder is called a *quadric cylinder*. Thus the equations

$$y^2 = 4ax, \qquad \frac{x^2}{a^2} + \frac{y^2}{b^2} = 1, \qquad \frac{x^2}{a^2} - \frac{y^2}{b^2} = 1$$

represent, respectively, a parabolic cylinder, an elliptic cylinder, and a hyperbolic cylinder in $\mathcal{E}_3$. Similarly, the equation $z^2 = 4ay$ (Fig. 6.11) represents a parabolic cylinder with generating lines parallel to the x-axis. In general, when one variable is missing in an equation the corresponding graph is a cylinder with generating lines parallel to the axis of the missing variable.

EXERCISE 6.4

1. Find equations of the following surfaces:

   (a) The cylinder, with generators parallel to the x-axis, that intersects the yz-plane in a circle with center $(0, 2, -1)$ and radius 5.

   (b) The paraboloid generated by rotating the parabola

$$x^2 = 6y,$$

$$z = 0,$$

   about its axis of symmetry.

   (c) The cone generated by rotating the line

$$y = mx,$$

$$z = 0,$$

   about the x-axis.

   (d) The cone generated by rotating the line

$$y = mx + b,$$
$$z = 0,$$

   about the y-axis.

2. Find an equation for the cone generated by rotating the line l_2 about l_1, these lines being

$$
\begin{array}{lrclr}
 & x & = & 2t & x = -t \\
l_1: & y & = & 3t & \quad l_2: \quad y = 4t \\
 & z & = & -t & z = 2t
\end{array}
$$

   Hint: The vertex will be at the origin, the point of intersection of l_1 and l_2. Let $P(x, y, z)$ be any point on the cone. Then the vector $\overrightarrow{OP}$ must make a constant angle with the vector $\overrightarrow{OQ}$ where Q is any point on l_1.

3. Show that an equation of a circular cone with vertex at the origin, axis in the direction of the unit vector $[\lambda, \mu, \nu]$, is

$$(\lambda x + \mu y + \nu z)^2 = k^2(x^2 + y^2 + z^2)$$

   where k is the cosine of the angle between the axis and a generator of the cone.

4. Identify and sketch each of the following surfaces

   (a) $x^2 - 3y^2 + z^2 = 1$,   (f) $4x = y^2 + z^2$,

   (b) $x^2 - 3y^2 + z^2 = 0$,   (g) $4y = x^2$,

   (c) $x^2 - 3y^2 + z^2 = -1$,   (h) $4z = y^2 - x^2$,

   (d) $x^2 - 9y^2 = 0$,   (i) $x^2 + 4y^2 + 4z^2 = 16$.

   (e) $x^2 - 9y^2 = 9$,

5. By a suitable translation of axes reduce each of the following equations to a form similar to those discussed in Section 6.6. Hence identify the surface represented by each equation:

(a) $x^2 + 4y^2 + 2z^2 - 2x + 32y + 8z = 27$,
(b) $x^2 + y^2 - 3x + 4y - 8z + 5 = 0$,
(c) $4x^2 + y^2 - z^2 + 12x - 2y + 4z = 12$.

6. The equation

(15)
$$\frac{x^2}{a^2} - \frac{y^2}{b^2} = cz$$

of a hyperbolic paraboloid can be written in the form

$$\left(\frac{x}{a} + \frac{y}{b}\right)\left(\frac{x}{a} - \frac{y}{b}\right) = cz.$$

Use this form of the equation to show that for every real number k the line defined by the equations

(16)
$$\frac{x}{a} + \frac{y}{b} = kc,$$

$$\frac{x}{a} - \frac{y}{b} = \frac{z}{k},$$

lies entirely in the surface (15). Similarly, for every real number m the line defined by

(17)
$$\frac{x}{a} + \frac{y}{b} = mz,$$

$$\frac{x}{a} - \frac{y}{b} = \frac{c}{m},$$

lies entirely in the surface (15). Show also that through every point of the hyperbolic paraboloid there passes exactly one line of the system (16) and exactly one line of the system (17). The surface is thus generated by the system of lines (16) or by (17), and each of these lines is called a generator of the surface. Such a surface is called a *ruled surface*.

7. Show that the hyperboloid of one sheet

$$\frac{x^2}{a^2} + \frac{y^2}{b^2} - \frac{z^2}{c^2} = 1$$

is a ruled surface and find two systems of generators as in Problem 6 by writing its equation in the form

$$\left(\frac{x}{a} + \frac{z}{c}\right)\left(\frac{x}{a} - \frac{z}{c}\right) = \left(1 + \frac{y}{b}\right)\left(1 - \frac{y}{b}\right).$$

6.7   Curves in $\mathcal{E}_3$

If

(18)
$$f(x, y, z) = 0,$$
$$g(x, y, z) = 0,$$

are equations of two surfaces, the simultaneous solutions of these two equations will represent the set of points that lie on both surfaces. We shall refer to this set as the curve of intersection of the two surfaces, although there will of course be cases when the intersection is the null set or a set of isolated points. Assuming that equations (18) do represent a curve, then for any real numbers k_1 and k_2 this curve lies entirely in the surface

(19)
$$k_1 f(x, y, z) + k_2 g(x, y, z) = 0.$$

This is clear because any simultaneous solution of (18) is necessarily a solution of (19). If k_1 and k_2 are different from zero, either of the equations (18) can be replaced by (19) and the resulting pair will have the same simultaneous solutions as (18) and hence represent the same curve. This principle, or an extension of it, can often be applied to find the orthogonal projection of a space curve onto one of the coordinate planes. We shall illustrate this with some examples.

Example 1. *Find equations of the projection of the curve*

(20)
$$x^2 + y^2 - 4z = 0,$$
$$x + 3y + 2z - 6 = 0,$$

onto the xy-plane.

Solution. The curve is the intersection of a paraboloid with a plane. Every point on the curve must also be on the surface

(21)
$$(x^2 + y^2 - 4z) + 2(x + 3y + 2z - 6) = 0, \qquad \text{or}$$
$$x^2 + y^2 + 2x + 6y - 12 = 0.$$

Since (21) is an equation of a cylinder with generators parallel to the z-axis, it must represent the projecting cylinder of the curve (20) onto the xy-plane. The projection of the curve (20) on the xy-plane is therefore the circle

$$x^2 + y^2 + 2x + 6y = 12,$$
$$z = 0,$$

with center at $(-1, -3, 0)$ and radius $\sqrt{22}$.

Example 2. *Find the projection on the xy-plane of the circle in which the plane $3x + 2y - z = 0$ intersects the sphere $x^2 + y^2 + z^2 = 16$.*

Solution. Every simultaneous solution of the two equations must also satisfy

(22) $$x^2 + y^2 + (3x + 2y)^2 = 16.$$

Conversely, every simultaneous solution of (22) and $3x + 2y = z$ must lie on the given sphere. Hence (22) is the projecting cylinder and the projection on the xy-plane is found, by simplifying (22), to be the curve

$$10x^2 + 12xy + 5y^2 = 16,$$
$$z = 0.$$

A curve in $\mathcal{E}_3$ is often most conveniently defined by equations of the form

$$x = f(t),$$
$$y = g(t),$$
$$z = h(t),$$

which give the coordinates of an arbitrary point on the curve in terms of a variable or *parameter* t. The curve then consists of all points $(f(t), g(t), h(t))$ where t varies over some stated domain, which may be the set of all real numbers. An example of this is the parametric equations of a line derived in Section 5.2. As another example consider the equations

(23) $$x = 3 \cos \theta,$$
$$y = 3 \sin \theta,$$
$$z = 2 \cos \theta - 5 \sin \theta.$$

The first two of these equations yield

(24) $$x^2 + y^2 = 9$$

and the third in combination with the first two yields

(25) $$3z = 2x - 5y.$$

Conversely if $x^2 + y^2 = 9$ there exists a value of θ such that $x = 3 \cos \theta$ and $y = 3 \sin \theta$ and hence every point on the curve of intersection of (24) and (25) can be written in the form (23). Hence equations (23) are parametric equations of the curve

$$x^2 + y^2 = 9,$$
$$2x - 5y - 3z = 0,$$

in which the plane (25) intersects the cylinder (24).

Similarly, a surface in $\mathcal{E}_3$ may often be conveniently defined by parametric equations of the form

(26)
$$x = F(u, v),$$
$$y = G(u, v),$$
$$z = H(u, v),$$

which define the coordinates of an arbitrary point (x, y, z) of the surface in terms of two independent parameters u and v, which vary over a stated domain. Thus, for example, the equations

$$x = r \cos \theta,$$
$$y = r \sin \theta, \qquad r \geq 0, \quad 0 \leq \theta < 2\pi$$
$$z = \frac{r}{5},$$

could be used as parametric equations for that part of the cone

$$25z^2 = x^2 + y^2,$$

which is above the xy-plane.

EXERCISE 6.5

1. Find equations of the projections on each of the coordinate planes of the following curves:

(a)
$$x^2 + y^2 + z^2 = 9,$$
$$x + y + z = 0.$$

(b)
$$x^2 + y^2 + z^2 = 9,$$
$$x + z = 0.$$

(c)
$$x^2 + y^2 = 4z,$$
$$x^2 + 4y^2 = z^2.$$

Draw figures showing each curve and at least one projection.

2. Prove that if two spheres intersect, the curve of intersection is a circle. Explain how to find an equation of the plane in which this circle lies.

3. Find an equation of the plane containing the circle of intersection of the spheres

$$x^2 + y^2 + z^2 = 25,$$
$$(x - 1)^2 + (y + 3)^2 + (z - 2)^2 = 14.$$

Find the center and radius of this circle.

4. Show that the curve defined by the parametric equations

$$x = 5 \cos \theta$$
$$y = 5 \sin \theta$$
$$z = 2\theta$$

lies in the cylinder $x^2 + y^2 = 25$ and that every generator of the cylinder cuts the curve in an infinite number of equally spaced points. This curve is called a helix.

5. Describe the curve defined by the parametric equations

(a) $x = 5 \cos \theta$,   (b) $x = 5 \cos \theta$,

$\quad y = 3 \sin \theta$, $\quad y = 3 \sin \theta$,

$\quad z = 2\theta$, $\quad z = 2 \cos \theta + 7 \sin \theta$.

6. Prove that any right circular cone with vertex at the origin and any sphere with center at the origin intersect in two plane curves. *Hint:* See Problem 3, Exercise 6.4.

7. Show that the equations

$$x = 5 \cos \phi \cos \theta$$
$$y = 5 \cos \phi \sin \theta$$
$$z = 5 \sin \phi$$

are parametric equations of a sphere of radius 5, center at the origin. Identify ϕ and θ as angles of latitude and longitude on this sphere.

CHAPTER 7

VECTOR SPACES AND TRANSFORMATIONS OF COORDINATES

7.1 Vector spaces

One of our main objectives in this chapter is to study general transformations by which we change from one Cartesian coordinate system to another. Translation of coordinate axes, discussed in Chapter 4, is one example of such a transformation of coordinates. In the present chapter we consider transformations from a given Cartesian coordinate system to any other such system having the same origin. Since this problem is best handled by vector methods we shall begin by developing further the algebra of vectors.

The basic laws of vector algebra are the five rules A.1 through A.5 for vector addition and the five rules S.1 through S.5 for multiplication by scalars which are listed in Sections 4.4 and 4.5. We now introduce the important concept of a *vector space*, which is essentially an algebraic system in which these ten rules are taken as postulates. We shall state the formal definition and then illustrate it by giving several examples of vector spaces.

Definition. *A set $\mathcal{S}$ of elements X_1, X_2, X_3, . . . , called vectors, is said to be a vector space if the following postulates hold:*

A1. *If X_1, X_2 are any two vectors in $\mathcal{S}$ their sum, a uniquely determined vector denoted by $X_1 + X_2$, is also in $\mathcal{S}$.*

A2. *Vector addition is commutative: $X_1 + X_2 = X_2 + X_1$.*

A3. *Vector addition is associative:*

$$(X_1 + X_2) + X_3 = X_1 + (X_2 + X_3).$$

A4. *There is a vector 0 in $\mathcal{S}$ such that $X + 0 = X$ for every vector X in $\mathcal{S}$.*

A5. *Every vector X in $\mathcal{S}$ has a negative $-X$ in $\mathcal{S}$ such that*

$$X + (-X) = 0.$$

S1. *If $X \in \mathcal{S}$ and k is a real number, there is a uniquely determined vector kX in $\mathcal{S}$ called the scalar product of X by k.*

S2. *If X_1, X_2, $\in \mathcal{S}$ and k is a real number,*

$$k(X_1 + X_2) = kX_1 + kX_2.$$

S3. *If $X \in \mathcal{S}$ and k_1, k_2 are real numbers, $(k_1 + k_2)X = k_1 X + k_2 X$.*

S4. *If $X \in \mathcal{S}$ and k_1, k_2 are real numbers, $k_1(k_2 X) = (k_1 k_2)X$.*

S5. *For every vector X in $\mathcal{S}$, $1X = X$.*

We make several remarks concerning this definition after which we shall give some examples.

Remark 1. This definition of a vector space can be made more general by allowing the scalars to be elements of any field. We shall have no occasion to use this greater generality and in this book a scalar will always be a real number. In the more general context a vector space as defined above would be called a *real* vector space or a vector space over the real numbers.

Remark 2. It can be proved from the postulates listed in the definition that for every vector X in $\mathcal{S}$, we have $0X = 0$ and $(-1)X = -X$ and for every scalar k, $k0 = 0$. These proofs are omitted partly because they seem out of place in a book of this nature and partly because in all the vector spaces that we shall be concerned with the three facts are obvious. The interested student can find the proofs in [3], p. 163.

Remark 3. The difference $X - Y$ of two vectors is defined to be $X + (-Y)$ and if k is a scalar, $k(X - Y) = kX - kY$ can be derived from the postulates.

Remark 4. The definition of a vector space has been given in an abstract form in which the nature of the "vectors" X_1, X_2, . . . in $\mathcal{S}$ is not specified. All that is required is that addition of these "vectors" and multiplication by scalars be defined and satisfy the ten postulates. The advantage of this is that our vectors may then be interpreted in many different ways and a single development of the algebra of vectors becomes applicable in many apparently diverse mathematical situations. One interpretation is of course the vectors in $\mathcal{E}_2$ or $\mathcal{E}_3$ already discussed in Chapter 4. A more general interpretation, and one of which we shall make considerable use, is given in Example 2.

Example 1. *It is clear from Section 4.4 and 4.5 that the set of all vectors* $[x_1, x_2, x_3]$ *in* $\mathcal{E}_3$ *(i.e., the set of all vectors in* $\mathcal{E}_3$ *with initial point at the origin) is a vector space. This space* will be denoted by* $\mathcal{V}_3$. *Similarly, the set of all vectors* $[x_1, x_2]$, *or all vectors in* $\mathcal{E}_2$ *with initial points at the origin, is a vector space which will be denoted by* $\mathcal{V}_2$.

Example 2. *If n is any fixed positive integer, consider the set* $\mathcal{V}_n$ *of all "vectors" of the form*

$$X = [x_1, x_2, \ldots, x_n]$$

where $x_1, x_2, \ldots, x_n$ are arbitrary real numbers. If

$$Y = [y_1, y_2, \ldots, y_n]$$

is also in $\mathcal{V}_n$ *and k is any real number, we define addition and scalar multiplication in* $\mathcal{V}_n$ *by*

$$X + Y = [x_1 + y_1, x_2 + y_2, \ldots, x_n + y_n]$$

and

$$kX = [kx_1, kx_2, \ldots, kx_n].$$

It is easy to verify that the ten postulates are satisfied and that $\mathcal{V}_n$ is a vector space under our definition. For example,

$$O = [0, 0, \ldots, 0]$$

and

$$-X = [-x_1, -x_2, \ldots, -x_n].$$

---

* When no confusion is likely "a space" will be used to mean "a vector space."

Definition. *If* $\mathcal{S}$ *is a vector space and* $\mathfrak{I}$ *is a subset of* $\mathcal{S}$ *which is itself a vector space (relative to the same addition and scalar multiplication as in* $\mathcal{S}$*), then* $\mathfrak{I}$ *is called a* subspace *of* $\mathcal{S}$.

Theorem 7.1. *If* $\mathcal{S}$ *is a vector space, any subset* $\mathfrak{I}$ *of* $\mathcal{S}$ *that satisfies A1 and S1 is a subspace of* $\mathcal{S}$.

Proof. If $X \in \mathfrak{I}$, $O = (0)X$ and $-X = (-1)X$ are both in $\mathfrak{I}$ since S1 holds in $\mathfrak{I}$. This proves A4 and A5. The remaining postulates all hold in $\mathfrak{I}$ because they hold in $\mathcal{S}$. Hence $\mathfrak{I}$ is a vector space and a subspace of $\mathcal{S}$.

Example 3. *The set* $\mathfrak{I}$ *of all vectors* $[x_1, x_2, 0]$ *with third coordinate* 0 *is a subspace of* $\mathcal{U}_3$*, because A1 and S1 clearly hold in* $\mathfrak{I}$:

$$[x_1, x_2, 0] + [y_1, y_2, 0] = [x_1 + y_1, x_2 + y_2, 0] \in \mathfrak{I}$$

$$k[x_1, x_2, 0] = [kx_1, kx_2, 0] \in \mathfrak{I}.$$

Definition. *If* $X_1, X_2, \ldots, X_r$ *are vectors in a space* $\mathcal{S}$*, any vector*

$$c_1X_1 + c_2X_2 + \cdots + c_rX_r$$

formed by adding scalar multiples of $X_1, X_2, \ldots, X_r$ *is called a* linear combination *of* $X_1, X_2, \ldots, X_r$.

Example 4. *Let* $\mathcal{S}$ *be any vector space and let* $X_1, X_2, \ldots, X_r$ *be any* r *vectors of* $\mathcal{S}$*. The set* $\mathfrak{I}$ *of all linear combinations of* $X_1, X_2, \ldots, X_r$ *is a subspace of* $\mathcal{S}$.

It is clear in Example 4 that $\mathfrak{I}$ satisfies A1 and S1. For if

$$X = a_1X_1 + a_2X_2 + \cdots + a_rX_r,$$

$$Y = b_1X_1 + b_2X_2 + \cdots + b_rX_r$$

are any two vectors in $\mathfrak{I}$ we have

$$X + Y = (a_1 + b_1)X_1 + (a_2 + b_2)X_2 + \cdots + (a_r + b_r)X_r$$

$$kX = (ka_1)X_1 + (ka_2)X_2 + \cdots + (ka_r)X_r.$$

Hence $X + Y$ and kX are linear combinations of $X_1, X_2, \ldots, X_r$ and therefore belong to $\mathfrak{I}$. It follows from Theorem 7.1 that $\mathfrak{I}$ is a vector space. It is possible that $\mathfrak{I} = \mathcal{S}$ and we agree to include the space $\mathcal{S}$ itself among the subspaces of $\mathcal{S}$.

Definition. *The subspace of* S *consisting of all linear combinations of the vectors* X_1, X_2, . . . , X_r *is called the subspace* generated *by (or* spanned *by)* X_1, X_2, . . . , X_r.

In the space $\mathcal{V}_3$ if we let

$$E_1 = [1, 0, 0],$$

$$E_2 = [0, 1, 0],$$

$$E_3 = [0, 0, 1],$$

we have

$$[x_1, x_2, x_3] = x_1 E_1 + x_2 E_2 + x_3 E_3.$$

It follows that every vector in $\mathcal{V}_3$ is a linear combination of E_1, E_2, E_3 and hence $\mathcal{V}_3$ itself is the space generated by these three vectors.

Although the terms vector and vector space are capable of many other interpretations in different areas of mathematics, we are primarily concerned in this book with the space $\mathcal{V}_n$ of Example 2 and its subspaces. Whereas the present chapter will be concerned mainly with $\mathcal{V}_2$ and $\mathcal{V}_3$ for which we have familiar geometric interpretations, the definitions and many of the theorems will be stated in terms of vectors in an arbitrary vector space in order that we may apply them in the next chapter to vectors in $\mathcal{V}_n$ to obtain important results about matrices and general systems of linear equations. It is mainly for this purpose that we introduce the spaces $\mathcal{V}_n$ for $n > 3$.

Theorem 7.2. *Let* X_1, X_2 *be any two vectors in* $\mathcal{V}_3$, *that is, two vectors in* $\mathcal{E}_3$ *with initial points at the origin. If* X_1 *and* X_2 *do not lie in the same straight line, the space generated by* X_1, X_2 *consists of all vectors in the same plane as* X_1 *and* X_2.

Proof. Let $V = c_1 X_1 + c_2 X_2$ be any linear combination of X_1, X_2. It is clear that V lies in the same plane as X_1 and X_2 since it is represented by the diagonal of the parallelogram whose sides $c_1 X_1$ and $c_2 X_2$ lie in the lines determined by X_1 and X_2. Conversely, let W be any vector (initial point at O) in the same plane as X_1 and X_2. Let P be the terminal point of W. Through P (see Fig. 7.1) draw lines parallel to X_1 and X_2 to cut the lines in which X_1 and X_2 lie in Q and R. It is then clear that $\overrightarrow{OQ} = k_1 X_1$ and $\overrightarrow{OR} = k_2 X_2$ for some scalars k_1, k_2 and

$$W = \overrightarrow{OP} = \overrightarrow{OQ} + \overrightarrow{OR} = k_1 X_1 + k_2 X_2$$

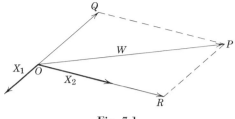

Fig. 7.1

Thus every vector in the plane of X_1, X_2 is a linear combination of X_1, X_2 and the theorem is proved.

Example 5. *Characterize the space generated by the vectors $X_1 = [2, -1, 6]$ and $X_2 = [1, 3, -1]$.*

Solution. (*a*) The space consists of all linear combinations $sX_1 + tX_2$ of the two vectors and hence of all vectors of the form

$$[2s + t, -s + 3t, 6s - t]$$

where s and t are real numbers.

(*b*) By Theorem 7.2 the space consists of all vectors in the plane of X_1 and X_2. A normal to this plane is

$$X_1 \times X_2 = [-17, 8, 7].$$

The space can therefore be characterized as the set of all vectors $[x, y, z]$ that are orthogonal to $[-17, 8, 7]$ or the set of all vectors $[x, y, z]$ whose coordinates satisfy the equation

$$-17x + 8y + 7z = 0.$$

Example 6. *If $\mathcal{S}$ and $\mathcal{T}$ are subspaces of $\mathcal{V}_3$, show that the set $\mathcal{W}$ of all vectors of the form $X + Y$ where $X \in \mathcal{S}$ and $Y \in \mathcal{T}$ is a vector space.*

Solution. If $V \in \mathcal{W}$, then $V = X_1 + Y_1$ where $X_1 \in \mathcal{S}$, $Y_1 \in \mathcal{T}$. Then if k is any scalar, $kV = kX_1 + kY_1$. Since $kX_1 \in \mathcal{S}$ and $kY_1 \in \mathcal{T}$, it follows that $kV \in \mathcal{W}$ and S1 is satisfied. Now if $U = X_2 + Y_2$ is another vector in W, we have

$$V + U = (X_1 + Y_1) + (X_2 + Y_2) = (X_1 + X_2) + (Y_1 + Y_2).$$

Since $X_1 + X_2 \in \mathcal{S}$ and $Y_1 + Y_2 \in \mathcal{T}$, it follows that $V + U \in \mathcal{W}$ and $A1$ is satisfied. Hence $\mathcal{W}$ is a vector space by Theorem 7.1.

EXERCISE 7.1

1. Show that the following are vector spaces.

   (a) The set of all vectors in $\mathcal{E}_3$ that lie in a fixed plane through the origin.
   (b) The set of all vectors in $\mathcal{E}_3$ that lie in a fixed line through the origin.
   (c) The set of all vectors of the form $[a, b, a + b]$ where a, b are real numbers.
   (d) The set of all vectors of the form $[2x - y, 3y, x + 2y]$ where x, y are real numbers.

2. Which of the following are vector spaces?

   (a) The set of all vectors $[x, y, z]$ whose coordinates x, y, z satisfy the equation $x - 5y + 7z = 0$.
   (b) The set of all vectors $[x, y, z]$ whose coordinates x, y, z satisfy the equation $x - 5y + 7z = 6$.
   (c) The set of all vectors of the form $[t + s, t - s, 2t]$ where t and s are real numbers.
   (d) The set of all vectors of the form $[2t + 1, t + s, 2s - 5]$ where t and s are real numbers.
   (e) The set of all vectors of the form $[s + t, s - t, s^2 + t^2]$ where s and t are real numbers.
   (f) The set of all vectors $[x, y, z]$ whose coordinates x, y, z satisfy the two equations

   $$x - y + 3z = 0,$$

   $$4x + y - 2z = 0.$$

   (g) The set of all vectors of the form $nX + mY$ where X, Y are two fixed vectors and n and m are integers.

3. If $\mathcal{S}$ and $\mathcal{T}$ are subspaces of $\mathcal{V}_3$, prove that $\mathcal{S} \cap \mathcal{T}$ is a subspace of $\mathcal{V}_3$.
4. Show that set consisting of the zero vector only is a subspace of $\mathcal{V}_3$.
5. Prove that the space generated by the vectors $[2, -1, 4]$ and $[5, 2, 1]$ consists of all vectors in $\mathcal{V}_3$ that lie in the plane $x - 2y - z = 0$.

7.2   Linear dependence

Basic to the algebra of vectors and vector spaces is the concept of linear dependence. It is defined as follows.

Definition. *A set of n vectors $\{X_1, X_2, \ldots, X_n\}$, $n \geq 1$, in any vector space $\mathcal{V}$, is said to be* linearly dependent, *or simply* dependent, *if there exist n scalars $c_1, c_2, \ldots, c_n$, not all zero, such that*

(1) $$c_1X_1 + c_2X_2 + \cdots + c_nX_n = 0.$$

A set of vectors that is not linearly dependent is said to be *linearly independent*. Thus if $\{X_1, X_2, \ldots, X_n\}$ is a linearly independent set, an equation of the form (1) can hold only if $c_1 = c_2 = \cdots = c_n = 0$.

Example 1. *The set consisting of the three vectors*

$$X = [2, -1, 4]$$

$$Y = [1, 2, 6]$$

$$Z = [1, -8, -10]$$

is linearly dependent since $2X - 3Y - Z = 0$. *The student should check this equation.*

An equation of the form (1) is called a *linear relation* among the vectors $X_1, X_2, \ldots, X_n$. If the coefficients $c_1, c_2, \ldots, c_n$ are not all zero, it is called a *nontrivial* linear relation. Thus a set of vectors is linearly dependent if and only if these vectors satisfy a nontrivial linear relation.

The following lemma draws attention to an important though obvious fact.

Lemma 7.1. *Let* $\mathcal{S}$ *be a non empty subset of the set of vectors*

$$\mathfrak{I} = \{X_1, X_2, \ldots, X_n\}.$$

If $\mathcal{S}$ *is a linearly dependent set, so also is the set* $\mathfrak{I}$.

Proof. Let $\mathcal{S}$ be the set $\{X_1, X_2, \ldots, X_r\}$, $r < n$. If $\mathcal{S}$ is linearly dependent, there is a nontrivial linear relation

$$c_1 X_1 + c_2 X_2 + \cdots + c_r X = 0.$$

It follows that

$$c_1 X_1 + c_2 X_2 + \cdots + c_r X_r + (0)X_{r+1} + \cdots + (0)X_n = 0$$

is a nontrivial linear relation among $X_1, X_2, \ldots, X_n$ which therefore form a linearly dependent set.

Corollary. *Any set of vectors* $\{X_1, X_2, \ldots, X_n\}$ *one of which is the zero vector is linearly dependent.*

Example 2. *Find a nontrivial linear relation that is satisfied by the vectors* $X_1 = [2, -1, 3]$, $X_2 = [-6, 3, -9]$, *and* $X_3 = [7, 2, -8]$

Solution. Since $X_2 = -3X_1$ a nontrivial relation is

$$3X_1 + X_2 + (0)X_3 = O$$

Example 3. *Prove that the vectors $X_1 = [2, -1, 5]$, $X_2 = [3, 0, 1]$, and $X_3 = [1, 4, -2]$ form a linearly independent set.*

Solution. Let c_1, c_2, c_3 be scalars such that

$$c_1 X_1 + c_2 X_2 + c_3 X_3 = O.$$

The left-hand side of this equation is the vector

$$[2c_1 + 3c_2 + c_3, \; -c_1 + 4c_3, \; 5c_1 + c_2 - 2c_3]$$

and hence c_1, c_2, c_3 must satisfy the equations

$$
\begin{aligned}
2c_1 + 3c_2 + \;\; c_3 &= 0, \\
-c_1 \qquad\quad + 4c_3 &= 0, \\
5c_1 + \;\; c_2 - 2c_3 &= 0.
\end{aligned}
$$

(2)

We now use the second equation of (2) to eliminate c_1 from the other two equations. This yields

$$
\begin{aligned}
-c_1 \qquad\;\; + \;\; 4c_3 &= 0, \\
3c_2 + \;\; 9c_3 &= 0, \\
c_2 + 18c_3 &= 0.
\end{aligned}
$$

(3)

where the second equation of (3) is obtained by multiplying the second equation of (2) by 2 and adding to the first, and third equation of (3) is obtained by multiplying the second equation of (2) by 5 and adding to the third. Finally, we divide the second equation of (3) by 3 and subtract from the third and we obtain

$$
\begin{aligned}
c_1 - \;\; 4c_3 &= 0, \\
c_2 + \;\; 3c_3 &= 0, \\
15c_3 &= 0.
\end{aligned}
$$

(4)

The third equation of (4) yields $c_3 = 0$. Substituting this in the second and first gives $c_2 = 0$ and $c_1 = 0$. Hence $c_1 X_1 + c_2 X_2 + c_3 X_3 = 0$ implies that $c_1 = c_2 = c_3 = 0$ and hence $\{X_1, X_2, X_3\}$ is a linearly independent set.

Example 4. *Find a nontrivial linear relation satisfied by the vectors*

$$X_1 = [1, -1, \ 4],$$
$$X_2 = [5, -4, 10],$$
$$X_3 = [3, \quad 1, 12],$$
$$X_4 = [1, \quad 7, \ 3].$$

Solution. If $c_1 X_1 + c_2 X_2 + c_3 X_3 + c_4 X_4 = O$, we find as previously that c_1, c_2, c_3, c_4 must satisfy the equations

$$c_1 + \ 5c_2 + \ 3c_3 + \ c_4 = 0,$$
$$-c_1 - \ 4c_2 + \ c_3 + 7c_4 = 0,$$
$$4c_1 + 10c_2 + 12c_3 + 3c_4 = 0.$$

Using the first equation to eliminate c_1 from the other two as in Example 3, we get

$$c_1 + \quad 5c_2 + 3c_3 + \ c_4 = 0,$$
$$c_2 + 4c_3 + 8c_4 = 0,$$
$$-10c_2 \qquad - \ c_4 = 0.$$

Now multiplying the second equation by 10 and adding to the third, we get

$$c_1 + 5c_2 + \ 3c_3 + \quad c_4 = 0,$$
(5) $$\qquad c_2 + \ 4c_3 + \ 8c_4 = 0,$$
$$40c_3 + 79c_4 = 0.$$

From (5) we can read off a solution. For example, $c_4 = 40$, $c_3 = -79$ is a solution of the third equation of (5). The second then gives $c_2 = -4$ and the first gives $c_1 = 217$. A nontrivial linear relation is therefore

$$217X_1 - 4X_2 - 79X_3 + 40X_4 = O$$

The student should verify this.

EXERCISE 7.2

1. Show that the set consisting of the zero vector only is linearly dependent but that the set consisting of a single nonzero vector is linearly independent.

2. Prove the corollary to Lemma 7.1.
3. Find nontrivial linear relations satisfied by each of the following sets of vectors

   (a) $X_1 = [1, 7]$, $X_2 = [3, -5]$, $X_3 = [2, 1]$.
   (b) $X_1 = [3, -2]$, $X_2 = [-2, \frac{4}{3}]$.
   (c) $X_1 = [0, 0, 0]$, $X_2 = [1, 2, 3]$, $X_3 = [7, -1, 6]$.
   (d) $X_1 = [3, 1, 2]$, $X_2 = [5, -1, 4]$, $X_3 = [1, -5, 2]$.
   (e) $X_1 = [3, -1, 6]$, $X_2 = [2, 1, 1]$, $X_3 = [-1, 7, 3]$, $X_4 = [2, 0, 3]$.

4. Prove that in any vector space two vectors are linearly dependent if and only if one is a scalar multiple of the other and hence that two vectors in $\mathcal{V}_2$ or $\mathcal{V}_3$ are dependent if and only if they lie in the same line through the origin.
5. Prove that three vectors in $\mathcal{V}_3$ are linearly dependent if and only if they lie in one plane. *Hint:* Use the method of Theorem 7.2.
6. If X, Y are linearly independent vectors in $\mathcal{V}_3$, show that the space generated by X and Y consist of all vectors perpendicular to $X \times Y$.
7. Show that the vectors $[a, b]$ and $[c, d]$ are linearly dependent if and only if

$$\begin{vmatrix} a & b \\ c & d \end{vmatrix} = 0.$$

8. Show that the three vectors X, Y, Z in $\mathcal{V}_3$ are linearly dependent if and only if $X \cdot (Y \times Z) = 0$.
9. Show that any set of three or more vectors of $\mathcal{V}_2$ is linearly dependent.
10. Show that the following definition of linear dependence is equivalent to that given in the text: A set of vectors is linearly dependent if and only if one of the vectors in the set belongs to the space generated by the others.
11. Find the value of t so that the following sets of vectors are linearly dependent

    (a) $X_1 = [2, -7]$, $X_2 = [t, 3]$.
    (b) $X_1 = [2, 1, 0]$, $X_2 = [3, -5, 2]$, $X_3 = [1, 4, t]$.

7.3 Dimension of a vector space

Let X_1, X_2, X_3 be any three vectors in $\mathcal{V}_2$. If X_1 and X_2 lie in the same line they are linearly dependent by Problem 4, Exercise 7.2. It then follows by Lemma 7.1 that X_1, X_2, X_3 form a linearly dependent set. If X_1, X_2 do not lie in the same line then $X_3 = c_1 X_1 + c_2 X_2$ by Theorem 7.2. Hence $c_1 X_1 + c_2 X_2 - X_3 = 0$ is a nontrivial relation and again X_1, X_2, X_3 are linearly dependent. This completes the proof of the following theorem.

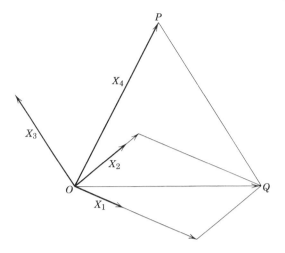

Fig. 7.2

Theorem 7.3. *Any three vectors in $\mathcal{U}_2$ are linearly dependent.*

It is common practice, which we shall adopt, to use the terminology "the vectors X_1, X_2, . . . , X_n are linearly dependent (independent)" to mean the same thing as "the set of vectors $\{X_1, X_2, \ldots, X_n\}$ is linearly dependent (independent)."

We now prove the three-dimensional analogue of Theorem 7.3.

Theorem 7.4. *Any four vectors X_1, X_2, X_3, X_4 of $\mathcal{U}_3$ are linearly dependent.*

Proof. We shall assume that no proper subset of the four vectors is linearly dependent since otherwise the theorem follows from Lemma 7.1. Hence each of the four vectors is nonzero and the sets $\{X_1, X_2\}$ and $\{X_1, X_2, X_3\}$ are both linearly independent. This means (Theorem 7.2) that X_1, X_2 determine a plane and that X_3 does not lie in this plane. Hence (see Fig. 7.2) a line through P, the terminal point of X_4, parallel to X_3 will cut the plane of X_1 and X_2 in a unique point Q. By Theorem 7.2 $\overrightarrow{OQ} = c_1X_1 + c_2X_2$. The points P and Q are distinct since otherwise X_1, X_2, X_4 would be linearly dependent contrary to our assumption. Since QP is parallel to X_3 we have $\overrightarrow{QP} = c_3X_3$ and

$$X_4 = \overrightarrow{OP} = \overrightarrow{OQ} + \overrightarrow{QP} = c_1X_1 + c_2X_2 + c_3X_3.$$

Thus X_4 is in the space generated by X_1, X_2, X_3 and the four vectors X_1, X_2, X_3, X_4 are linearly dependent.

Corollary. *Any set of n vectors of $\mathcal{U}_3$ with $n > 3$ is linearly dependent.*

This follows from Lemma 7.1.

It is interesting to interpret Theorem 7.4 algebraically. Suppose we are given four vectors

$$X_1 = [a_1, b_1, c_1],$$

$$X_2 = [a_2, b_2, c_2],$$

$$X_3 = [a_3, b_3, c_3],$$

$$X_4 = [a_4, b_4, c_4].$$

To assert that these vectors are linearly dependent is to assert that there exist four numbers x_1, x_2, x_3, x_4, not all zero, such that

$$x_1 X_1 + x_2 X_2 + x_3 X_3 + x_4 X_4 = O.$$

This in turn is to assert that the system of equations

$$a_1 x_1 + a_2 x_2 + a_3 x_3 + a_4 x_4 = 0,$$

(6) $$b_1 x_1 + b_2 x_2 + b_3 x_3 + b_4 x_4 = 0,$$

$$c_1 x_1 + c_2 x_2 + c_3 x_3 + c_4 x_4 = 0,$$

has a nontrivial solution, i.e., a solution other than $x_1 = x_2 = x_3 = x_4 = 0$. Conversely, the existence of a nontrivial solution of (6) implies the linear dependence of the four vectors X_1, X_2, X_3, X_4. A linear equation with zero constant term is said to be *homogeneous*. It is now clear that the statement (Theorem 7.4) that any four vectors in $\mathcal{U}_3$ are linearly dependent is equivalent to the algebraic statement that any system of three linear homogeneous equations in four unknowns has a nontrivial solution. Similarly, the corollary to Theorem 7.4 states that any system of three linear homogeneous equations in four *or more* unknowns has a nontrivial solution. Applying the same argument to three or more vectors in $\mathcal{U}_2$ and using Theorem 7.3 we can see that any system of two linear homogeneous equations in three or more unknowns has a nontrivial solution.

Now let $\mathcal{S}$ be any subspace of $\mathcal{U}_3$. This does not exclude the case when $\mathcal{S}$ is $\mathcal{U}_3$ itself. By Theorem 7.4 any linearly independent set of vectors from $\mathcal{S}$ contains at most three vectors. Hence there is an integer n, less than or equal to 3, such that $\mathcal{S}$ contains a set of n linearly independent vectors but no set of $n + 1$ linearly independent vectors.

Definition. *If $\mathcal{S}$ is a vector space that contains a linearly independent set of n vectors but no linearly independent set of $n + 1$ vectors, then $\mathcal{S}$ is said to be a* space of dimension n.

The three vectors

$$E_1 = [1, 0, 0]$$

$$E_2 = [0, 1, 0]$$

$$E_3 = [0, 0, 1]$$

in $\mathcal{U}_3$ are clearly linearly independent. For since

$$c_1 E_1 + c_2 E_2 + c_3 E_3 = [c_1, c_2, c_3]$$

we have that $c_1 E_1 + c_2 E_2 + c_3 E_3 = O$ implies $c_1 = c_2 = c_3 = 0$. Thus $\mathcal{U}_3$ contains a set of three linearly independent vectors but, by Theorem 7.4, no set of more than three independent vectors. Hence $\mathcal{U}_3$ has dimension 3. Similarly, because $[1, 0]$ and $[0, 1]$ are clearly independent, Theorem 7.3 tells us that $\mathcal{U}_2$ has dimension 2.

We have now used the concept of linear dependence to do two things. On the one hand we have used it to give an algebraic definition of the dimension of a vector space which is compatible with our geometric intuition that a line is one-dimensional, a plane two-dimensional, and "physical space" three-dimensional. On the other hand we have shown (Theorem 7.4) that the geometric fact that any four vectors in $\mathcal{U}_3$ are linearly dependent is equivalent to the algebraic fact that any system of three linear homogeneous equations in four unknowns has a nontrivial solution. We now generalize this theorem on homogeneous linear equations, and this will enable us to find the dimension of the space $\mathcal{U}_n$ for any value of n. The basic result is the following.

Theorem 7.5. *If $r > n$, a system of n homogeneous linear equations in r unknowns has a nontrivial solution.*

A detailed proof of this theorem can be found in [5], pp. 14–15 and will not be given here. We simply remark that the proof consists in observing that the method used in Example 4, Section 7.2, to find a solution of three equations in four unknowns is perfectly general and will provide a nontrivial solution of a homogeneous system whenever the number of unknowns is greater than the number of equations.

Now let

$$X_1 = [a_{11}, a_{12}, \ldots, a_{1n}],$$

$$X_2 = [a_{21}, a_{22}, \ldots, a_{2n}],$$

$$\cdots \cdots \cdots \cdots \cdots \cdots \cdots$$

$$X_r = [a_{r1}, a_{r2}, \ldots, a_{rn}],$$

be any set of r vectors in $\mathcal{U}_n$. The linear relation

(7)
$$x_1 X_1 + x_2 X_2 + \cdots + x_r X_r = O$$

is equivalent to the system of equations

(8)
$$a_{11}x_1 + a_{21}x_2 + \cdots + a_{r1}x_r = 0,$$
$$a_{12}x_1 + a_{22}x_2 + \cdots + a_{r2}x_r = 0,$$
$$\cdots \cdots \cdots \cdots \cdots \cdots \cdots \cdots \cdots$$
$$a_{1n}x_1 + a_{2n}x_2 + \cdots + a_{rn}x_r = 0,$$

since the left members of equations (8) are exactly the coordinates of the vector on the left side of (7).

If $r > n$, Theorem 7.5 asserts that there exists a nontrivial solution for (8) and hence a set of real numbers $x_1, x_2, \ldots, x_r$, not all zero, for which (7) holds. This proves that *if $r > n$, any r vectors in $\mathcal{U}_n$ are linearly dependent.*

On the other hand, it is easy to exhibit a linearly independent set of n vectors in $\mathcal{U}_n$. Let

$$E_1 = [1, 0, 0, \ldots, 0],$$

$$E_2 = [0, 1, 0, \ldots, 0],$$

$$\cdots \cdots \cdots \cdots \cdots \cdots$$

$$E_n = [0, 0, 0, \ldots, 1].$$

Since

$$x_1 E_1 + x_2 E_2 + \cdots + x_n E_n = [x_1, x_2, \ldots, x_n],$$

it is clear that

$$x_1E_1 + x_2E_2 + \cdots + x_nE_n = O$$

only if $x_1 = x_2 = \cdots = x_n = 0$. Hence $E_1, E_2, \ldots, E_n$ are linearly independent. This completes the proof of the following.

Theorem 7.6. *The vector space $\mathcal{U}_n$ has dimension n.*

It is clear that any subspace of $\mathcal{U}_n$ has dimension $\leq n$.

EXERCISE 7.3

1. Prove that in any vector space $\mathcal{U}$:

   (a) The subspace consisting of the zero vector only has dimension 0.
   (b) A subspace generated by a single nonzero vector X has dimension 1.
   (c) A subspace generated by two linearly independent vectors has dimension 2.
   (d) A subspace generated by three linearly independent vectors has dimension 3.

2. Prove that a subspace of $\mathcal{U}_3$ that has dimension 3 must be $\mathcal{U}_3$ itself.
3. Prove that every subspace of $\mathcal{U}_3$ is either:

   (a) The space consisting of the zero vector only.
   (b) A space consisting of the set of all vectors that lie in some fixed line through the origin.
   (c) A space consisting of the set of all vectors that lie in some fixed plane through the origin.
   (d) The space $\mathcal{U}_3$ itself.

4. Show that the set of all vectors of the form $[2t, -5t, 4t]$ where t is a real number is a vector space. What is the dimension of this space?
5. Show that the set of all vectors of the form

$$[2s + 3t, 4s + 5t, 7s - t],$$

   where s and t are real numbers is a vector space. What is the dimension of this space?
6. Show that the set $\mathcal{S}$ of all vectors $[x, y, z]$ whose coordinates satisfy a homogeneous linear equation

   (9) $$ax + by + cz = 0$$

   is a vector space. What is the dimension of $\mathcal{S}$? The space $\mathcal{S}$ is called the *solution space* of equation (9).

7. Let $\mathcal{S}$ be the solution space (see Problem 6) of the equation (9) and let $\mathcal{J}$ be the solution space of

(10)
$$dx + ey + fz = 0.$$

Prove that the set $\mathcal{W}$ of all vectors that are solution vectors of both (9) and (10) is a vector space and that $\mathcal{W} = \mathcal{S} \cap \mathcal{J}$. What are the dimensions of $\mathcal{S}$, $\mathcal{J}$, and $\mathcal{W}$ (a) if $\mathcal{S}$ and $\mathcal{J}$ are different spaces? (b) if $\mathcal{S} = \mathcal{J}$?

8. Find two vectors that generate the solution space of the equation

$$2x - y + 7z = 0.$$

9. Find a vector that generates the solution space of the system of equations

$$x - y + 4z = 0,$$
$$2x + y - 3z = 0.$$

10. If $\mathcal{S}$ is a vector space of dimension n and $X_1, X_2, \ldots, X_r$ ($r \leq n$) are r linearly independent vectors of $\mathcal{S}$, prove that the subspace of $\mathcal{S}$ generated by $X_1, X_2, \ldots, X_r$ has dimension r.

11. Prove that the set of all vectors $[x, y, z, t]$ whose coordinates satisfy the equation

(11)
$$2x - y + 7z + 3t = 0$$

is a subspace $\mathcal{S}$ of $\mathcal{V}_4$.

12. Show that the subspace $\mathcal{S}$ of Problem 11 has dimension 3. *Hint:* Show that (11) has three linearly independent solution vectors of the form $[x_1, 0, 0, 1]$, $[x_2, 0, 1, 0]$, $[x_3, 1, 0, 0]$, and that these three vectors generate the solution space.

13. Use the method of Example 4, Section 7.2, to solve the following system for x, y, z in terms of t:

$$x - y + 2z + t = 0,$$
$$3x - 2y + z + t = 0,$$
$$x + y - 5z + 8t = 0.$$

From this solution deduce that the solution space of this system has dimension 1. Find a vector that generates this solution space.

14. Find two linearly independent solution vectors of the system

$$x + 2y - 6z + t = 0,$$
$$3x - y + z - 2t = 0$$

and show that they generate the solution space of the system. What is the dimension of the solution space?

7.4   Bases of a vector space

Let $\mathcal{S}$ be any vector space of dimension n. Thus, for example, $\mathcal{S}$ might be $\mathcal{V}_n$ or perhaps a subspace of $\mathcal{V}_m$ for some integer $m > n$. By the definition of dimension, $\mathcal{S}$ contains a linearly independent set of n vectors, say $X_1, X_2, \ldots, X_n$. If X is any vector in $\mathcal{S}$ it follows, again from the definition of dimension, that the set $\{X, X_1, X_2, \ldots, X_n\}$ is linearly dependent. Hence there exist scalars $c, c_1, c_2, \ldots, c_n$ not all zero such that

$$(12) \qquad cX + c_1X_1 + c_2X_2 + \cdots + c_nX_n = 0.$$

Moreover $c \neq 0$ for otherwise (12) would be a nontrivial linear relation among the vectors $X_1, X_2, \ldots, X_n$ contrary to their linear independence. Hence we can divide (12) by c and express X as a linear combination of $X_1, X_2, \ldots, X_n$. Thus

$$(13) \qquad X = a_1X_1 + a_2X_2 + \cdots + a_nX_n$$

where $a_i = -c_i/c$ $(i = 1, 2, \ldots, n)$. Moreover, the coefficients a_1, $a_2, \ldots, a_n$ in (13) are uniquely determined by X. For if in addition we have

$$X = b_1X_1 + b_2X_2 + \cdots + b_nX_n,$$

we get by subtracting (13)

$$0 = (b_1 - a_1)X_1 + (b_2 - a_2)X_2 + \cdots + (b_n - a_n)X_n.$$

The linear independence of $X_1, \ldots, X_n$ then implies that $b_i - a_i = 0$ or $b_i = a_i$ $(i = 1, 2, \ldots, n)$. We have therefore proved the following.

Theorem 7.7. *If $X_1, X_2, \ldots, X_n$ is any set of n linearly independent vectors in a space $\mathcal{S}$ of dimension n, then every vector X in $\mathcal{S}$ has a unique representation as a linear combination of $X_1, X_2, \ldots, X_n$.*

Definition. *If $\mathcal{S}$ is a vector space of dimension n, any set of n linearly independent vectors of $\mathcal{S}$ is called a basis of $\mathcal{S}$.*

Thus if $X_1, X_2, \ldots, X_n$ is a basis of $\mathcal{S}$, Theorem 7.7 tells us that every vector X in $\mathcal{S}$ can be written in exactly one way in the form

$$X = a_1X + a_2X_2 + \cdots + a_nX_n.$$

The coefficients $a_1, a_2, \ldots, a_n$ are called the *coordinates of X relative to the basis* $X_1, X_2, \ldots, X_n$.

Example 1. *Show that the vectors* $X_1 = [2, -1]$, $X_2 = [1, 5]$ *constitute a basis of* $\mathcal{V}_2$. *Find the coordinates of the vector* $[7, 4]$ *relative to this basis.*

Solution. Since neither of the two vectors X_1, X_2 is a scalar multiple of the other, they are linearly independent. Since $\mathcal{V}_2$ has dimension 2 it follows that X_1, X_2 is a basis. To find the required coordinates we must write $[7, 4]$ as a linear combination of X_1 and X_2. If

$$[7, 4] = x[2, -1] + y[1, 5],$$

we must have

$$2x + y = 7,$$
$$-x + 5y = 4.$$

Solving these we get $x = \frac{31}{11}$; $y = \frac{15}{11}$ and hence

$$[7, 4] = \tfrac{31}{11}X_1 + \tfrac{15}{11}X_2,$$

and the coordinates of $[7, 4]$ relative to the basis X_1, X_2 are $[\frac{31}{11}, \frac{15}{11}]$.

Example 2. *Find a basis for the solution space* $\mathcal{S}$ *of the system of equations*

$$x - y + 2z + t + u = 0,$$
$$2x + y - z + 2t + 3u = 0.$$

Solution. Since there are five unknowns, the solution vectors belong to $\mathcal{V}_5$. The equations may be written

$$x - y = -2z - t - u,$$
$$2x + y = z - 2t - 3u,$$

and from these, eliminating y and x in turn, we get

(14)
$$x = -\tfrac{1}{3}z - t - \tfrac{4}{3}u,$$
$$y = \tfrac{5}{3}z - \tfrac{1}{3}u.$$

It is clear from these equations that solutions can be found by assigning arbitrary values to z, t, and u and computing the corresponding values of x and y. For example if we put each of z, t, u in turn equal to 1 and the other two equal to 0, we find the following three solution vectors.

$$X_1 = [-\tfrac{1}{3}, \tfrac{5}{3}, 1, 0, 0],$$

$$X_2 = [-1, 0, 0, 1, 0],$$

$$X_3 = [-\tfrac{4}{3}, -\tfrac{1}{3}, 0, 0, 1].$$

These are linearly independent since

$$c_1 X_1 + c_2 X_2 + c_3 X_3 = \left[\frac{-c_1 - 3c_2 - 4c_3}{3}, \frac{5c_1 - c_3}{3}, c_1, c_2, c_3 \right]$$

and is therefore O only if $c_1 = c_2 = c_3 = 0$. Moreover, X_1, X_2, X_3 generate the solution space $\mathcal{S}$. For if $X = [x_1, x_2, x_3, x_4, x_5]$ is any vector in $\mathcal{S}$, the vector $X - x_3 X_1 - x_4 X_2 - x_5 X_3$ also belongs to $\mathcal{S}$ and its last three coordinates are 0. Since its coordinates satisfy (14) it follows that its first two coordinates must also be 0. Hence $X = x_3 X_1 + x_4 X_2 + x_5 X_3$ and every vector of $\mathcal{S}$ is a linear combination of X_1, X_2, X_3. It follows that $\mathcal{S}$ has dimension 3 and that X_1, X_2, X_3 is a basis of $\mathcal{S}$.

EXERCISE 7.4

Note: When the problems in this exercise require the solution of a system of linear equations the student should use the method illustrated in Examples 3 and 4 of Section 7.2.

1. Show that the vectors $X_1 = [2, -1]$, $X_2 = [1, 3]$ form a basis of $\mathcal{V}_2$.
2. If $\{X_1, X_2\}$ is a basis of $\mathcal{V}_2$, show that $\{X_1, X_2 + kX_1\}$, for any scalar k, is also a basis of $\mathcal{V}_2$.
3. Let $X_1 = [2, 1, -5]$, $X_2 = [3, -1, 4]$. Prove that the vector $X = [13, -1, 2]$ lies in the same plane as X_1, X_2 and write X as a linear combination of X_1, X_2.
4. If X_1, X_2, X_3 are linearly independent vectors in a space $\mathcal{S}$, prove that the vectors

$$Y_1 = X_1 + aX_2 + bX_3$$

$$Y_2 = \qquad X_2 + cX_3$$

$$Y_3 = \qquad\qquad X_3$$

are also linearly independent for any values of a, b, c.
5. Show that the vectors $X_1 = [1, 0, 5]$, $X_2 = [3, -1, 4]$, and $X_3 = [2, 9, 7]$ form a basis of $\mathcal{V}_3$. Express the vector $X = [2, 5, 3]$ as a linear combination

of X_1, X_2, X_3. What are the coordinates of X relative to the basis X_1, X_2, X_3?

6. Let $\mathcal{S}$ be a vector space of dimension n. If $\mathcal{3}$ is a subspace of $\mathcal{S}$ and $\mathcal{3}$ also has dimension n, prove that $\mathcal{3} = \mathcal{S}$.

7. Find a basis for the solution space of each of the following

(a) $3x - y + z - 2t = 0$. (d) $x + 2y - 2z = 0$.

(b) $x + y - z + t = 0$, (e) $x - y + 3z = 0$,

       $2x + y - 2z + 4t = 0$. $x + 2y - z = 0$.

(c) $x + 2y + z - t + u = 0$, (f) $2x - y + z - 5t + u = 0$.

       $3x + y - z + 2t + 3u = 0$.

7.5   General coordinate systems

We now return to geometry in $\mathcal{E}_2$ and $\mathcal{E}_3$ and use the concepts that have been introduced to study general Cartesian coordinate systems. We shall deal first with coordinate systems in the plane $\mathcal{E}_2$. Since vector methods will be used, the student should first be clear on the relationship between $\mathcal{E}_2$ and the vector space $\mathcal{V}_2$. We have identified $\mathcal{E}_2$ with the set of all points (x, y) in a plane and $\mathcal{V}_2$ with the set of all vectors $[x, y]$ where x, y are arbitrary real numbers. Thus from one point of view the *elements* of these two sets differ only in the shape of the brackets used, certainly a trivial distinction. The significant difference between the two sets lies rather in what we *do* with these elements. In $\mathcal{E}_2$ we are concerned with points, distances between them, lines joining two points, and such questions as whether a given point lies on a given line. The elements $[x, y]$ of $\mathcal{V}_2$, on the other hand, are vectors with initial point $(0, 0)$ and terminal point (x, y). As vectors, they can be added, multiplied by scalars, and used to designate directions in the plane $\mathcal{E}_2$. We can of course also think of $\mathcal{E}_2$ simply as the set of all points in a plane and of $\mathcal{V}_2$ as the set of all vectors in this plane with fixed initial point 0. It is important to remember that when we replace these geometric objects, points, and vectors by their algebraic counterparts (x, y) and $[x, y]$, a fixed coordinate system is assumed. A different choice of coordinate system would assign a different pair of real numbers to a given point or vector.

We now consider any Cartesian coordinate system in $\mathcal{E}_2$ as described in Section 2.2. We shall designate the axes by x_1 and x_2 rather than the conventional x and y because this notation has some advantages

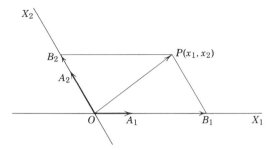

Fig. 7.3

when two or more coordinate systems are being considered. Let A_1, A_2 be the unit points on the x_1- and x_2-axes and denote the vectors $\overrightarrow{OA}_1$ and $\overrightarrow{OA}_2$ by E_1 and E_2. Since E_1 and E_2 do not lie in the same line, they are linearly independent and form a basis of $\mathcal{V}_2$. Let $P(x_1, x_2)$ be an arbitrary point in the plane and let lines through P parallel to the coordinate axes cut these axes in B_1 and B_2 as in Fig. 7.3. It is then clear that $\overrightarrow{OB}_1 = x_1 E_1$, $\overrightarrow{OB}_2 = x_2 E_2$, and $\overrightarrow{OP} = x_1 E_1 + x_2 E_2$. Thus every Cartesian coordinate system in $\mathcal{E}_2$ gives rise in a natural way to a basis E_1, E_2 of $\mathcal{V}_2$.

Conversely, suppose we are given any two linearly independent vectors E_1, E_2 (in a plane $\mathcal{E}_2$) with the same initial point 0. These vectors determine a coordinate system in $\mathcal{E}_2$ with origin O and with the terminal points of E_1 and E_2 as unit points of the x_1- and x_2-axes. Thus every basis E_1, E_2 of $\mathcal{V}_2$ determines a Cartesian coordinate system in $\mathcal{E}_2$, and conversely. Moreover, the relation between the basis E_1, E_2 and the corresponding coordinate system is such that if P is any point in $\mathcal{E}_2$ with coordinates (x_1, x_2) then

$$\overrightarrow{OP} = x_1 E_1 + x_2 E_2.$$

Thus x_1, x_2 are both the coordinates of P and the coordinates of $\overrightarrow{OP}$ relative to the basis E_1, E_2. Figure 7.4 shows the grid or "graph paper" for the coordinate system defined by the vectors E_1, E_2. We refer to this as the x-coordinate system.

Now suppose we choose another pair of basis vectors F_1, F_2 for $\mathcal{V}_2$ having the same initial point O, and consider the corresponding coordinate system (see Fig. 7.5). The coordinate axes determined by F_1 and F_2 will be called the y_1-axis and the y_2-axis. Since E_1, E_2 form a

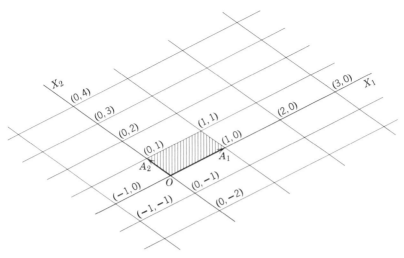

Fig. 7.4

basis of $\mho_2$, F_1 and F_2 can be expressed as linear combinations of E_1 and E_2. Thus we have

$$F_1 = a_1 E_1 + a_2 E_2,$$
(15)
$$F_2 = b_1 E_1 + b_2 E_2,$$

where (a_1, a_2), (b_1, b_2) are the coordinates of the unit points on the y_1- and y_2-axes relative to the x-coordinate system. Now let P be any

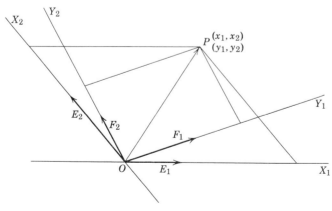

Fig. 7.5

point in the plane. Let (x_1, x_2) be the x-coordinates of P and (y_1, y_2) its y-coordinates. This means that

$$
\begin{aligned}
\overrightarrow{OP} &= y_1F_1 + y_2F_2 \\
&= y_1(a_1E_1 + a_2E_2) + y_2(b_1E_1 + b_2E_2) \qquad \text{by (15)} \\
&= (a_1y_1 + b_1y_2)E_1 + (a_2y_1 + b_2y_2)E_2 \\
&= x_1E_1 + x_2E_2.
\end{aligned}
$$

But by Theorem 7.7 the representation of $\overrightarrow{OP}$ as a linear combination of E_1 and E_2 is unique, and hence

(16)
$$
\begin{aligned}
x_1 &= a_1y_1 + b_1y_2, \\
x_2 &= a_2y_1 + b_2y_2.
\end{aligned}
$$

Equations (16) relate the x-coordinates and the y-coordinates of an arbitrary point P. Note that the coefficients a_1, b_1, a_2, b_2 in (16) depend only on the two coordinate systems and not on the point P. Equations (16) are called the equations of the transformation from the x-coordinate system to the y-coordinate system.

Example 1. *Given a rectangular coordinate system with origin O and equal units on the x_1- and x_2-axes, find equations of the transformation of coordinates to the y-coordinate system with origin O if the unit points on the y_1- and y_2-axes are $U_1(2, -1)$ and $U_2(1, 1)$, respectively. Find an equation relative to the y-coordinate system for the circle $x_1{}^2 + x_2{}^2 = 4$.*

Solution. Let P be any point in the plane. Let (x_1, x_2) be the coordinates of P relative to the x-coordinate system and (y_1, y_2) the coordinates of P relative to the y-coordinate system. Let F_1 be the vector $\overrightarrow{OU}_1$ and F_2 the vector $\overrightarrow{OU}_2$ so that relative to the x-coordinate system

$$
F_1 = [2, -1],
$$
$$
F_2 = [1, 1].
$$

Referring to Fig. 7.6 we have

$$
\begin{aligned}
\overrightarrow{OP} = [x_1, x_2] = y_1F_1 + y_2F_2 &= y_1[2, -1] + y_2[1, 1] \\
&= [2y_1 + y_2, -y_1 + y_2]
\end{aligned}
$$

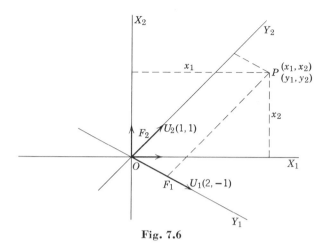

Fig. 7.6

and therefore

(17)
$$x_1 = 2y_1 + y_2,$$
$$x_2 = -y_1 + y_2.$$

These are the equations of the transformation of coordinates.

Now if $P(x_1, x_2)$ is constrained to lie on the given circle we have

(18) $$x_1{}^2 + x_2{}^2 = 4.$$

Hence if (y_1, y_2) are the y-coordinates of P, we have from (17) and (18)

$$(2y_1 + y_2)^2 + (-y_1 + y_2)^2 = 4$$

or

$$5y_1{}^2 + 2y_1y_2 + 2y_2{}^2 = 4,$$

which is an equation of the given circle in the y-coordinate system.

Example 2. *Find a formula for the distance between the points $P(y_1, y_2)$, $P'(y_1', y_2')$ in the y-coordinate system of Example 1.*

Solution. Let the x-coordinates of P, P' be (x_1, x_2) and (x_1', x_2'). Hence

$$PP'^2 = (x_1 - x_1')^2 + (x_2 - x_2')^2$$
$$= \{(2y_1 + y_2) - (2y_1' + y_2')\}^2 + \{(-y_1 + y_2) - (-y_1' + y_2')\}^2$$
$$= 5(y_1 - y_1')^2 + 2(y_1 - y_1')(y_2 - y_2') + 2(y_2 - y_2')^2$$

The required formula results on taking square roots. If we put $y_1' = y_2' = 0$, we get for the square of the distance from the origin to the point $P(y_1, y_2)$ the expression

$$5y_1{}^2 + 2y_1y_2 + 2y_2{}^2.$$

Thus $P(y_1, y_2)$ lies on a circle with center O and radius 2 if and only if

$$5y_1{}^2 + 2y_1y_2 + 2y_2{}^2 = 4,$$

the same result that we obtained in Example 1.

We shall now state in general terms the results we have obtained.

Theorem 7.8. *Let E_1, E_2 be basis vectors corresponding to an x-coordinate system and F_1, F_2 be basis vectors corresponding to a y-coordinate system. Then if*

$$F_1 = a_1E_1 + a_2E_2,$$

$$F_2 = b_1E_1 + b_2E_3,$$

the x-coordinates (x_1, x_2) and the y-coordinates (y_1, y_2) of any point P are connected by the equations

$$x_1 = a_1y_1 + b_1y_2,$$

$$x_2 = a_2y_1 + b_2y_2.$$

Similarly, given a system of coordinates in $\mathcal{E}_3$ the vectors E_1, E_2, E_3 drawn from the origin to the unit points of the three coordinate axes will serve as a basis for $\mathcal{V}_3$—the basis corresponding to the given coordinate system. Conversely, given an origin O and any three linearly independent vectors with initial points at O, a coordinate system is determined by choosing the terminal points of these vectors as the unit points on the three coordinate axes.

The three-dimensional form of Theorem 7.8 is the following.

Theorem 7.9. *Let E_1, E_2, E_3 be basis vectors corresponding to an x-coordinate system in $\mathcal{E}_3$ and let F_1, F_2, F_3 be basis vectors corresponding to a y-coordinate system. Then if*

$$F_1 = a_1E_1 + a_2E_2 + a_3E_3,$$

$$F_2 = b_1E_1 + b_2E_2 + b_3E_3,$$

$$F_3 = c_1E_2 + c_2E_2 + c_3E_3,$$

the x-coordinates (x_1, x_2, x_3) and the y-coordinates (y_1, y_2, y_3) of any point P are connected by the equations

$$x_1 = a_1y_1 + b_1y_2 + c_1y_3,$$

$$x_2 = a_2y_1 + b_2y_2 + c_2y_3,$$

$$x_3 = a_3y_1 + b_3y_2 + c_3y_3.$$

The proof is similar to that of Theorem 7.8 and will be left as an exercise. (See Exercise 7.5, Problem 5.)

EXERCISE 7.5

Note: In all the following problems the x-coordinate system is assumed to be rectangular with equal units on the coordinate axes.

1. Find equations of the transformation of coordinates from an x-coordinate system to:

   (a) A y-coordinate system corresponding to the basis vectors $F_1 = [2, 1]$, $F_2 = [-1, 3]$.

   (b) A y-coordinate system in which the y_1-axis is the line $3x_1 = x_2$ and the y_2-axis the line $x_1 + x_2 = 0$ and the units are the same on the y_1- and y_2-axes as on the x_1- and x_2-axes.

   (c) A y-coordinate system corresponding to the basis vectors

   $$F_1 = [\sqrt{2}/2, \sqrt{2}/2] \text{ and } F_2 = [-\sqrt{2}/2, \sqrt{2}/2].$$

2. Find an equation of the circle $x_1^2 + x_2^2 = 9$ in each of the three y-coordinate systems in Problem 1.

3. Find an equation of the ellipse $x_1^2/a^2 + x_2^2/b^2 = 1$ in the y-coordinate system corresponding to the basis vectors $F_1 = [a, 0]$, $F_2 = [0, b]$.

4. Find an equation of the hyperbola $x_1^2/a^2 - x_2^2/b^2 = 1$ in a y-coordinate system in which the coordinate axes are the asymptotes of the hyperbola and the units on the y-coordinate axes are the same as on the x-coordinate axes.

5. Write out a proof of Theorem 7.9.

6. Given an ellipsoid $(x_1^2/a^2) + (x_2^2/b^2) + (x_3^2/c^2) = 1$, explain how to choose a y-coordinate system in which the ellipsoid has the equation

$$y_1^2 + y_2^2 + y_3^2 = 1.$$

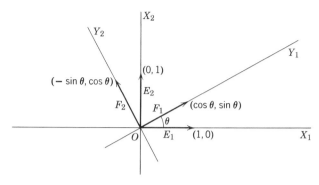

Fig. 7.7

7.6 Rotation of axes in $\mathcal{E}_2$

We assume again that the x-coordinate system in $\mathcal{E}_2$ is rectangular with equal units on the coordinate axes. This means that the corresponding basis vectors E_1, E_2 of $\mathcal{V}_2$ are mutually orthogonal unit vectors. Such a basis is called an *orthonormal basis* of $\mathcal{V}_2$. Now suppose the y-coordinate axes are obtained by rotating the x-coordinate axes, about the origin, counterclockwise through an angle θ, orthogonality being preserved. The basis vectors F_1, F_2 corresponding to the y-coordinate system are also an orthonormal basis and are given by (Fig. 7.7)

$$F_1 = [\cos \theta, \sin \theta] = (\cos \theta)E_1 + (\sin \theta)E_2$$

$$F_2 = [-\sin \theta, \cos \theta] = (-\sin \theta)E_1 + (\cos \theta)E_2$$

It therefore follows by Theorem 7.8 that the x-coordinates and the y-coordinates are related by the equations

(19)
$$x_1 = y_1 \cos \theta - y_2 \sin \theta,$$
$$x_2 = y_1 \sin \theta + y_2 \cos \theta.$$

Thus equations (19) are the equations of a rotation of coordinate axes (counterclockwise) through an angle θ.

Example 1. *Show that a circle $x_1{}^2 + x_2{}^2 = r^2$ has an equation $y_1{}^2 + y_2{}^2 = r^2$ relative to any y-coordinate system obtained from the x-system by a rotation.*

Solution. Using (19) to transform the equation $x_1{}^2 + x_2{}^2 = r^2$, we get

$$(y_1 \cos \theta - y_2 \sin \theta)^2 + (y_1 \sin \theta + y_2 \cos \theta)^2 = r^2.$$

Simplifying and using $\cos^2 \theta + \sin^2 \theta = 1$ this equation reduces to

$$y_1{}^2 + y_2{}^2 = r^2.$$

Since this equation is independent of θ, it holds for any y-coordinate system obtained by rotation.

Example 2. *Find an equation of the hyperbola* $x_1{}^2 - x_2{}^2 = a^2$ *relative to a y-coordinate system obtained by rotating the coordinate axes counterclockwise through 45°.*

Solution. Since $\theta = 45°$, the equations (19) become

$$x_1 = \frac{y_1 - y_2}{\sqrt{2}}$$

$$x_2 = \frac{y_1 + y_2}{\sqrt{2}}.$$

The equation $x_1{}^2 - x_2{}^2 = a^2$ therefore becomes

$$\frac{(y_1 - y_2)^2}{2} - \frac{(y_1 + y_2)^2}{2} = a^2,$$

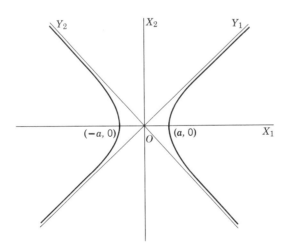

Fig. 7.8

which simplifies to $2y_1y_2 = -a^2$. The hyperbola and the two sets of coordinate axes are shown in Fig. 7.8.

Example 3. *Find equations of a rotation of axes that will reduce the equation*

$$(20) \qquad\qquad 8x_1{}^2 - 12x_1x_2 + 17x_2{}^2 = 20$$

to an equation in y_1 and y_2 which lacks the term in y_1y_2. Use the y-equation to sketch the graph of (20) and show both the x- and the y-coordinate axes.

Solution. If we rotate the axes through an angle θ, the y-equation of the curve is obtained by substituting (19) in (20). The result is

$$8(y_1 \cos \theta - y_2 \sin \theta)^2 - 12(y_1 \cos \theta - y_2 \sin \theta)(y_1 \sin \theta + y_2 \cos \theta)$$
$$+ 17(y_1 \sin \theta + y_2 \cos \theta)^2 = 20.$$

This simplifies to

$$ay_1{}^2 + by_1y_2 + cy_2{}^2 = 20,$$

where the coefficients a, b, c are given by

$$
\begin{aligned}
a &= 8 \cos^2 \theta - 12 \sin \theta \cos \theta + 17 \sin^2 \theta, \\
b &= 18 \sin \theta \cos \theta - 12(\cos^2 \theta - \sin^2 \theta), \\
&= 9 \sin 2\theta - 12 \cos 2\theta, \\
c &= 8 \sin^2 \theta + 12 \sin \theta \cos \theta + 17 \cos^2 \theta.
\end{aligned}
$$

(21)

We now choose θ so that the coefficient b of y_1y_2 is zero, i.e., so that

$$9 \sin 2\theta - 12 \cos 2\theta = 0$$

or

$$(22) \qquad\qquad \tan 2\theta = \tfrac{4}{3}.$$

Any solution of (22) will serve our purpose. We choose the solution for which $0 < 2\theta < 90°$. We then have $\sin 2\theta = \tfrac{4}{5}$ and $\cos 2\theta = \tfrac{3}{5}$ and since θ is an acute angle,

$$\sin \theta = \sqrt{\frac{1 - \cos 2\theta}{2}} = \frac{1}{\sqrt{5}},$$

$$\cos \theta = \sqrt{\frac{1 + \cos 2\theta}{2}} = \frac{2}{\sqrt{5}}.$$

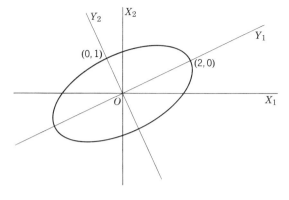

Fig. 7.9

The angle θ is therefore approximately $26°\ 34'$ and from (19) the equations of the required rotation are

$$x_1 = \frac{2y_1 - y_2}{\sqrt{5}},$$

$$x_2 = \frac{y_1 + 2y_2}{\sqrt{5}}.$$

From (21) we have $a = 5$, $b = 0$, $c = 20$. The transformed equation is therefore

$$5y_1{}^2 + 20y_2{}^2 = 20$$

or

$$\frac{y_1{}^2}{4} + y_2{}^2 = 1.$$

The graph is therefore an ellipse with major axis 4 and minor axis 2. Its graph, with both sets of coordinate axes, is shown in Fig. 7.9.

In Chapter 9 we shall give an alternative method for the solution of Example 3 which is not only simpler than the preceding one but has the added advantage that it can readily be generalized to three- (or higher) dimensional space.

EXERCISE 7.6

1. Transform the following equations by rotating the coordinate axes through the angle indicated. Sketch the graph of the equation showing both sets of coordinate axes.

   (a) $x_1 x_2 = 4$, $\theta = 45°$.
   (b) $x_1^2 + 2x_1 x_2 + x_2^2 - 2x_1 + 2x_2 = 0$, $\theta = 45°$.
   (c) $4x_1^2 + 4x_1 x_2 + x_2^2 + 6x_1 - x_2 = 0$, θ such that $\tan \theta = \frac{1}{2}$.
   (d) $x_1^2 - 3x_2^2 = 5$, θ such that $\tan \theta = 3$.

2. Find a rotation of axes that will reduce the equation

$$2x_1^2 - 12x_1 x_2 - 3x_2^2 = 42$$

   to an equation in y_1, y_2 that lacks the term in $y_1 y_2$. Use the y-equation to sketch the graph and show both sets of coordinate axes.

3. Show that if $a \neq c$, the equation

$$ax_1^2 + bx_1 x_2 + cx_2^2 = d$$

   can be reduced to an equation of the form

$$a' y_1^2 + c' y_2^2 = d$$

   by rotating the x_1- and x_2-axes through an angle θ chosen to satisfy $\tan 2\theta = b/(a - c)$.

4. Show that if $a = c$, the result stated in Problem 3 can be achieved by rotating the axes through an angle of $45°$.

CHAPTER **8**

MATRICES, DETERMINANTS, AND LINEAR EQUATIONS

8.1 Matrices

Before discussing rotation of axes and other transformations of coordinates in $\mathcal{E}_3$, it is desirable to introduce some matrix algebra for this provides a very flexible and compact language in which quite general results can be stated.

A *matrix* is any rectangular array of numbers such as, for example,

$$A = \begin{bmatrix} 2 & -6 \\ 3 & 4 \end{bmatrix} \quad \text{or} \quad B = \begin{bmatrix} 5 & 1 & 0 & 3 \\ 2 & 6 & -1 & 4 \\ 3 & -5 & 7 & 0 \end{bmatrix}.$$

If a matrix has m rows and n columns, it is said to be of *type* (m, n). The preceding examples are therefore of type $(2, 2)$ and $(3, 4)$. Two matrices are said to be *equal* only if they are of the same type and if the numbers in corresponding positions in the two matrices are equal. A matrix of type (n, n) is said to be a square matrix of *order* n. The vector $[x_1, x_2, x_3]$ is a matrix of type $(1, 3)$. The numbers that make up a matrix are called the *elements* of the matrix. For the most part we shall deal with matrices whose elements are real numbers. However, the elements of a matrix might also be complex numbers or even polynomials (see Chapter 10). Matrices will be denoted by capital Latin letters.

Associated with any matrix M is another matrix, called the transpose of M, which is obtained by writing the rows of M as columns. The transpose of M is denoted by M^T. Thus if A and B are the two preceding matrices, we have

$$A^T = \begin{bmatrix} 2 & 3 \\ -6 & 4 \end{bmatrix} \qquad B^T = \begin{bmatrix} 5 & 2 & 3 \\ 1 & 6 & -5 \\ 0 & -1 & 7 \\ 3 & 4 & 0 \end{bmatrix}.$$

Clearly, if M is of type (m, n), M^T is of type (n, m). A vector of $\mathcal{V}_n$ (sometimes called a vector of order n), such as

$$X = [x_1, x_2, \ldots, x_n],$$

will be called a *row vector* to distinguish it from its transpose

$$X^T = \begin{bmatrix} x_1 \\ x_2 \\ \cdot \\ \cdot \\ \cdot \\ x_n \end{bmatrix}$$

which is called a *column vector*. The rows of a matrix, considered as vectors, are called the row vectors of the matrix. Similarly, the columns are called the column vectors. Thus the matrix B has three row vectors (of order 4) and four column vectors (of order 3).

If A is any matrix of type (m, n), a double subscript notation is often used to designate the elements of A whereby the element in the ith row and jth column is denoted by a_{ij} (or b_{ij}, c_{ij}, etc.). Thus we would write

$$A = \begin{bmatrix} a_{11} & a_{12} & \cdots & a_{1n} \\ a_{21} & a_{22} & \cdots & a_{2n} \\ \cdot & \cdot & \cdot & \cdot \\ a_{m1} & a_{m2} & \cdots & a_{mn} \end{bmatrix}.$$

The first subscript, called the row index, designates the number of the row and the second subscript, the column index, designates the number of the column in which the element occurs. If the number of rows and columns is clear from the context, the above matrix may be written in the abbreviated form $A = [a_{ij}]$. If $m = n$ so that the matrix is square the diagonal from the upper left- to lower right-hand corner of the matrix is called the *main diagonal* of A. The elements $a_{11}, a_{22}, \ldots, a_{nn}$ that lie on the main diagonal are called the *diagonal elements* of A. A square matrix in which all elements not on the main diagonal are zero is called a *diagonal matrix*.

If two matrices are of the same type, their *sum* is defined to be the matrix obtained by adding corresponding elements. Thus if

$$A = \begin{bmatrix} a_1 & a_2 \\ b_1 & b_2 \end{bmatrix} \quad \text{and} \quad C = \begin{bmatrix} c_1 & c_2 \\ d_1 & d_2 \end{bmatrix}$$

we define the sum $A + C$ to be the matrix

$$A + C = \begin{bmatrix} a_1 + c_1 & a_2 + c_2 \\ b_1 + d_1 & b_2 + d_2 \end{bmatrix}.$$

Note that the sum of two matrices is defined only when they are of the same type. Note also that the sum of two vectors in $\mathcal{U}_n$ is a special case of a matrix sum.

If A is a matrix and k is any real number, it is useful to define the *scalar multiple* kA of A to be the matrix obtained by multiplying all the elements of A by k. Thus

$$k \begin{bmatrix} a_1 & a_2 \\ b_1 & b_2 \end{bmatrix} = \begin{bmatrix} ka_1 & ka_2 \\ kb_1 & kb_2 \end{bmatrix}.$$

We write $-A$ for $(-1)A$ and $A - C$ for $A + (-C)$. Thus

$$-C = \begin{bmatrix} -c_1 & -c_2 \\ -d_1 & -d_2 \end{bmatrix} \quad \text{and} \quad A - C = \begin{bmatrix} a_1 - c_1 & a_2 - c_2 \\ b_1 - d_1 & b_2 - d_2 \end{bmatrix}.$$

It is easy to show that matrix addition and scalar multiplication obey exactly the same rules as the corresponding operations for vectors which are listed in Sections 4.4 and 4.5. The role of the "zero matrix" is filled by a matrix all elements of which are zero. Whatever its type such a matrix will be denoted by O.

Before defining the product of two matrices, we consider the following motivation of our definition. Suppose a coordinate transformation

(1)
$$x_1 = a_1y_1 + a_2y_2,$$
$$x_2 = b_1y_1 + b_2y_2$$

from an x-coordinate system in $\mathcal{E}_2$ to a y-coordinate system is followed by a second transformation

(2)
$$y_1 = c_1z_1 + c_2z_2$$
$$y_2 = d_1z_1 + d_2z_2$$

from the y-coordinate system to a z-coordinate system. The transformation (1) is characterized by the matrix

$$A = \begin{bmatrix} a_1 & a_2 \\ b_1 & b_2 \end{bmatrix},$$

called the *matrix of the transformation*. Similarly, the matrix

$$C = \begin{bmatrix} c_1 & c_2 \\ d_1 & d_2 \end{bmatrix}$$

is the matrix of the transformation (2). By substituting (2) for y_1, y_2 in (1) we get equations of the transformation that takes us directly from the x-coordinates to the z-coordinates. These equations are, as the student should verify,

(3)
$$x_1 = (a_1c_1 + a_2d_1)z_1 + (a_1c_2 + a_2d_2)z_2,$$
$$x_2 = (b_1c_1 + b_2d_1)z_1 + (b_1c_2 + b_2d_2)z_2.$$

The matrix of this transformation is called the product of the matrices A and C (in that order) and we write

$$AC = \begin{bmatrix} a_1c_1 + a_2d_1 & a_1c_2 + a_2d_2 \\ b_1c_1 + b_2d_1 & b_1c_2 + b_2d_2 \end{bmatrix}.$$

Note that the first row of AC is found by forming inner products of the first row vector of A with the column vectors of C. Similarly, the second row of AC consists of inner products of the second row vector of A with the column vectors of C. We use this principle to state the general definition of a matrix product.

Definition. *Let* $A = [a_{ij}]$ *be a matrix of type* (m, n) *whose* i*th row vector is* $[a_{i1}, a_{i2}, \ldots, a_{in}]$ *and let* $B = [b_{ij}]$ *be a matrix of type* (n, r) *whose* j*th column vector is*

$$\begin{bmatrix} b_{1j} \\ b_{2j} \\ \cdot \\ \cdot \\ \cdot \\ b_{nj} \end{bmatrix}.$$

The product AB *is the matrix of type* (m, r) *such that the element in its* i*th row and* j*th column is* $a_{i1}b_{1j} + a_{i2}b_{2j} + \cdots + a_{in}b_{nj}$, $(i = 1, 2, \ldots, m; j = 1, 2, \ldots, r)$.

Example 1. *The student should verify the following matrix products*

(a)
$$\begin{bmatrix} 2 & 1 & -4 \\ 5 & 0 & 3 \end{bmatrix} \begin{bmatrix} 2 & 1 & 0 \\ 1 & -1 & 3 \\ 1 & 1 & 4 \end{bmatrix} = \begin{bmatrix} 1 & -3 & -13 \\ 13 & 8 & 12 \end{bmatrix}.$$

For example, the first row of the product consists of the inner products of $[2, 1, -4]$ *with the three column vectors of the right-hand factor.*

(b)
$$[1 \quad 3] \begin{bmatrix} 1 & -1 & 2 \\ 2 & 2 & 3 \end{bmatrix} = [7 \quad 5 \quad 11]$$

(c)
$$\begin{bmatrix} 1 & 2 & -5 \\ 3 & 1 & 4 \\ 2 & 9 & 7 \end{bmatrix} \begin{bmatrix} x_1 \\ x_2 \\ x_3 \end{bmatrix} = \begin{bmatrix} x_1 + 2x_2 - 5x_3 \\ 3x_1 + x_2 + 4x_3 \\ 2x_1 + 9x_2 + 7x_3 \end{bmatrix}$$

Note that the matrix product AC *is defined only if the number of columns in the left-hand factor* A *is equal to the number of rows in the right-hand factor* C.

Returning now to the two transformations of coordinates (1) and (2), suppose a third transformation

(4)
$$z_1 = e_1 w_1 + e_2 w_2,$$
$$z_2 = f_1 w_1 + f_2 w_2$$

from the z-coordinate system to a w-coordinate system is applied. The matrix of the transformation going directly from the x's to the w's could be found by substituting (4) in (3). As before, this matrix would be the product $(AC)D$ where

$$D = \begin{bmatrix} e_1 & e_2 \\ f_1 & f_2 \end{bmatrix}$$

is the matrix of the transformation (4). However the same result, namely, the equations giving the x's in terms of the w's, could be obtained by first substituting (4) in (2) to get the equations with matrix CD giving the y's in terms of the w's. These could then be substituted in (1) to get equations with matrix $A(CD)$ giving the x's in terms of the w's. Since these last equations must be the same as those already found, it follows that the two matrix products $(AC)D$ and $A(CD)$ must be the same. This illustrates the following general law which holds for matrix products.

Associative law for matrix multiplication. *If A, C, D are any three matrices of type (m, n), (n, r) and (r, s) respectively, then*

$$(AC)D = A(CD).$$

Matrix multiplication also satisfies the following.

Distributive laws for matrix multiplication. *Let B and C be any two matrices of type (m, n). Let A and D be of type (r, m) and (n, s) respectively. Then*

$$A(B + C) = AB + AC$$

and

$$(B + C)D = BD + CD.$$

We shall not prove the distributive law in general but shall ask the student to verify special cases of it in Problem 7, Exercise 8.1.

In general, matrix multiplication is not commutative. Thus even if A and B are matrices for which both AB and BA are defined, these two products will in general be different (see Problem 1, Exercise 8.1). In special cases, AB and BA may be equal and we then say A *commutes* with B, or B with A. If, for example, A is a square matrix and we denote the product AA by A^2, the associative law gives

$$AA^2 = A(AA) = (AA)A = A^2A$$

and therefore A commutes with A^2. Thus we can define A^3 unambiguously to be AA^2 (or A^2A). Indeed, for any positive integer n we can define A^n to be AA^{n-1} and show that A commutes with every positive integral power of A.

The diagonal matrix, of any order, whose diagonal elements are all equal to 1 is called a *unit* or *identity* matrix and is denoted by I. If A is any square matrix and if I is the unit matrix of the same order then it is easy to verify that $IA = AI = A$. Note that a transformation of coordinates in $\mathcal{E}_2$ with matrix I leaves the coordinates of every point unchanged, since it has the form $x_1 = y_1$, $x_2 = y_2$; hence the term *identity* matrix.

EXERCISE 8.1

1. If
$$A = \begin{bmatrix} 2 & 1 \\ -1 & 6 \end{bmatrix} \quad \text{and} \quad B = \begin{bmatrix} 1 & 5 \\ 2 & -3 \end{bmatrix},$$
compute the matrices AB and BA, A^2, A^2B, and A^3.

2. If
$$A = \begin{bmatrix} 2 & 1 & 4 \\ 3 & -1 & 2 \end{bmatrix} \quad \text{and} \quad B = \begin{bmatrix} 5 & 2 & -1 \\ 3 & 0 & 1 \\ 2 & 4 & -3 \end{bmatrix},$$
compute AB, B^2, AA^T, A^TA, BB^T.

3. If
$$A = \begin{bmatrix} \cos\theta & -\sin\theta \\ \sin\theta & \cos\theta \end{bmatrix}, \quad B = \begin{bmatrix} \cos\phi & -\sin\phi \\ \sin\phi & \cos\phi \end{bmatrix},$$
show that $AB = BA = \begin{bmatrix} \cos(\theta+\phi) & -\sin(\theta+\phi) \\ \sin(\theta+\phi) & \cos(\theta+\phi) \end{bmatrix}$.

Interpret this geometrically by considering A and B as the matrices of two rotations of coordinate axes.

4. If A is the matrix given in Problem 3, find A^2, A^3 and A^{57}.

5. If $A = \begin{bmatrix} \dfrac{1}{\sqrt{2}} & -\dfrac{1}{\sqrt{2}} \\ \dfrac{1}{\sqrt{2}} & \dfrac{1}{\sqrt{2}} \end{bmatrix}$, compute A^2, A^4, and A^8. Explain the results in terms of rotations of axes.

6. If $A = \begin{bmatrix} \dfrac{\sqrt{3}}{2} & -\dfrac{1}{2} \\ \dfrac{1}{2} & \dfrac{\sqrt{3}}{2} \end{bmatrix}$, can you write down A^{12} without doing any matrix multiplication?

7. If A and B are the matrices in Problem 1 and if

$$C = \begin{bmatrix} 8 & -3 \\ 2 & 5 \end{bmatrix} \quad \text{and} \quad X = \begin{bmatrix} x \\ y \end{bmatrix},$$

verify the distributive laws $C(A + B) = CA + CB$ and $(A + B)X = AX + BX$.

8. Let D be the diagonal matrix of order n with the element k_i in the ith row and ith column. Show that (a) the product DA is the matrix obtained from A by multiplying the ith row of A by k_i $(i = 1, 2, \ldots, n)$ and (b) the product AD is the matrix obtained from A by multiplying the ith column of A by k_i $(i = 1, 2, \ldots, n)$.

9. Verify the statements of Problem 8 by computing the products AD and DA if

$$D = \begin{bmatrix} 2 & 0 & 0 \\ 0 & -3 & 0 \\ 0 & 0 & 7 \end{bmatrix} \quad \text{and} \quad A = \begin{bmatrix} 1 & 4 & -2 \\ 3 & 5 & 8 \\ 2 & -1 & 6 \end{bmatrix}.$$

10. Let $\mathfrak{M}$ be the set of all second order square matrices with real elements. With addition and scalar multiplication defined as in Section 8.1, show that $\mathfrak{M}$ is a real vector space. Exhibit a set of four matrices which are linearly independent "vectors" of this space and which generate the space $\mathfrak{M}$. Hence prove that the dimension of $\mathfrak{M}$ as a vector space is 4. Now show that the set of all m by n matrices is a space of dimension mn.

11. If $A = \begin{bmatrix} 2 & -1 \\ 3 & 5 \end{bmatrix}$, solve the matrix equation $AX = I$, that is find u, v, x, y, such that

$$\begin{bmatrix} 2 & -1 \\ 3 & 5 \end{bmatrix} \begin{bmatrix} u & x \\ v & y \end{bmatrix} = \begin{bmatrix} 1 & 0 \\ 0 & 1 \end{bmatrix}.$$

12. (a) Can you solve the matrix equation $AX = I$ if

$$A = \begin{bmatrix} 1 & -2 \\ 3 & -6 \end{bmatrix}.$$

(b) Can you solve the matrix equation $AX = 0$ for A as in Problem 12a? How many solutions are there?

(c) Can you solve $AX = 0$ for A as in Problem 11? How many solutions are there?

13. Let $\mathfrak{S}$ be the set of all square matrices of fixed order n, with addition and multiplication defined as in Section 8.1. Which of the field postulates listed in Section 1.2 hold in $\mathfrak{S}$ and which do not?

14. If A, B are any two matrices for which the product AB is defined, prove that $(AB)^T = B^T A^T$.
    Hint: Let $A = [a_{ij}]$, $B = [b_{ij}]$. Compute the element in the ith row and jth column of $(AB)^T$ and show that it is equal to the element in the same position in $B^T A^T$.

15. Verify the result in Problem 14 for the matrices

(a) $A = \begin{bmatrix} 2 & 1 \\ -6 & 4 \end{bmatrix}$ $B = \begin{bmatrix} a & b \\ c & d \end{bmatrix}$,

(b) $A = \begin{bmatrix} 2 & 0 & 1 \\ 5 & -1 & 6 \\ 8 & 2 & 9 \end{bmatrix}$ $B = \begin{bmatrix} 3 \\ 2 \\ -1 \end{bmatrix}$.

16. Prove (from the definition of matrix product) that the row vectors of the matrix AB are R_1B, R_2B, . . . , R_nB where R_1, . . . , R_n are the row vectors of A.
17. Prove that the column vectors of AB are AC_1^T, AC_2^T, . . . , AC_m^T where C_1^T, . . . , C_m^T are the column vectors of B.
18. Verify the results of Problems 16 and 17 when

$$A = \begin{bmatrix} 2 & 9 & 1 \\ 0 & -1 & 4 \\ 5 & 3 & 2 \end{bmatrix} \quad B = \begin{bmatrix} 4 & 1 & 2 \\ -1 & 0 & 1 \\ 2 & 3 & 1 \end{bmatrix}.$$

8.2   Matrices and systems of linear equations

Consider the system of linear equations

(5)
$$2x_1 + 3x_2 - x_3 = 4,$$
$$x_1 + 4x_2 + 2x_3 = 10,$$
$$5x_1 - 4x_2 + 4x_3 = 2.$$

One problem associated with such a system is to find a solution. By this we mean to find three numbers x_1, x_2, x_3 that satisfy the three equations. This problem can be solved by the method described in Example 3, Section 7.2 and will be dealt with later in this section. (See Example 1 below). A more basic problem is to determine the conditions under which such a solution exists and if it exists, the conditions under which it is unique. We consider first problems of the latter kind.

We note first that equations (5) can be written in the vector-matrix form,

(6)
$$\begin{bmatrix} 2 & 3 & -1 \\ 1 & 4 & 2 \\ 5 & -4 & 4 \end{bmatrix} \begin{bmatrix} x_1 \\ x_2 \\ x_3 \end{bmatrix} = \begin{bmatrix} 4 \\ 10 \\ 2 \end{bmatrix},$$

for if we compute the matrix product on the left we get a column vector whose three elements are the left members of equations (5). Equating these to the corresponding elements of the vector on the right side of equation (6) equations (5) result. The matrix

$$A = \begin{bmatrix} 2 & 3 & -1 \\ 1 & 4 & 2 \\ 5 & -4 & 4 \end{bmatrix}$$

is called the coefficient matrix of the system (5). If we denote by X the vector $[x_1, x_2, x_3]$ and by C the vector $[4, 10, 2]$, we can write equations (5) in the compact form

(7) $$A X^T = C^T.$$

This is a useful shorthand notation for the system (5).

Another way to write (5) as a vector equation is

(8) $$x_1 \begin{bmatrix} 2 \\ 1 \\ 5 \end{bmatrix} + x_2 \begin{bmatrix} 3 \\ 4 \\ -4 \end{bmatrix} + x_3 \begin{bmatrix} -1 \\ 2 \\ 4 \end{bmatrix} = \begin{bmatrix} 4 \\ 10 \\ 2 \end{bmatrix}.$$

In this form the equations ask us to express the vector of the constant terms as a linear combination of the column vectors of A. If the column vectors of A are linearly independent and hence form a basis of $\mathcal{V}_3$, Theorem 7.7 tells us that (8), and therefore (7), has a unique solution for x_1, x_2, x_3, whatever the vector of constant terms may be. In fact, Theorem 7.7 ensures that, for any n, an arbitrary vector of $\mathcal{V}_n$ can be expressed in one and only one way as a linear combination of any given set of n linearly independent vectors of $\mathcal{V}_n$. We can therefore state the following general result.

Theorem 8.1. *Let $A X^T = C^T$ be a system of n linear equations in n unknowns, with coefficient matrix A. If the column vectors of A are linearly independent, then the system has a unique solution.*

It is easy to show that if the row vectors of a square matrix are linearly dependent, the column vectors are also. We give the proof for the 3-by-3 matrix

$$M = \begin{bmatrix} a_1 & a_2 & a_3 \\ b_1 & b_2 & b_3 \\ c_1 & c_2 & c_3 \end{bmatrix}.$$

Denote the row vectors of this matrix by A, B, and C.
We consider the system of equations $AX^T = O$ or

$$a_1x_1 + a_2x_2 + a_3x_3 = 0,$$
(9)
$$b_1x_1 + b_2x_2 + b_3x_3 = 0,$$
$$c_1x_1 + c_2x_2 + c_3x_3 = 0.$$

If the row vectors of A are linearly dependent, one of them, say C, is a linear combination of the other two. Now if $C = pA + qB$, the third equation of (9) can be obtained by multiplying the first by p, the second by q, and adding and is therefore satisfied by every solution of the first two. The third equation is therefore redundant and every solution of the system

$$a_1x_1 + a_2x_2 + a_3x_3 = 0,$$
(10)
$$b_1x_1 + b_2x_2 + b_3x_3 = 0$$

is also a solution of (9). But by Theorem 7.5 the system (10) has a nontrivial solution. Hence (9) has a nontrivial solution. Since (9) can be written in the form

$$x_1 \begin{bmatrix} a_1 \\ b_1 \\ c_1 \end{bmatrix} + x_2 \begin{bmatrix} a_2 \\ b_2 \\ c_2 \end{bmatrix} + x_3 \begin{bmatrix} a_3 \\ b_3 \\ c_3 \end{bmatrix} = 0,$$

the existence of a nontrivial solution implies that the column vectors of M are linearly dependent.

Conversely, if the columns of M are linearly dependent, the rows of M^T (which are the columns of M) are dependent. Hence by the preceding proof the columns of M^T, that is, the rows of M, are linearly dependent.

The preceding proof, although stated for the third-order matrix M, is perfectly general and applies with minor rewording to any square matrix of order n. We state the general result.

Theorem 8.2. *In any square matrix M the column vectors are linearly dependent if and only if the row vectors are linearly dependent.*

Definition. *A square matrix is said to be* singular *if its rows (and therefore its columns) are linearly dependent. If its rows (and columns) are linearly independent, it is said to be* nonsingular.

We can now prove the following important property of a nonsingular matrix.

Theorem 8.3. *If P is a nonsingular square matrix of order n, there exists a uniquely determined matrix P^{-1}, also of order n, such that $PP^{-1} = P^{-1}P = I$ where I is the unit matrix. This matrix P^{-1} is called the* inverse *of P.*

Proof. We seek a matrix X that satisfies the equation $PX = I$. It follows from the definition of a matrix product that the column vectors of PX are $PX_1^T, PX_2^T, \ldots, PX_n^T$ where $X_1^T, X_2^T, \ldots, X_n^T$ are the column vectors of X (see Problem 17, Exercise 8.1). Hence the matrix equation $PX = I$ is equivalent to the n systems of n linear equations

$$PX_1^T = E_1^T, PX_2^T = E_2^T, \ldots, PX_n^T = E_n^T$$

where $E_1^T, \ldots, E_n^T$ are the column vectors of I. Since P is nonsingular each of these systems has a unique solution by Theorem 8.1, and hence the matrix equation $PX = I$ has a unique solution. Denote this solution by $X = P^{-1}$.

Since P^T is also nonsingular there is a unique matrix Y such that $P^TY = I$. Since $I^T = I$ we have by Problem 14, Exercise 8.1, $Y^TP = I$. Hence there is a matrix $Q = Y^T$ such that $QP = I$. If we multiply this equation on the right by P^{-1}, we get $(QP)P^{-1} = P^{-1}$ or since $(QP)P^{-1} = Q(PP^{-1}) = QI = Q$, we have $Q = P^{-1}$. Hence $P^{-1}P = PP^{-1} = I$ as required.

On the other hand a singular matrix has no inverse. For if P is singular its columns are dependent and hence the system of equations

(11) $$PX^T = 0$$

has a nontrivial solution. Thus there exists a nonzero vector X satisfying (11). But if P had an inverse, we could multiply each side of (11) on the left by P^{-1} to get

$$X^T = P^{-1}0 = 0$$

contrary to $X \neq O$. We have therefore proved the following theorem.

Theorem 8.4. *A square matrix has an inverse if and only if it is nonsingular.*

If $X = [x_1, x_2, \ldots, x_n]$ and P is a nonsingular matrix of order n, the system of equations

(12) $$P X^T = C^T$$

is called a *regular* or *nonsingular* system. If the inverse P^{-1} of the matrix of coefficients is known, the solution of (12) can be written immediately in the form

$$X^T = P^{-1} C^T.$$

In practice, however, it is more difficult to compute P^{-1} than it is to solve the system (12) directly by the method of successive elimination of the unknowns used in Examples 3 and 4, Section 7.2. If $n > 3$, the computation involved in finding the inverse of a matrix is very tedious. If $n > 8$ or 9, it is prohibitive. Such problems today are solved by electronic computers. The basic method used, however, by man or machine is still that of successive elimination. We now illustrate a streamlined form of this method which is carried through by operating on the associated matrix rather than on the equations themselves.

Example 1. *Solve the system of equations* (5).

Solution. In the method of successive elimination of the unknowns illustrated in Example 3, Section 7.2, we can omit the x's and the $+$, $-$, and $=$ signs from the equations and work as follows with the associated matrix. First we write down the *"augmented matrix"* of the system. This is the matrix of the coefficients with the column vector of constant terms adjoined. In our case it is

$$\begin{bmatrix} 2 & 3 & -1 & 4 \\ 1 & 4 & 2 & 10 \\ 5 & -4 & 4 & 2 \end{bmatrix}.$$

At each stage we denote the row vectors by R_1, R_2, R_3 and proceed as follows. The operations performed on the rows of the matrix (i.e., on the equations of the system) are recorded on the left and the resulting matrix on the right.

$$\text{Interchange } R_1, R_2 \rightarrow \begin{bmatrix} 1 & 4 & 2 & 10 \\ 2 & 3 & -1 & 4 \\ 5 & -4 & 4 & 2 \end{bmatrix},$$

$$\begin{matrix} R_2 - 2R_1 \longrightarrow \\ R_3 - 5R_1 \longrightarrow \end{matrix} \begin{bmatrix} 1 & 4 & 2 & 10 \\ 0 & -5 & -5 & -16 \\ 0 & -24 & -6 & -48 \end{bmatrix},$$

$$\begin{matrix} -\frac{1}{5}R_1 \longrightarrow \\ \frac{1}{6}R_2 \longrightarrow \end{matrix} \begin{bmatrix} 1 & 4 & 2 & 10 \\ 0 & 1 & 1 & 3.2 \\ 0 & -4 & -1 & -8 \end{bmatrix},$$

$$R_3 + 4R_2 \longrightarrow \begin{bmatrix} 1 & 4 & 2 & 10 \\ 0 & 1 & 1 & 3.2 \\ 0 & 0 & 3 & 4.8 \end{bmatrix},$$

$$\frac{1}{3}R_3 \longrightarrow \begin{bmatrix} 1 & 4 & 2 & 10 \\ 0 & 1 & 1 & 3.2 \\ 0 & 0 & 1 & 1.6 \end{bmatrix}.$$

This is the matrix of the system

$$x_1 + 4x_2 + 2x_3 = 10,$$

$$x_2 + x_3 = 3.2,$$

$$x_3 = 1.6.$$

The third equation yields $x_3 = 1.6$. This can be substituted in the second equation to find x_2, and then x_1 can be computed from the first equation. Alternatively, we can continue to operate on the matrix as follows

$$\begin{matrix} R_1 - 2R_3 \rightarrow \\ R_2 - R_3 \longrightarrow \end{matrix} \begin{bmatrix} 1 & 4 & 0 & 6.8 \\ 0 & 1 & 0 & 1.6 \\ 0 & 0 & 1 & 1.6 \end{bmatrix},$$

$$R_1 - 4R_2 \rightarrow \begin{bmatrix} 1 & 0 & 0 & 0.4 \\ 0 & 1 & 0 & 1.6 \\ 0 & 0 & 1 & 1.6 \end{bmatrix}.$$

Since this is the augmented matrix of the equivalent system

$$x_1 = 0.4,$$

(13) $$\qquad x_2 = 1.6,$$

$$x_3 = 1.6,$$

(13) is the solution of (5).

The operations on the rows of the matrices used in Example 1 are of the following three types:

(a) Interchange of two row vectors.
(b) Multiplication of a row vector by a nonzero scalar.
(c) Addition of a nonzero scalar multiple of one row vector to another row vector.

These are called the *elementary row transformations*. They correspond to the following operations on the associated system of equations.

(a) Changing the order of the equations of the system.
(b) Multiplying each side of an equation by the same nonzero constant.
(c) Adding corresponding sides of two equations after applying (b) to one of them.

It is clear that application of these operations produces a new system of equations that is *equivalent* to the original system in the sense that the two systems have the same solutions. Similarly, if a matrix B can be obtained by a sequence of elementary row transformations from a matrix A, we say A is *row equivalent* to B. Since each elementary transformation can be "undone" by another elementary transformation, it follows that B is also row equivalent to A and we say simply that A and B are row equivalent. It is clear from the preceding remarks that row equivalent matrices belong to equivalent systems of equations.

In a matrix

$$A = \begin{bmatrix} a_{11} & a_{12} & \cdots & a_{1n} \\ a_{21} & a_{22} & \cdots & a_{2n} \\ \cdot & \cdot \cdot \cdot \cdot \cdot \cdot \cdot \cdot & \cdot \\ a_{m1} & a_{m2} & \cdots & a_{mn} \end{bmatrix}$$

elements a_{ij} for which $i > j$ occur below the main diagonal. It can be shown quite easily (for complete proofs see [3], pp. 173–174) that every matrix is row equivalent to one in which all elements below the diagonal are zero. The solutions, if any, of the corresponding system of equations can then be found at once as in Example 1. If no solutions exist, this fact also becomes apparent. Both cases are illustrated in the following examples.

Example 2. *Show that the following system has no solution:*

$$x_1 + 3x_2 + 5x_3 = 7,$$

$$2x_1 - x_2 + 3x_3 = 0,$$

$$5x_1 - 2x_2 + 8x_3 = 11.$$

Solution. The augmented matrix is

$$\begin{bmatrix} 1 & 3 & 5 & 7 \\ 2 & -1 & 3 & 0 \\ 5 & -2 & 8 & 11 \end{bmatrix}.$$

Reduction by elementary transformations gives successively:

$$\begin{matrix} R_2 - 2R_1 \longrightarrow \\ R_3 - 5R_1 \longrightarrow \end{matrix} \begin{bmatrix} 1 & 3 & 5 & 7 \\ 0 & -7 & -7 & -14 \\ 0 & -17 & -17 & -24 \end{bmatrix},$$

$$\begin{matrix} \frac{1}{7}R_2 \longrightarrow \\ -R_3 \longrightarrow \end{matrix} \begin{bmatrix} 1 & 3 & 5 & 7 \\ 0 & 1 & 1 & 2 \\ 0 & 17 & 17 & 24 \end{bmatrix},$$

$$\begin{matrix} \\ \\ R_3 - 17R_2 \longrightarrow \end{matrix} \begin{bmatrix} 1 & 3 & 5 & 7 \\ 0 & 1 & 1 & 2 \\ 0 & 0 & 0 & -10 \end{bmatrix}.$$

Hence an equivalent system of equations is

$$x_1 + 3x_2 + 5x_3 = 7,$$

$$x_2 + x_3 = 2,$$

$$0x_3 = -10.$$

since the last equation clearly has no solution, the original system has no solution.

Example 3. *Find all solutions of the system*

$$x_1 + 3x_2 + 5x_3 = 7,$$
$$2x_1 - x_2 + 3x_3 = 0,$$
$$5x_1 - 2x_2 + 8x_3 = 1.$$

Solution. The augmented matrix

$$\begin{bmatrix} 1 & 3 & 5 & 7 \\ 2 & -1 & 3 & 0 \\ 5 & -2 & 8 & 1 \end{bmatrix}$$

differs from that of Example 2 only in the element in the lower right-hand corner. The same elementary row transformations used in Example 2 reduce it to

$$\begin{bmatrix} 1 & 3 & 5 & 7 \\ 0 & 1 & 1 & 2 \\ 0 & 0 & 0 & 0 \end{bmatrix},$$

and hence

$$R_1 - 3R_2 \rightarrow \begin{bmatrix} 1 & 0 & 2 & 1 \\ 0 & 1 & 1 & 2 \\ 0 & 0 & 0 & 0 \end{bmatrix}.$$

Hence the given system is equivalent to

$$x_1 = 1 - 2x_3,$$
$$x_2 = 2 - x_3,$$

and every solution vector has the form

$$[1 - 2x_3, 2 - x_3, x_3]$$

where x_3 may be chosen arbitrarily. This means that the given system actually contained only two independent equations and the number of solutions is infinite.

Example 4. *Find all solutions of the system*

$$x_1 + x_2 - 3x_3 - 2x_4 = 1,$$
$$2x_1 - 3x_2 + 9x_3 - x_4 = 3,$$
$$2x_2 - 6x_3 + x_4 = 4,$$
$$3x_1 + 4x_2 - 12x_3 - 10x_4 = -4.$$

Solution. The augmented matrix is

$$\begin{bmatrix} 1 & 1 & -3 & -2 & 1 \\ 2 & -3 & 9 & -1 & 3 \\ 0 & 2 & -6 & 1 & 4 \\ 3 & 4 & -12 & -10 & -4 \end{bmatrix}.$$

Reduction by elementary transformations as indicated gives successively

$$\begin{matrix} & \\ R_2 - 2R_1 \rightarrow \\ & \\ R_4 - 3R_1 \rightarrow \end{matrix} \begin{bmatrix} 1 & 1 & -3 & -2 & 1 \\ 0 & -5 & 15 & 3 & 1 \\ 0 & 2 & -6 & 1 & 4 \\ 0 & 1 & -3 & -4 & -7 \end{bmatrix},$$

$$\begin{matrix} R_4 \longrightarrow \\ R_2 + 5R_4 \rightarrow \\ R_3 - 2R_4 \rightarrow \end{matrix} \begin{bmatrix} 1 & 1 & -3 & -2 & 1 \\ 0 & 1 & -3 & -4 & -7 \\ 0 & 0 & 0 & -17 & -34 \\ 0 & 0 & 0 & 9 & 18 \end{bmatrix},$$

$$\begin{matrix} \\ \\ -\frac{1}{17}R_3 \longrightarrow \\ \frac{1}{9}R_4 \longrightarrow \end{matrix} \begin{bmatrix} 1 & 1 & -3 & -2 & 1 \\ 0 & 1 & -3 & -4 & -7 \\ 0 & 0 & 0 & 1 & 2 \\ 0 & 0 & 0 & 1 & 2 \end{bmatrix},$$

$$\begin{matrix} R_1 - R_2 \rightarrow \\ \\ \\ R_4 - R_3 \longrightarrow \end{matrix} \begin{bmatrix} 1 & 0 & 0 & 2 & 8 \\ 0 & 1 & -3 & -4 & -7 \\ 0 & 0 & 0 & 1 & 2 \\ 0 & 0 & 0 & 0 & 0 \end{bmatrix},$$

$$\begin{matrix} R_1 - 2R_3 \rightarrow \\ R_2 + 4R_3 \rightarrow \\ \\ \end{matrix} \begin{bmatrix} 1 & 0 & 0 & 0 & 4 \\ 0 & 1 & -3 & 0 & 1 \\ 0 & 0 & 0 & 1 & 2 \\ 0 & 0 & 0 & 0 & 0 \end{bmatrix}.$$

This is the matrix of the system

$$x_1 \qquad\quad = 4,$$
$$x_2 - 3x_3 = 1,$$
$$x_4 = 2.$$

The general solution of this (and also, therefore, of the original system) is

$$x_1 = 4, \quad x_2 = 3x_3 + 1, \quad x_4 = 2,$$

where x_3 may be assigned any value. There are infinitely many solutions, one for each value assigned to x_3.

EXERCISE 8.2

1. Solve the following systems of equations by the method of Example 1

(a) $x + 5y = 2,$
    $2x + 6y = 5.$

(c) $x + 4y - 3z = 11,$
    $3x - y + 2z = 5,$
    $2x + 3y - 4z = 9.$

(b) $x + y + 2z = 12,$
    $2x - 3y - z = 3,$
    $7x + 2y - 3z = 1.$

(d) $2x + y - z + w = 4,$
    $x + 2y + 7w = 11,$
    $5x - 4z + 2w = 18,$
    $2x + y + z - w = 22.$

2. Use the method of Example 2 to show that the following systems have no solution

(a) $2x - 7y = 14,$
    $-6x + 21y = 20.$

(b) $2x + 3y + z = 6,$
    $4x + 2y + 6z = 24,$
    $x - 2y + 4z = 1.$

3. Show by using the method of Example 3 that each of the following systems has infinitely many solutions and find formulas for these in terms of one or more parameters.

(a) $x + 3y + 4z = 0,$
    $3x - 2y + z = 0,$
    $x - 12y - 11z = 0.$

(c) $x + y - z = 7,$
    $3x - 5y + 2z = 8,$
    $2x - 14y + 8z = -12.$

(b) $2x + y - z + 3w = 0,$
    $5x + 3y + 7z - w = 0,$
    $4x + 3y + 17z - 11w = 0,$
    $x + y + 9z - 7w = 0.$

(d) $x + 9y - 6z + w = 0,$
    $3x + y - z + 7w = 0,$
    $x + 5y + 2z - 7w = 0.$

4. Let
$$A = \begin{bmatrix} 2 & 3 & -1 \\ 1 & 4 & 2 \\ 5 & -4 & 4 \end{bmatrix}.$$

Find A^{-1} by solving the three systems $AX^T = E_1{}^T$, $AX^T = E_2{}^T$, $AX^T = E_3{}^T$ where E_1, E_2, E_3 are the column vectors of the unit matrix I of order 3. Check your answer by computing AA^{-1}.

5. Show that the three systems of Problem 4 can all be solved at once by applying the elementary row transformations of Example 1 to the matrix

$$B = \begin{bmatrix} 2 & 3 & -1 & 1 & 0 & 0 \\ 1 & 4 & 2 & 0 & 1 & 0 \\ 5 & -4 & 4 & 0 & 0 & 1 \end{bmatrix}.$$

Hint: When the matrix Z (the first three columns of B) has been reduced to the unit matrix by row transformations on B (as in Example 1), the solution vectors of the three systems in Problem 4 will appear in the last three columns of the transformed matrix. Thus when B is transformed by row transformations to the form

$$B' = \begin{bmatrix} 1 & 0 & 0 & p_1 & p_2 & p_3 \\ 0 & 1 & 0 & q_1 & q_2 & q_3 \\ 0 & 0 & 1 & r_1 & r_2 & r_3 \end{bmatrix},$$

we shall have

$$A^{-1} = \begin{bmatrix} p_1 & p_2 & p_3 \\ q_1 & q_2 & q_3 \\ r_1 & r_2 & r_3 \end{bmatrix}.$$

6. Use the method of Problem 5 to find A^{-1} and B^{-1} if

$$A = \begin{bmatrix} 5 & -2 \\ -4 & 2 \end{bmatrix} \quad \text{and} \quad B = \begin{bmatrix} 1 & 2 & 2 \\ 2 & 3 & 2 \\ 3 & 3 & 1 \end{bmatrix}.$$

7. Prove that if A and B are both nonsingular matrices of order n, then $(AB)^{-1} = B^{-1}A^{-1}$ and hence AB is nonsingular.
8. Prove that if either A or B is singular, AB is singular.
9. Prove that a system $AX^T = O$ where A is a square matrix of order n has a nonzero solution vector if and only if A is singular.
10. Let E_1, E_2, E_3 be any basis of $\mathcal{U}_3$, that is, any three linearly independent vectors. Let

$$F_1 = p_{11}E_1 + p_{12}E_2 + p_{13}E_3$$
$$F_2 = p_{21}E_1 + p_{22}E_2 + p_{23}E_3$$
$$F_3 = p_{31}E_1 + p_{32}E_2 + p_{33}E_3$$

be any three vectors of $\mathcal{U}_3$. Prove that the vectors F_1, F_2, F_3 are linearly independent if and only if the matrix $P = [p_{ij}]$ is nonsingular. *Hint:* Show that if $x_1F_1 + x_2F_2 + x_3F_3 = O$, it follows that

$$P^TX^T = O,$$

where $X = [x_1, x_2, x_3]$. This system has a nontrivial solution if and only if P^T, and hence P, is singular.
11. Show that the matrix of any transformation of coordinates in $\mathcal{E}_3$ is nonsingular. *Hint:* Use Problem 10 and Theorem 7.9. The matrix of a transformation of coordinates in $\mathcal{E}_3$ is (as in $\mathcal{E}_2$) the matrix P of the equations $X^T = PY^T$ connecting the original x-coordinates with the new y-coordinates.
12. If P is the matrix of a transformation of coordinates from an x-coordinate to a y-coordinate system, show that P^{-1} is the matrix of the transformation from the y-coordinate to the x-coordinate system.
13. Prove that if P is nonsingular, $(P^T)^{-1} = (P^{-1})^T$.

8.3   Determinants of order 2

In Section 5.3 we have already introduced the concept of the second-order determinant

$$\begin{vmatrix} a & c \\ b & d \end{vmatrix} = ad - bc.$$

It is now clear that such a determinant can be thought of as a number, namely, $ad - bc$, associated with the square matrix

$$A = \begin{bmatrix} a & c \\ b & d \end{bmatrix}.$$

We call this determinant the determinant of the matrix A and denote it by det A. Determinants of order 2 were used in Section 5.3 simply as a notational convenience. In this section we shall indicate their geometric significance in connection with transformations of coordinates. Later we shall show how a determinant can also be associated with a square matrix of order 3 or higher. First we ask the student to verify certain properties of second-order determinants in the following exercise.

EXERCISE 8.3

Verify the following properties of second-order determinants. When the letters A, B are used, they represent square matrices of order 2.

1. $\begin{vmatrix} a & c \\ b & d \end{vmatrix} = \begin{vmatrix} a & b \\ c & d \end{vmatrix}.$

2. $\begin{vmatrix} ka & kc \\ b & d \end{vmatrix} = \begin{vmatrix} ka & c \\ kb & d \end{vmatrix} = k \begin{vmatrix} a & c \\ b & d \end{vmatrix}.$

3. $\begin{vmatrix} a + x & c + y \\ b & d \end{vmatrix} = \begin{vmatrix} a & c \\ b & d \end{vmatrix} + \begin{vmatrix} x & y \\ b & d \end{vmatrix}.$

4. $\begin{vmatrix} a & c \\ b + ka & d + kc \end{vmatrix} = \begin{vmatrix} a & c \\ b & d \end{vmatrix}.$

5. $\begin{vmatrix} a & c \\ b & d \end{vmatrix} = - \begin{vmatrix} c & a \\ d & b \end{vmatrix} = - \begin{vmatrix} b & d \\ a & c \end{vmatrix}.$

6. $\begin{vmatrix} a + kc & c \\ b + kd & d \end{vmatrix} = \begin{vmatrix} a & c \\ b & d \end{vmatrix}.$

7. det $(AB) = (\det A)(\det B)$.

8. det $A = 0$ if and only if the row vectors of A are linearly dependent.

9. If det $A = d \neq 0$ and $A = \begin{bmatrix} e & f \\ g & h \end{bmatrix}$,

then
$$A^{-1} = \frac{1}{d} \begin{bmatrix} h & -f \\ -g & e \end{bmatrix}.$$

10. If A is nonsingular, $\det(A^{-1}) = (\det A)^{-1}$.

Suppose now that we are given a rectangular coordinate system (the x-system) with equal units on the coordinate axes, and we let $E_1 = [1, 0]$, $E_2 = [0, 1]$ be the corresponding basis for $\mathcal{V}_2$. We know from Theorem 7.8 that if we transform to a y-coordinate system for which the corresponding basis vectors are

$$F_1 = [a, b] = aE_1 + bE_2,$$
$$F_2 = [c, d] = cE_1 + dE_2$$

that the coordinates (x_1, x_2) and (y_1, y_2) of a point relative to the x- and y-systems are connected by the equations

$$x_1 = ay_1 + cy_2,$$
$$x_2 = by_1 + dy_2.$$

These may be written $X^T = A Y^T$ (or $X = YA^T$) where $X = [x_1, x_2]$, $Y = [y_1, y_2]$, and A is the matrix of the transformation.

The basis vectors of $\mathcal{V}_2$ that correspond to a given coordinate system (i.e., the vectors drawn from the origin to the unit points on the coordinate axes) determine a parallelogram of which they are adjacent sides. This we shall call the *fundamental parallelogram* of the coordinate system. It is the basic cell of the "graph paper" corresponding to the given coordinate system which is shaded in Fig. 7.4. For the x-coordinate system the fundamental parallelogram is a square whose edge is one unit in length. Its area is therefore 1. We now compute the area of the fundamental parallelogram in the y-coordinate system (see Fig. 8.1). If θ is the angle between F_1 and F_2, we have for this area, if we denote by r_1, r_2 the lengths of F_1 and F_2,

$$\text{Area} = (\text{base}) (\text{altitude}) = r_1 r_2 \sin \theta$$

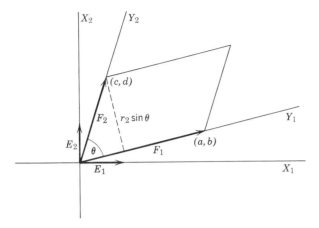

Fig. 8.1

Hence

$$(\text{Area})^2 = r_1{}^2r_2{}^2 \sin^2 \theta = r_1{}^2r_2{}^2 - r_1{}^2r_2{}^2 \cos^2 \theta$$

$$= r_1{}^2r_2{}^2 - (F_1 \cdot F_2)^2$$

$$= (a^2 + b^2)(c^2 + d^2) - (ac + bd)^2$$

$$= a^2d^2 - 2acbd + b^2c^2$$

$$= (ad - bc)^2 = \begin{vmatrix} a & c \\ b & d \end{vmatrix}^2.$$

Thus the square of the required area is $(\det A)^2$ where A is the matrix of the transformation. The area itself is therefore $|\det A|$.

Now suppose we apply a second transformation of coordinates (with matrix B) to a z-coordinate system. The matrix of the transformation from the x- to the z-system is AB and the area of the fundamental parallelogram in the z-system is $|\det AB|$. But by Problem 7, Exercise 8.3, this is $|\det A| \, |\det B|$ and we have the relation

$$\frac{\text{Area of } z\text{-parallelogram}}{\text{Area of } y\text{-parallelogram}} = \frac{|\det A| \, |\det B|}{|\det A|} = |\det B|$$

We have therefore proved the following general result.

Theorem 8.5. *In a transformation from one Cartesian coordinate system in $\mathcal{E}_2$ to another the area of the fundamental parallelogram is multiplied by $|\det B|$ where B is the matrix of the transformation.*

8.4   Determinants of order 3

We now define third-order determinants as follows. Consider the matrix

$$A = \begin{bmatrix} a_{11} & a_{12} & a_{13} \\ a_{21} & a_{22} & a_{23} \\ a_{31} & a_{32} & a_{33} \end{bmatrix}.$$

We define the determinant of A to be the expression:

(14) $\det A = a_{11}a_{22}a_{33} + a_{13}a_{21}a_{32} + a_{12}a_{23}a_{31} - a_{13}a_{22}a_{31}$
$$- a_{11}a_{23}a_{32} - a_{12}a_{21}a_{33}$$

Although this definition may at first seem somewhat arbitrary, we shall show that the third-order determinant so defined plays a role in three-dimensional problems entirely analogous to that of the second-order determinant discussed previously.

In order to derive the basic properties of third-order determinants we first make some observations about the definition of det A in (14). We have used the double subscript notation which was described in Section 8.1. Thus the element a_{ij} occurs in the ith row and jth column of A. In each of the six terms of det A each possible row index 1, 2, 3, and each possible column index, occurs exactly once. This means that each term of det A is formed by multiplying three elements of A chosen one from each row and one from each column. Note that in (14) the row indices in each term are written in their natural order and that *all possible* permutations of the column indices occur, namely, 123, 312, 231, 321, 132, and 213. Hence all possible products of three elements, one from each row and one from each column, are included.

Note that three of the terms of det A in (14) have plus signs and three have minus signs preceding them. In order to explain how the sign before each term is determined, we have to study the relevant permutations of the column indices when the row indices are in natural order. In particular we need to know the number of interchanges of two column indices needed to achieve the given permutation. This information is given in Table 8.1. To explain the construction of this table we note that the second line, for example, means that the order 312 of the column indices (when the row indices are in natural order 123) can be

Table 8.1

Term	Order of Column Indices	Interchanges of Indices Required	Number of Interchanges
$a_{11}a_{22}a_{33}$	123	None	0
$a_{13}a_{21}a_{32}$	312	First 1,3 then 1,2	2
$a_{12}a_{23}a_{31}$	231	First 1,2 then 1,3	2
$a_{13}a_{22}a_{31}$	321	1,3	1
$a_{11}a_{23}a_{32}$	132	2,3	1
$a_{12}a_{21}a_{33}$	213	1,2	1

obtained from the natural order in two steps as follows:

from 123 to 321   by interchange of 1 and 3,

from 321 to 312   by interchange of 1 and 2.

It is clear that the number of interchanges from the natural order required to achieve a given permutation is not uniquely determined since the same interchange performed twice produces no change. It can be shown, however (see Section 8.7), that for a given permutation this number either is always even or always odd. Thus we can classify the six possible permutations of the three column indices as *even* or *odd* according as the number of interchanges required to achieve them is even or odd. Note that half of the six possible permutations are odd and half are even.

We can now define det A to be the sum of the six terms of the form

$$\epsilon(i_1, i_2, i_3)a_{1i_1}a_{2i_2}a_{3i_3}$$

where i_1, i_2, i_3 ranges over the six possible permutations of 1, 2, 3 and $\epsilon(i_1, i_2, i_3)$ is 1 when i_1, i_2, i_3 is an even permutation and -1 when i_1, i_2, i_3 is an odd permutation of 1, 2, 3. In Section 8.8 we shall define in a similar way the determinant of a square matrix of arbitrary order n. But first we shall derive the main properties of determinants for the case $n = 3$ and discuss some applications.

8.5   Properties of determinants

We shall now prove a number of basic theorems about determinants. We shall give the proofs for determinants of order 3, although as pointed out in Section 8.8 most of these proofs, like the definition of determinant, are immediately applicable to determinants of arbitrary order n. The case $n = 2$ is usually trivial and the theorems in this case have already been verified by the student in Exercise 8.3.

Theorem 8.6. *If A is a square matrix of order 3, $\det A^T = \det A$.*

Proof. 1. Since A^T is obtained from A by interchanging rows and columns, $\det A^T$ is obtained from $\det A$ by interchanging row and column indices of each a_{ij} in (14). This operation leaves all terms of (14) unchanged except $a_{13}a_{21}a_{32}$ and $a_{12}a_{23}a_{31}$ which are simply interchanged. Thus $\det A^T = \det A$.

2. We give an alternative proof that is also applicable to determinants of order greater than 3. It is clear that except possibly for the signs the terms in the expansion of $\det A^T$ are exactly the same as those in $\det A$. This is because each expansion consists of all terms obtained by forming products of three elements, one from each row and one from each column. This prescription gives the same six terms whether applied to A or A^T. We must show that the signs attached to these terms are the same. Let

$$\epsilon(i_1, i_2, i_3)a_{1i_1}a_{2i_2}a_{3i_3}$$

be a typical term of $\det A$. If the column indices are put in natural order, this term becomes

$$\epsilon(i_1, i_2, i_3)a_{j_11}a_{j_22}a_{j_33}.$$

Now if i_1, i_2, i_3 is obtained from 1, 2, 3 by r interchanges, the same r interchanges applied in *reverse order* will change i_1, i_2, i_3 to 1, 2, 3 and hence will change 1, 2, 3 to j_1, j_2, j_3. It follows that $\epsilon(i_1, i_2, i_3) = \epsilon(j_1, j_2, j_3)$ and hence the term $a_{1i_1}a_{2i_2}a_{3i_3}$ occurs with the same sign in both $\det A$ and $\det A^T$. Hence $\det A^T = \det A$ as required.

Corollary. *Any true statement about the rows of a determinant remains true if the word row is replaced by the word column, and conversely.*

Theorem 8.7. *If A' is the matrix obtained from A by interchanging two columns (or two rows), then $\det A' = - \det A$.*

Proof. Suppose first that two adjacent columns, say the jth and $(j + 1)$th are interchanged. The effect is to interchange the column indices j and $j + 1$ in (14). This introduces one additional interchange in the column indices of each term. Hence in the expansion of det A' each term in det A appears but with $+$ signs before the terms corresponding to odd permutations of the column indices and $-$ signs before the terms corresponding to even permutations. Hence det $A' =$ $-$ det A as required, and the theorem is proved for the case of adjacent columns. The interchange of the jth and the $(j + p)$th columns can be achieved by $2p - 1$ successive interchanges of adjacent columns. For example, to interchange the first and third we proceed as follows:

$$C_1C_2C_3 \rightarrow C_2C_1C_3 \rightarrow C_2C_3C_1 \rightarrow C_3C_2C_1$$

a total of three interchanges of adjacent columns. Since this means $2p - 1$ (an odd number) of changes in sign, we have det $A' = -$ det A in all cases. For the interchange of two rows the theorem follows from the corollary to Theorem 8.6.

Corollary. *If two rows (or two columns) of A are identical, then det A = 0.*

Proof. The interchange of the two identical rows clearly makes no change in det A but by Theorem 8.7 it must change the sign of det A. Hence det $A = -$ det A and det $A = 0$.

Theorem 8.8. *Suppose the ith row vector of A is the sum of two vectors B_i and C_i. Then det A = det B + det C where B is the matrix obtained from A by replacing the ith row by B_i and C is the matrix obtained from A by replacing the ith row by C_i. For example,*

$$\begin{vmatrix} a & b & c \\ d & e & f \\ x + w & y + v & z + w \end{vmatrix} = \begin{vmatrix} a & b & c \\ d & e & f \\ x & y & z \end{vmatrix} + \begin{vmatrix} a & b & c \\ d & e & f \\ u & v & w \end{vmatrix}.$$

Proof. This theorem follows at once from (14). If, for example, $a_{1j} = b_{1j} + c_{1j}$ $(j = 1, 2, 3)$, then $a_{11}a_{22}a_{33} = (b_{11} + c_{11})a_{22}a_{33} = b_{11}a_{22}a_{33} + c_{11}a_{22}a_{33}$, and similarly for each of the other terms. The six terms containing b's add up to det B and the six terms containing c's to det C. Thus det $A =$ det $B +$ det C as stated.

Theorem 8.9. *If A' is the matrix obtained when the ith row vector A_i of A is replaced by a scalar multiple kA_i of itself, then det $A' = k$ det A.*

Proof. Since each term in the expansion of det A contains one and only one factor from the ith row, each term of det A' is k times the corresponding term in det A.

Corollary. *If one row (or column) of A is the zero vector, then det A = 0.*

Theorem 8.10. *If A' is the matrix obtained from A by replacing the ith row vector A_i by $A_i + kA_j$ where A_j is the jth row vector, $j \neq i$, then det $A' =$ det A.*

Proof. By Theorems 8.8 and 8.9, det $A' =$ det $A + k$ det B where B is the matrix obtained from A by replacing the ith row by the jth row. But since B then has two rows (the ith and jth) identical, det $B = 0$ by the corollary to Theorem 8.7. Hence det $A' =$ det A as stated.

Let a_{ij} be the element in the ith row and jth column of A. If the ith row and jth column are deleted, the remaining elements of A form a second-order "submatrix" of A which we shall denote by A_{ij}. For example,

$$A_{11} = \begin{vmatrix} a_{22} & a_{23} \\ a_{32} & a_{33} \end{vmatrix}, \qquad A_{32} = \begin{vmatrix} a_{11} & a_{13} \\ a_{21} & a_{23} \end{vmatrix}.$$

Definition. *The determinant det A_{ij} is called the* minor *of the element a_{ij} in A, and $(-1)^{i+j}$ det A_{ij} is called the* cofactor *of a_{ij} in A. Thus the cofactors of the elements in the first row of A are det A_{11}, $-$ det A_{12} and det A_{13}.*

Theorem 8.11. *Let b_{ij} be the cofactor of a_{ij} in A. Then for any values of i and j (chosen from 1, 2, 3),*

$$det\ A = a_{i1}b_{i1} + a_{i2}b_{i2} + a_{i3}b_{i3}$$
$$= a_{1j}b_{1j} + a_{2j}b_{2j} + a_{3j}b_{3j}.$$

In other words, if the elements of any row or column are multiplied by their cofactors, the sum of the products so obtained is det A.

Proof. We prove the theorem first for the first row.

1. From (14) det A can be written in the form

$$a_{11}(a_{22}a_{23} - a_{23}a_{32}) - a_{12}(a_{21}a_{33} - a_{23}a_{31}) + a_{13}(a_{21}a_{32} - a_{22}a_{31})$$

or

$$(15)\quad \det A = a_{11}\begin{vmatrix} a_{22} & a_{23} \\ a_{32} & a_{33} \end{vmatrix} - a_{12}\begin{vmatrix} a_{21} & a_{23} \\ a_{31} & a_{33} \end{vmatrix} + a_{13}\begin{vmatrix} a_{21} & a_{22} \\ a_{31} & a_{32} \end{vmatrix}.$$

This is the required result for the first row. The result for other rows can be as easily checked and the result for columns follows from the corollary to Theorem 8.6.

2. We now give an alternative proof which has the advantage that it is applicable to determinants of order greater than 3. First we consider all terms in det A that contain the factor a_{11}. Since each term of det A contains one element from each row and each column and since a_{11} lies in the first row and first column the other factors must be chosen in all possible ways from the second and third rows and columns, i.e., from the matrix A_{11}. Moreover, since the first factor of each of these terms is a_{11} the number of interchanges in the column indices of the remaining factors, say $a_{2j_2}a_{3j_3}$ is the same for this product as for the term $a_{11}a_{2j_2}a_{3j_3}$. It follows that the total coefficient of a_{11} in det A is precisely the minor, det A_{11}.

We now seek the coefficient of a_{ij} in det A. By $i-1$ successive interchanges of adjacent rows the ith row of A can be brought into first position without changing the relative order of the other rows. Having done this the jth column can be brought into first position similarly by $j-1$ successive interchanges. The new matrix A' so obtained will have a_{ij} in the first row and first column and the minor of a_{ij} in A' will be exactly det A_{ij}, the same as its minor in A. Since by Theorem 8.7

$$\det A' = (-1)^{i+j-2} \det A = (-1)^{i+j} \det A,$$

we have also

$$\det A = (-1)^{i+j} \det A'.$$

Now by the case for a_{11} (already proved) applied to det A', the coefficient of a_{ij} in det A' is det A_{ij}. Hence the coefficient of a_{ij} in det A is $(-1)^{i+j} \det A_{ij}$ or the cofactor of a_{ij} in A. Since every term in det A contains exactly one factor from the ith row the theorem now follows.

Corollary 1. *If A_1, A_2, A_3 are the row vectors of A, then*

$$\det A = A_1 \cdot (A_2 \times A_3).$$

Proof. From the definition of the cross product (Section 5.3)

$$A_2 \times A_3 = [\det A_{11},\ -\det A_{12},\ \det A_{13}]$$

and hence from (15)

$$A_1 \cdot (A_2 \times A_3) = a_{11} \det A_{11} - a_{12} \det A_{12} + a_{13} \det A_{13} = \det A.$$

Corollary 2. *If the elements of any row (column) are multiplied by the cofactors of any other row (column), the sum of the products so formed is zero.*

Proof. This follows from the corollary to Theorem 8.7 for the sum described is the expansion of a determinant with two identical rows. For example,

$$a_{21} \det A_{11} - a_{22} \det A_{12} + a_{23} \det A_{13} = \begin{vmatrix} a_{21} & a_{22} & a_{23} \\ a_{21} & a_{22} & a_{23} \\ a_{31} & a_{32} & a_{33} \end{vmatrix} = 0.$$

Corollary 3. *Let $b_{ij} = (-1)^{i+j} \det A_{ij}$ be the cofactor in A of the element a_{ij} and let $B = [b_{ij}]$. Then $AB^T = (\det A)I$ and if $\det A \neq 0$, $A^{-1} = (\det A)^{-1} B^T$.*

Proof. This follows at once on forming the matrix product AB^T and using Theorem 8.11 and Corollary 2. This gives a method of computing A^{-1}.

It follows from Corollary 3 that if $\det A \neq 0$, the inverse matrix A^{-1} exists and therefore A is nonsingular by Theorem 8.4. Conversely, suppose $\det A = 0$ so that by Corollary 1

$$A_1 \cdot (A_2 \times A_3) = 0.$$

This implies that either

        (*a*) $A_1 = 0$,

        (*b*) $A_2 \times A_3 = 0$,

or   (*c*) A_1 is perpendicular to $A_2 \times A_3$.

If (*a*) holds, the three row vectors are linearly dependent by Lemma 7.1. If (*b*) holds, A_2 and A_3 are linearly dependent by Section 5.3 and so also are A_1, A_2, A_3 by Lemma 7.1. If (*c*) holds, A_1 lies in the plane of A_2 and A_3 and hence the three vectors are linearly dependent by Problem 5, Exercise 7.2. We have therefore proved the following theorem.

Theorem 8.12. *A square matrix A of order 3 is singular if and only if det A = 0.*

If in a square matrix A all the elements below (or above) the main diagonal are zero, then A is called a *triangular* matrix. A diagonal matrix is a special case of a triangular matrix.

Theorem 8.13. *If A is a triangular matrix (of order 2 or 3), then det A is equal to the product of the diagonal elements of A.*

Proof. Every term in the expansion of det A except the product of the diagonal elements must contain as a factor at least one element from below the diagonal and one from above, and must therefore be 0 if A is triangular.

Theorems 8.11 and 8.13 can be used to evaluate determinants as in the following example.

Example 1. *Evaluate det A if*

$$A = \begin{bmatrix} 2 & 3 & 7 \\ 3 & -1 & 4 \\ 5 & 4 & 1 \end{bmatrix}.$$

Solution 1. By Theorem 8.11.

$$\det A = 2 \begin{vmatrix} -1 & 4 \\ 4 & 1 \end{vmatrix} - 3 \begin{vmatrix} 3 & 4 \\ 5 & 1 \end{vmatrix} + 7 \begin{vmatrix} 3 & -1 \\ 5 & 4 \end{vmatrix}$$

$$= 2(-17) - 3(-17) + 7(17) = 136.$$

Solution 2. By using Theorem 8.10 we can reduce A to triangular form without changing det A. For example, if R_1, R_2, R_3 are the row vectors at any stage we have

$$\begin{vmatrix} 2 & 3 & 7 \\ 3 & -1 & 4 \\ 5 & 4 & 1 \end{vmatrix} = \begin{vmatrix} -33 & -25 & 0 \\ -17 & -17 & 0 \\ 5 & 4 & 1 \end{vmatrix} \begin{matrix} \leftarrow R_1 - 7R_3 \\ \leftarrow R_2 - 4R_3 \\ \end{matrix}$$

$$= \begin{vmatrix} -8 & 0 & 0 \\ -17 & -17 & 0 \\ 5 & 4 & 1 \end{vmatrix} \begin{matrix} \leftarrow R_1 - \frac{25}{17}R_2 \\ \\ \end{matrix}$$

$$= (-8)(-17)(1) = 136.$$

EXERCISE 8.4

1. Evaluate the following determinants (*a*) by using Theorem 8.11, (*b*) by reducing to triangular form and using Theorem 8.13

(i) $\begin{vmatrix} 2 & -6 & 0 \\ 3 & 9 & 4 \\ 2 & 4 & 3 \end{vmatrix}$,

(ii) $\begin{vmatrix} 1 & -2 & -2 \\ 2 & -1 & 2 \\ -2 & -2 & 1 \end{vmatrix}$,

(iii) $\begin{vmatrix} 5 & 1 & 6 \\ 2 & 2 & 3 \\ 7 & 4 & 1 \end{vmatrix}$,

(iv) $\begin{vmatrix} 1 & 1 & 1 \\ a & b & c \\ a^2 & b^2 & c^2 \end{vmatrix}$.

2. Prove without expanding the determinants but by using the theorems of Section 8.5 that

(*a*) $\begin{vmatrix} 1 & 2 & 3 \\ 4 & 5 & 6 \\ 7 & 8 & 9 \end{vmatrix} = 0.$

(*b*) $\begin{vmatrix} 5 & -21 & 16 \\ 7 & 3 & -10 \\ 3 & -7 & 4 \end{vmatrix} = 0.$

3. If

$$A = \begin{bmatrix} 2 & 1 & 3 \\ 4 & 3 & 1 \\ 2 & 2 & 3 \end{bmatrix},$$

use the method of Theorem 8.11, Corollary 3, to compute A^{-1} and check the result by the method of Problem 5, Exercise 8.2.

4. Prove, without expanding, that

$$\begin{vmatrix} a+x & b+y & c+z \\ x+u & y+v & z+w \\ u+a & v+b & w+c \end{vmatrix} = 2 \begin{vmatrix} a & b & c \\ x & y & z \\ u & v & w \end{vmatrix}.$$

8.6   Cramer's rule and multiplication of determinants

Theorem 8.11 and its Corollary 2 provide a method of solving any system of three equations in three unknowns whose coefficient matrix is nonsingular. Consider the system

$$a_{11}x_1 + a_{12}x_2 + a_{13}x_3 = c_1,$$

(16) $\qquad a_{21}x_1 + a_{22}x_2 + a_{23}x_3 = c_2,$

$$a_{31}x_1 + a_{32}x_2 + a_{33}x_3 = c_3,$$

and let $b_{ij} = (-1)^{i+j} \det A_{ij}$ be the cofactor of a_{ij} in the matrix $A = [a_{ij}]$. If we multiply the first equation by b_{11}, the second by b_{21}, the third by b_{31}, and add we get

(17) $(a_{11}b_{11} + a_{21}b_{21} + a_{31}b_{31})x_1 = c_1b_{11} + c_2b_{21} + c_3b_{31}$,

since the coefficients of x_2 and x_3 are 0 by Corollary 2 of Theorem 8.11. By Theorem 8.11 the coefficient of x_1 is $\det A$ and the right-hand side of (17) is $\det A_1$ where A_1 is the matrix obtained from A by replacing the first column by the column vector C^T where $C = [c_1, c_2, c_3]$. Hence (17) becomes

$$(\det A)x_1 = \det A_1.$$

Similarly, by multiplying the three equations of (16) in turn by the cofactors of the elements of the second and third columns of A, we get

$$(\det A)x_2 = \det A_2,$$

$$(\det A)x_3 = \det A_3,$$

where A_2 and A_3 are the matrices obtained from A by replacing in turn the second and third columns by C^T. Now if A is nonsingular, we have $\det A \neq 0$ by Theorem 8.12 and hence the solution of (16) is

$$x_1 = \frac{\det A_1}{\det A}, \qquad x_2 = \frac{\det A_2}{\det A}, \qquad x_3 = \frac{\det A_3}{\det A}.$$

This method of solution of (16) is known as *Cramer's rule*. It requires the evaluation of four third-order determinants. As a practical method the successive elimination process of Example 1, Section 8.2, is usually preferable. However, Cramer's rule is of considerable theoretical importance and we use it now to give an elegant proof of an important property of determinants.

Theorem 8.14. *If A and B are square matrices of order 3, then*

$$\det (AB) = (\det A)(\det B).$$

Proof. If either A or B is singular, then AB is also singular by Problem 8, Exercise 8.2. Hence in this case by Theorem 8.12, $\det AB = \det A \det B = 0$. We therefore assume that both A and B are nonsingular. By Cramer's rule the system of equations

(18) $BX^T = C^T$

has solutions

(19) $\qquad x_1 = \dfrac{\det B_1}{\det B}, \qquad x_2 = \dfrac{\det B_2}{\det B}, \qquad x_3 = \dfrac{\det B_3}{\det B},$

where B_i is the matrix obtained from B by replacing the ith column by C^T. Since $\det B \neq 0$, we can choose C so that x_1, x_2, x_3 and hence also $\det B_1$, $\det B_2$, and $\det B_3$ are not zero. Now since A is nonsingular the system (18) is equivalent to the system

(20) $\qquad\qquad\qquad (AB)X^T = AC^T$

for (20) holds if and only if (18) does. Applying Cramer's rule to (20) we get

(21) $\quad x_1 = \dfrac{\det (AB)_1}{\det AB}, \qquad x_2 = \dfrac{\det (AB)_2}{\det AB}, \qquad x_3 = \dfrac{\det (AB)_3}{\det AB},$

where $(AB)_i$ is the matrix obtained from AB on replacing the ith column by AC^T. Equating the values for x_1, x_2, x_3 in (19) and (21) we get

(22) $\qquad \dfrac{\det AB}{\det B} = \dfrac{\det (AB)_1}{\det B_1} = \dfrac{\det (AB)_2}{\det B_2} = \dfrac{\det (AB)_3}{\det B_3}.$

Now by Problem 17, Exercise 8.1, the column vectors of AB are AC_1^T, AC_2^T, AC_3^T where C_1^T, C_2^T, C_3^T are the column vectors of B. Thus $\det (AB)_1$ and $\det B_1$ are both independent of the first column vector C_1^T of B. Similarly, $\det (AB)_2/\det B_2$ is independent of the second column vector C_2^T of B and $\det (AB)_3/\det B_3$ is independent of the third column vector C_3^T of B. Hence by (22), the quotient $\det AB/\det B$ is independent of B altogether, and has the same value for every nonsingular matrix B. We can therefore evaluate it by putting $B = I$ and we find

$$\frac{\det AB}{\det B} = \frac{\det AI}{\det I} = \det A$$

since $\det I = 1$ by Theorem 8.13. Hence $\det AB = \det A \det B$, as required.

8.7   Permutations

The definition of det A when A is a square matrix of order n is suggested by the discussion in Section 8.4 following the definition of a determinant of order 3. Before stating the definition it is necessary to discuss permutations of n objects.

Any arrangement in a definite order of the n integers $1, 2, \ldots, n$ is called a permutation of these integers. The three digits $1, 2, 3$ give rise to six permutations, namely, $123, 132, 213, 231, 312, 321$. To compute the number of permutations of the four digits 1234 we note that any one of the four can be chosen for first place and that there are then six ways of arranging the remaining three digits. This gives rise to 4×6 or 24 permutations and clearly there can be no others. The same argument tells us that if P_r is the number of permutations of the first r integers, then

$$P_{r+1} = (r + 1)P_r.$$

Since $P_1 = 1$, n applications of this rule yields

$$P_n = nP_{n-1} = n(n - 1)P_{n-2} = \cdots$$
$$= n(n - 1)(n - 2) \cdots 3 \cdot 2 \cdot 1.$$

This product of the first n positive integers is denoted by $n!$ which is read n *factorial*. It is the total number of permutations of n distinct objects.

Every permutation of $1, 2, \ldots, n$ can be obtained from the natural order by a succession of interchanges of two integers. For example, to obtain 342165 from the natural order we can proceed as follows

1	2	3	4	5	6	
3	2	1	4	5	6	by interchanging 1 and 3
3	4	1	2	5	6	by interchanging 2 and 4
3	4	2	1	5	6	by interchanging 1 and 2
3	4	2	1	6	5	by interchanging 5 and 6

The number of interchanges required to achieve a given permutation is not uniquely determined but it can be shown that it is either always even or always odd. To do this we consider the following expression in the n variables $x_1, x_2, \ldots, x_n$:

$$A(x_1, x_2, \ldots, x_n) = \prod_{\substack{i,j=1 \\ i<j}}^{n} (x_i - x_j).$$

By this notation we mean the product of all factors $x_i - x_j$ where $i < j$ and i and j run through the values $1, 2, 3, \ldots, n$. We consider the effect on $A(x_1, \ldots, x_n)$ of interchanging two specific x's, say x_r and x_s, where we assume $r < s$. The only factors affected by this interchange are those containing x_r, x_s or both. The changes are as follows

(a) For each $i < r$, $x_i - x_r$ and $x_i - x_s$ are interchanged and this produces no change in A.

(b) For each $i > s$, $x_s - x_i$, $x_r - x_i$ are interchanged and this produces no change in A.

(c) For each i such that $r < i < s$

$$x_r - x_i \text{ becomes } x_s - x_i = -(x_i - x_s)$$

$$x_i - x_s \text{ becomes } x_i - x_r = -(x_r - x_i)$$

This produces an even number of sign changes in the factors of A and hence no change in A.

(d) The factor $x_r - x_s$ becomes $x_s - x_r = -(x_r - x_s)$. This changes the sign of one factor and therefore changes the sign of A.

Thus every interchange of two subscripts $1, 2, \ldots, n$ changes the sign of A. It follows that every permutation of $1, 2, \ldots, n$, since it is a succession of such interchanges, either leaves A unchanged or changes its sign. Those permutations that leave A unchanged we call *even* because they must correspond to an even number of interchanges; those that change the sign of A are called *odd* because they must correspond to an odd number of interchanges.

8.8   Determinants of order n

If $i_1, i_2, \ldots, i_n$ is any permutation of $1, 2, \ldots, n$, we define the symbol $\epsilon(i_1, i_2, \ldots, i_n)$ to be equal to 1 when $i_1, i_2, \ldots, i_n$ is an even permutation and equal to -1 when $i_1, i_2, \ldots, i_n$ is an odd permutation. We can now formulate the definition of a determinant of order n.

Definition. *If* $A = [a_{ij}]$ *is a square matrix of order* n, *the determinant of* A, *denoted by det* A, *is the sum of the* $n!$ *terms of the form*

$$\epsilon(i_1, i_2, \ldots, i_n)a_{1i_1}a_{2i_2} \cdots a_{ni_n}$$

where $i_1, i_2, \ldots, i_n$ *varies over all permutations of* $1, 2, \ldots, n$.

We note that if $n = 2$ or 3, this definition reduces to the determinants of order 2 and 3 already discussed. With this definition, moreover, Theorems 8.6 through 8.14 all hold for determinants of any order. In fact, with the single exception of Theorem 8.12, the proofs given for these theorems are valid with minor rewording for determinants of order n. For the proof of Theorem 8.12 in the general case the reader is referred to [5], pp. 45–46. Cramer's rule also applies, using determinants of order n, to the solution of a regular system of n linear equations in n unknowns.

Example 1. *Evaluate the determinant of the matrix*

$$A = \begin{bmatrix} 2 & 1 & 3 & 5 \\ 7 & 2 & 1 & 4 \\ 2 & -1 & 6 & 5 \\ 9 & 4 & 2 & 12 \end{bmatrix}.$$

Solution 1. We denote the row vectors by R_1, R_2, R_3, R_4 and replace R_2 by $R_2 - 2R_1$, R_3 by $R_3 + R_1$, and R_4 by $R_4 - 4R_1$. By the general form of Theorem 8.10, we have

$$\det A = \begin{vmatrix} 2 & 1 & 3 & 8 \\ 3 & 0 & -5 & -6 \\ 4 & 0 & 9 & 10 \\ 1 & 0 & -10 & -8 \end{vmatrix}.$$

Expanding by the cofactors of the second column we get

$$\det A = - \begin{vmatrix} 3 & -5 & -6 \\ 4 & 9 & 10 \\ 1 & -10 & -8 \end{vmatrix}$$

$$= -3 \begin{vmatrix} 9 & 10 \\ -10 & -8 \end{vmatrix} - 5 \begin{vmatrix} 4 & 10 \\ 1 & -8 \end{vmatrix} + 6 \begin{vmatrix} 4 & 9 \\ 1 & -10 \end{vmatrix}$$

$$= -3(28) + 5(42) - 6(49) = -168.$$

Solution 2. Reduce to triangular form by elementary row or column transformations and use the general form of Theorem 8.13. Thus

$$
\det A = - \begin{vmatrix} 1 & 2 & 3 & 5 \\ 2 & 7 & 1 & 4 \\ -1 & 2 & 6 & 5 \\ 4 & 9 & 2 & 12 \end{vmatrix}
$$

$$
= - \begin{vmatrix} 1 & 2 & 3 & 5 \\ 0 & 3 & -5 & -6 \\ 0 & 4 & 9 & 10 \\ 0 & 1 & -10 & -8 \end{vmatrix} \begin{matrix} \\ \leftarrow R_2 - 2R_1 \\ \leftarrow R_3 + R_1 \\ \leftarrow R_4 - 4R_1 \end{matrix}
$$

$$
= - \begin{vmatrix} 1 & 2 & 3 & 5 \\ 0 & 1 & -10 & -8 \\ 0 & 0 & 25 & 18 \\ 0 & 0 & 49 & 42 \end{vmatrix} \begin{matrix} \\ \leftarrow R_4 \\ \leftarrow R_2 - 3R_4 \\ \leftarrow R_3 - 4R_4 \end{matrix}
$$

$$
= -7 \begin{vmatrix} 1 & 2 & 3 & 5 \\ 0 & 1 & -10 & -8 \\ 0 & 0 & 25 & 18 \\ 0 & 0 & 7 & 6 \end{vmatrix} \begin{matrix} . \\ \\ \\ \leftarrow \frac{1}{7}R_4 \end{matrix}
$$

$$
= -7 \begin{vmatrix} 1 & 2 & 3 & 5 \\ 0 & 1 & -10 & -8 \\ 0 & 0 & 25 & 18 \\ 0 & 0 & 0 & .96 \end{vmatrix} \begin{matrix} \\ \\ \\ \leftarrow R_4 - .28R_3 \end{matrix}
$$

$$
= -7(24) = -168.
$$

EXERCISE 8.5

1. State and prove Cramer's rule for two equations in two unknowns and use it to solve the systems

   (a) $3x + 4y = 7,$ $\quad\quad\quad$ (b) $2x - y = 8,$
   $\quad\;\; 2x + 3y = 15.$ $\quad\quad\quad\quad\quad\;\; 2x + 3y = 24.$

2. Evaluate the following determinants (a) by using the general (order n) form of Theorem 8.11 and (b) by using the general form of Theorem 8.13.

   (a) $\begin{vmatrix} 3 & 1 & 2 & -1 \\ 1 & 5 & 2 & -3 \\ 4 & -1 & -1 & 2 \\ -1 & 3 & 2 & 3 \end{vmatrix},$ $\quad$ (b) $\begin{vmatrix} 4 & 2 & 1 & 1 \\ 2 & 1 & 3 & -1 \\ 5 & 3 & -2 & -3 \\ -2 & 3 & 2 & 1 \end{vmatrix}.$

3. Prove that

$$\begin{vmatrix} 1 & 1 & 1 & 1 \\ a & b & c & d \\ a^2 & b^2 & c^2 & d^2 \\ a^3 & b^3 & c^3 & d^3 \end{vmatrix} = \begin{vmatrix} b-a & c-a & d-a \\ b^2-a^2 & c^2-a^2 & d^2-a^2 \\ b^3-a^3 & c^3-a^3 & d^3-a^3 \end{vmatrix}$$

$$= (b-a)(c-a)(d-a) \begin{vmatrix} 1 & 1 & 1 \\ b & c & d \\ b^2 & c^2 & d^2 \end{vmatrix}$$

$$= (b-a)(c-a)(d-a)(c-b)(d-b)(d-c).$$

4. Use Cramer's rule to solve the systems 1(a), (b), and (c) of Exercise 8.2.
5. By the generalization of Corollary 3, Theorem 8.11, to matrices of order n we know that if A is nonsingular of order n

$$A^{-1} = \left(\frac{1}{\det A} \right) B^T$$

where $B = [b_{ij}]$ and b_{ij} is the cofactor of a_{ij} in A. Use this to show that the statement that $X^T = A^{-1}C^T$ is the solution of the system $AX^T = C^T$ is exactly the statement of Cramer's rule for n equations in n unknowns.
6. In Section 5.3 it was shown that a solution of the two equations

$$a_1x_1 + a_2x_2 + a_3x_3 = 0,$$

$$b_1x_1 + b_2x_2 + b_3x_3 = 0,$$

is given by

$$x_1 = \begin{vmatrix} a_2 & a_3 \\ b_2 & b_3 \end{vmatrix}, \qquad x_2 = - \begin{vmatrix} a_1 & a_3 \\ b_1 & b_3 \end{vmatrix}, \qquad x_3 = \begin{vmatrix} a_1 & a_2 \\ b_1 & b_2 \end{vmatrix}.$$

Show that this follows at once from Theorem 8.11 because

$$\begin{vmatrix} a_1 & a_2 & a_3 \\ a_1 & a_2 & a_3 \\ b_1 & b_2 & b_3 \end{vmatrix} = \begin{vmatrix} b_1 & b_2 & b_3 \\ a_1 & a_2 & a_3 \\ b_1 & b_2 & b_3 \end{vmatrix} = 0$$

by the Corollary to Theorem 8.7.
7. Generalize Problem 6 and write a solution of

(a) three equations in four unknowns.
(b) $n-1$ equations in n unknowns.

8.9   Volume of a parallelepiped

If the three vectors

$$A = [a_1, a_2, a_3],$$

$$B = [b_1, b_2, b_3],$$

$$C = [c_1, c_2, c_3]$$

are linearly independent, they are three adjacent edges of a uniquely determined parallelepiped with one vertex at the origin. The parallelepiped is illustrated in Fig. 8.2. The volume of a parallelepiped is the product of the area of its base by its altitude. If we choose as base the parallelogram of which B and C are adjacent sides, and let this area be a we have, if θ is the angle between B and C,

$$a^2 = \|B\|^2\|C\|^2 \sin^2 \theta$$

$$= \|B\|^2\|C\|^2(1 - \cos^2 \theta)$$

$$= \|B\|^2\|C\|^2 - (B \cdot C)^2.$$

Since $B \cdot C = C \cdot B$ and $\|B\|^2 = B \cdot B$ this can be written

$$(23) \qquad a^2 = \begin{vmatrix} B \cdot B & B \cdot C \\ C \cdot B & C \cdot C \end{vmatrix}.$$

Now the altitude of the parallelepiped, measured perpendicular to the base, is the length of the projection of the vector A onto a line perpendicular to the base. Referring to Fig. 8.3, we let R be the terminal point of A, P the projection of R onto the plane of B and C, and Q the projection of R onto the normal to this plane through O.

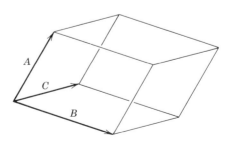

Fig. 8.2

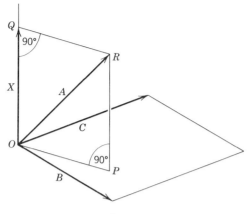

Fig. 8.3

We then let $X = \overrightarrow{OQ}$, and $\|X\|$ is the altitude of the parallelepiped. Since $\overrightarrow{OP}$ is in the plane of B and C we have

$$\overrightarrow{OP} = xB + yC$$

and since $A = \overrightarrow{OQ} + \overrightarrow{OP}$, $A = X + xB + yC$ and

(24) $$X = A - xB - yC.$$

Since X is perpendicular to B and C we have $X \cdot B = X \cdot C = 0$. Taking inner products of each side of (24) with B, C, and X in turn and using $X \cdot B = X \cdot C = 0$, we get the three equations

(25)
$$xB \cdot B + yB \cdot C = B \cdot A,$$
$$xC \cdot B + yC \cdot C = C \cdot A,$$
$$X \cdot X = A \cdot X.$$

We now solve the first two equations of (25) for x and y using Cramer's rule and noting from (23) that the determinant of the coefficients is a^2. The result is

(26) $$a^2 x = \begin{vmatrix} B \cdot A & B \cdot C \\ C \cdot A & C \cdot C \end{vmatrix}, \qquad a^2 y = \begin{vmatrix} B \cdot B & B \cdot A \\ C \cdot B & C \cdot A \end{vmatrix}.$$

Let v be the volume of the parallelepiped. Since its altitude is $\|X\|$ and its base area is a we have, using the third equation of (25),

$$v^2 = a^2\|X\|^2 = a^2(X \cdot X) = a^2(A \cdot X).$$

We now substitute for X from (24) and get

$$v^2 = a^2 A \cdot (A - xB - yC)$$
$$= a^2(A \cdot A) - a^2 x(A \cdot B) - a^2 y(A \cdot C).$$

Now using the value of a^2 from (23) and $a^2 x$ and $a^2 y$ from (26) we find

$$(27) \quad v^2 = A \cdot A \begin{vmatrix} B \cdot B & B \cdot C \\ C \cdot B & C \cdot C \end{vmatrix} - A \cdot B \begin{vmatrix} B \cdot A & B \cdot C \\ C \cdot A & C \cdot C \end{vmatrix}$$
$$+ A \cdot C \begin{vmatrix} B \cdot A & B \cdot B \\ C \cdot A & C \cdot B \end{vmatrix}$$

where the sign before the third determinant has been changed to compensate for an interchange of the two columns. But (27) is the expansion of a third-order determinant by cofactors of its first row and we can therefore write

$$v^2 = \begin{vmatrix} A \cdot A & A \cdot B & A \cdot C \\ B \cdot A & B \cdot B & B \cdot C \\ C \cdot A & C \cdot B & C \cdot C \end{vmatrix}$$

$$= \begin{vmatrix} a_1 & a_2 & a_3 \\ b_1 & b_2 & b_3 \\ c_1 & c_2 & c_3 \end{vmatrix} \begin{vmatrix} a_1 & b_1 & c_1 \\ a_2 & b_2 & c_2 \\ a_3 & b_3 & c_3 \end{vmatrix}$$

$$= \begin{vmatrix} a_1 & b_1 & c_1 \\ a_2 & b_2 & c_2 \\ a_3 & b_3 & c_3 \end{vmatrix}^2 .$$

Here the second equality follows from Theorem 8.14 and the third from Theorem 8.6. This completes the proof of the following theorem.

Theorem 8.15. *If A is any nonsingular matrix of order* 3, $|\det A|$ *is the volume of the parallelepiped defined by its three column (or row) vectors.*

The basis vectors in $\mathcal{U}_3$ corresponding to a given coordinate system in $\mathcal{E}_3$ (i.e., the vectors drawn from the origin to the unit points on the coordinate axes) determine a parallelepiped of which they are adjacent edges. This we shall call the *fundamental parallelepiped* of the coordinate system. For a rectangular coordinate system with equal units on the coordinate axes, the fundamental parallelepiped is a unit cube, of volume 1. Suppose now that we transform from such a coordinate system (the x-system) to a y-system with corresponding basis vectors,

$$F_1 = [a_1, a_2, a_3],$$

$$F_2 = [b_1, b_2, b_3],$$

$$F_3 = [c_1, c_2, c_3].$$

The coordinate vectors X and Y of a point relative to the two coordinate systems are then connected by the equations $X^T = PY^T$ where

$$P = \begin{vmatrix} a_1 & b_1 & c_1 \\ a_2 & b_2 & c_2 \\ a_3 & b_3 & c_3 \end{vmatrix}$$

is the matrix of the transformation. By Theorem 8.15 the volume of the fundamental parallelepiped of the y-system is $|\det P|$.

Now suppose we apply a second transformation, from the y-system to a z-system, with matrix Q. The matrix of the transformation from the x-system to the z-system is therefore PQ and the volume of the fundamental parallelepiped of the z-system is

$$|\det PQ| = |\det P| \, |\det Q|.$$

Hence in transforming from an arbitrary y-system to a z-system the volume of the fundamental parallelepiped is multiplied by $|\det Q|$ where Q is the matrix of the transformation. We have therefore proved a three-dimensional analogue of Theorem 8.5 as follows.

Theorem 8.16. *In a transformation from one Cartesian coordinate system in $\mathcal{E}_3$ to another the volume of the fundamental parallelepiped is multiplied by $|\det Q|$ where Q is the matrix of transformation.*

EXERCISE 8.6

1. Find the area of the parallelogram in $\mathcal{E}_2$ the vertices of which are $(0, 0)$, $(-1, 6)$, $(3, 4)$, and $(2, 10)$.
2. Find the area of the parallelogram in $\mathcal{E}_2$ the vertices of which are $(7, -1)$, $(4, 2)$, $(5, 8)$, $(8, 5)$. *Hint.* Translate axes so that the new origin is at one vertex.

3. If $X = [x_1, x_2, x_3]$, $Y = [y_1, y_2, y_3]$, prove that

$$\|X \times Y\|^2 = \|X\|^2\|Y\|^2 - (X \cdot Y)^2$$

4. Find the area of the parallelogram with vertices at $(0, 0, 0)$, $(2 - 3, 5)$, $(7, 5, 4)$, and $(9, 2, 9)$.

5. Find the area of the parallelogram with vertices at $(4, 1, -6)$, $(6, 9, 2)$, $(12, 8, -4)$, and $(14, 16, 4)$.

6. Find the volume of the parallelepiped of which the vectors $[2, 1, 9]$, $[-1, 5, 2]$, $[-4, -2, 7]$ are three adjacent edges.

7. If the vectors $A_i = [a_{i1}, a_{i2}, a_{i3}]$ $(i = 1, 2, 3)$ are three adjacent edges of a parallelepiped, show that the eight vertices of the parallelepiped are the terminal points of the vectors, O, A_1, A_2, A_3, $A_1 + A_2$, $A_2 + A_3$, $A_1 + A_3$, $A_1 + A_2 + A_3$.

8. Find the coordinates of all the vertices of the parallelepiped in Problem 6.

9. Given the four points $A(1, 2, -2)$, $B(3, 7, 8)$, $C(-6, 5, 1)$, and $D(3, 0, 4)$, find the other four vertices and the volume of the parallelepiped of which AB, AC, AD are adjacent edges.

10. A tetrahedron is a figure with four plane triangular faces formed by joining every pair of four non-coplanar points. These four points are the vertices of the tetrahedron. The volume of a tetrahedron is $\frac{1}{3}bh$ where b is the area of a base and h the altitude. Prove that the volume of the tetrahedron with vertices $(0, 0, 0)$, (x_1, x_2, x_3), (y_1, y_2, y_3), (z_1, z_2, z_3) is $\frac{1}{6}|\det A|$ where

$$A = \begin{bmatrix} x_1 & y_1 & z_1 \\ x_2 & y_2 & z_2 \\ x_3 & y_3 & z_3 \end{bmatrix}.$$

11. Give a geometric interpretation in terms of areas of parallelograms of the identity

$$\begin{vmatrix} a + kc & c \\ b + kd & d \end{vmatrix} = \begin{vmatrix} a & c \\ b & d \end{vmatrix}.$$

Illustrate by drawing a figure.

12. Give a geometric interpretation in terms of volumes of parallelepipeds of the identity

$$\begin{vmatrix} a_1 + kb_1 + hc_1 & b_1 & c_1 \\ a_2 + kb_2 + hc_2 & b_2 & c_2 \\ a_3 + kb_3 + hc_3 & b_3 & c_3 \end{vmatrix} = \begin{vmatrix} a_1 & b_1 & c_1 \\ a_2 & b_2 & c_2 \\ a_3 & b_3 & c_3 \end{vmatrix}.$$

Illustrate by drawing a figure.

CHAPTER 9

ORTHOGONAL
TRANSFORMATIONS AND
ROTATIONS IN $\mathcal{E}_3$

9.1 Orthonormal bases and orthogonal transformations

In this chapter we shall be concerned only with rectangular Cartesian coordinate systems all of which have the same origin and in which a single fixed unit of length is used on the coordinate axes. We shall assume also that the same unit is used in all coordinate systems considered. The basis vectors of $\mathcal{U}_3$ corresponding to such a coordinate system are mutually perpendicular unit vectors. Such a basis is called an *orthonormal* (or *normal orthogonal*) *basis*. Since a coordinate system is uniquely determined by the corresponding basis vectors, a transformation of coordinates simply means a change to a new set of basis vectors. We speak then of a transformation of coordinates either as a transformation from one coordinate system to another or (what is the same thing) as a transformation from one basis to another. In this chapter, therefore, we are fixing our attention on transformations from one orthonormal basis to another.

We start from a fixed rectangular coordinate system with the orthonormal basis

$$E_1 = [1, 0, 0],$$

(1) $$E_2 = [0, 1, 0],$$

$$E_3 = [0, 0, 1].$$

If $F_j = [p_{1j}, p_{2j}, p_{3j}]$ $(j = 1, 2, 3)$ is any other orthonormal basis, we have

$$F_1 = p_{11}E_1 + p_{21}E_2 + p_{31}E_3,$$

$$F_2 = p_{12}E_1 + p_{22}E_2 + p_{32}E_3,$$

$$F_3 = p_{13}E_1 + p_{23}E_2 + p_{33}E_3.$$

By Theorem 7.9 the coordinates in the two systems are connected by the equation $X^T = PY^T$ where

$$P = \begin{bmatrix} p_{11} & p_{12} & p_{13} \\ p_{21} & p_{22} & p_{23} \\ p_{31} & p_{32} & p_{33} \end{bmatrix}$$

is the matrix of the transformation. Since F_1, F_2, F_3 are mutually orthogonal unit vectors, we have for each i and each $j \neq i$, $F_i \cdot F_i = 1$ and $F_i \cdot F_j = 0$. These facts can be expressed by the matrix equation

(2) $$\begin{bmatrix} p_{11} & p_{21} & p_{31} \\ p_{12} & p_{22} & p_{32} \\ p_{13} & p_{23} & p_{33} \end{bmatrix} \begin{bmatrix} p_{11} & p_{12} & p_{13} \\ p_{21} & p_{22} & p_{23} \\ p_{31} & p_{32} & p_{33} \end{bmatrix} = \begin{bmatrix} 1 & 0 & 0 \\ 0 & 1 & 0 \\ 0 & 0 & 1 \end{bmatrix}$$

or $P^T P = I$.

Definition. *A matrix P whose elements are real numbers is said to be orthogonal if it satisfies the condition $P^T P = I$.*

The condition $P^T P = I$ that defines an orthogonal matrix states as in (2) that the columns of P are mutually orthogonal unit vectors. Since the condition can also be written in the form $P^T = P^{-1}$, it implies also $PP^T = I$ which states that the row vectors of P are also mutually orthogonal unit vectors.

Theorem 9.1. *If P is an orthogonal matrix, so also are P^{-1} and P^T. If P and Q are orthogonal, so also is PQ.*

Proof. The first statement is obvious from the preceding remarks. If P and Q are orthogonal

$$(PQ)^T PQ = Q^T P^T PQ = Q^T Q = I$$

since $P^T P = Q^T Q = I$, and hence PQ is orthogonal.

Theorem 9.2. *The matrix of a transformation of coordinates from one orthonormal basis to another is orthogonal.*

Proof. We have already shown that the matrix P of the transformation from the special basis E_1, E_2, E_3 to the arbitrary orthonormal basis F_1, F_2, F_3 is orthogonal. Now suppose the transformation from the F-basis to any other orthonormal basis G_1, G_2, G_3 has matrix Q. The matrix of the transformation from the E-basis to the G-basis is PQ and must be orthogonal as already shown. Hence by Theorem 9.1 $Q = P^{-1}(PQ)$ is orthogonal.

We can also prove a partial converse of Theorem 9.2. Suppose F_1, F_2, F_3 is an orthonormal basis and $P = [p_{ij}]$ is an orthogonal matrix. It is then easy to show that the basis G_1, G_2, G_3 defined by

$$G_1 = p_{11}F_1 + p_{21}F_2 + p_{31}F_3,$$

$$G_2 = p_{12}F_1 + p_{22}F_2 + p_{32}F_3,$$

$$G_3 = p_{13}F_1 + p_{23}F_2 + p_{33}F_3,$$

is also orthonormal. For we have, since $F_i \cdot F_j = 0$ if $i \neq j$ and 1 if $i = j$,

$$G_i \cdot G_j = (p_{1i}F_1 + p_{2i}F_2 + p_{3i}F_3) \cdot (p_{1j}F_1 + p_{2j}F_2 + p_{3j}F_3)$$

$$= p_{1i}p_{1j} + p_{2i}p_{2j} + p_{3i}p_{3j}$$

$$= 0 \quad \text{if } i \neq j \text{ and 1 if } i = j \text{ since } P \text{ is orthogonal.}$$

Thus if we start from one orthonormal basis the orthogonal transformations (i.e., those with orthogonal matrix) are exactly those that transform to another orthonormal basis.

Finally, we remark that if P is orthogonal, since $P^T P = I$ we have

$$\det (P^T P) = \det (P^T) \det P = \det I = 1.$$

Since $\det (P^T) = \det P$ this implies $(\det P)^2 = 1$ and hence

$$\det P = \pm 1.$$

Hence we can distinguish two types of orthogonal matrices, those with determinant 1 and those with determinant -1.

Definition. *An orthogonal matrix P such that* $\det P = 1$ *is called a proper orthogonal matrix. If* $\det P = -1$ *then P is an improper orthogonal matrix.*

EXERCISE 9.1

1. Verify that the following matrices are orthogonal and determine whether they are proper or improper.

$$A = \begin{bmatrix} \frac{1}{3} & \frac{2}{3} & \frac{2}{3} \\ \frac{2}{3} & -\frac{2}{3} & \frac{1}{3} \\ \frac{2}{3} & \frac{1}{3} & -\frac{2}{3} \end{bmatrix} \qquad B = \begin{bmatrix} \frac{6}{7} & \frac{3}{7} & -\frac{2}{7} \\ \frac{2}{7} & -\frac{6}{7} & -\frac{3}{7} \\ \frac{3}{7} & -\frac{2}{7} & \frac{6}{7} \end{bmatrix}.$$

2. Compute the product AB and verify that it is orthogonal.
3. Prove that if P and Q are both proper or both improper orthogonal, and of the same order, then PQ is proper orthogonal. If one is proper and the other improper, show that the product is improper orthogonal.
4. Show that a second-order orthogonal matrix must have one of the two forms

$$\begin{bmatrix} \cos\theta & -\sin\theta \\ \sin\theta & \cos\theta \end{bmatrix} \quad \text{or} \quad \begin{bmatrix} \cos\theta & \sin\theta \\ \sin\theta & -\cos\theta \end{bmatrix}$$

for a suitably chosen angle θ.

9.2 Rotations and reflections

We have distinguished two types of orthogonal transformation: proper and improper. We now investigate the geometric meaning of this distinction. First we introduce a related division of orthonormal bases into two classes. We associate with any basis F_1, F_2, F_3 the matrix F of which F_1^T, F_2^T, and F_3^T are the first, second, and third column vectors, respectively. If the F-basis is orthonormal, F is an orthogonal matrix and hence $\det F$ is either 1 or -1. If $\det F = 1$, we say that the basis F_1, F_2, F_3 is *positively oriented;* if $\det F = -1$, then this basis is *negatively oriented.* We note that the orientation depends on the order of the three basis vectors. Note also that if *one* of the basis vectors is multiplied by -1 (i.e., its direction is reversed) the orientation is changed although the basis is still orthonormal.

Theorem 9.3. *A proper orthogonal transformation preserves the orientation of the basis vectors; an improper orthogonal transformation changes the orientation.*

Proof. Let P be the matrix of the transformation from the basis F_1, F_2, F_3 to a new basis G_1, G_2, G_3. Let E_1, E_2, E_3 be the basis (1). The matrix F associated with the F-basis is actually the matrix of the transformation from the E-basis to the F-basis, for its columns are the coordinates of F_1, F_2, F_3 relative to the E-basis. Similarly, G is the matrix of the transformation from the E-basis to the G-basis. By Problem 12, Exercise 8.2, F^{-1} is the matrix of the transformation from the F-basis to the E-basis and hence $F^{-1}G$ is the matrix of the transformation from the F-basis to the G-basis. Hence $F^{-1}G = P$, $G = FP$ and $\det G = (\det F)(\det P)$. Thus if $\det P = 1$, $\det G$ and $\det F$ have the same sign; if $\det P = -1$, $\det G$ and $\det F$ have opposite signs. Hence a proper orthogonal transformation preserves, but an improper orthogonal transformation changes, the orientation of the basis vectors.

Definition. *By a rotation of axes in $\mathcal{E}_3$ we shall mean a transformation to a new basis obtained from the original by a continuous rigid motion of the basis vectors leaving the origin fixed, and preserving orthogonality.*

Definition. *By a reflection of axes in $\mathcal{E}_3$ we shall mean a reversal in direction of one of the basis vectors.*

Since either a rotation or a reflection takes us from one orthonormal basis to another, they are both orthogonal transformations. Moreover every orthogonal transformation of coordinates is either a rotation or a rotation followed by a reflection. To see this let F_1, F_2, F_3, and G_1, G_2, G_3 be any two orthonormal bases. It is clear that a succession of rotations (continuous rigid motions) is again a rotation. The F-basis vectors can clearly be rotated until F_1 coincides with G_1. This having been done, a further rotation will bring F_2 into coincidence with G_2. The fact that both are orthonormal then requires that F_3 coincide either with G_3 or $-G_3$. In the first case the transformation from the F-basis to the G-basis is a rotation; in the second it is a rotation followed by a reflection. We state this result formally.

Theorem 9.4. *Every orthogonal transformation of coordinates in $\mathcal{E}_3$ is either a rotation of axes or a rotation of axes followed by a reflection.*

Next we show that the rotations are precisely the proper orthogonal transformations. We do this by showing that a rotation preserves the orientation of the basis vectors, whereas a reflection changes the orientation. The proof of this actually depends on basic properties of continuous functions which are proved by calculus. However, since the proof is one with particularly strong appeal to the mathematical intuition of the average student, we shall give it here as an intuitive argument. The student should understand that the basic property of continuous functions that is used requires proof and that this can be given only after considerable knowledge of calculus has been acquired.

Let F_1, F_2, F_3 where $F_j = [f_{1j}, f_{2j}, f_{3j}]$ be any orthonormal basis and let these be transformed by a rotation to a new orthonormal basis G_1, G_2, G_3 with $G_j = [g_{1j}, g_{2j}, g_{3j}]$. Let $X_j = [x_{1j}, x_{2j}, x_{3j}]$ be the coordinates of the basis vectors at any intermediate position so that x_{ij} varies continuously from f_{ij} to g_{ij} in the course of the rotation. Let F, G, and X be the matrices corresponding to the three bases. Since a rotation is a continuous transformation, and since a determinant is a continuous function of the elements of a matrix, it follows that $\det X$ must vary continuously from the value $\det F$ to the value $\det G$. Now suppose $\det F = 1$ and $\det G = -1$. A basic property of continuous functions states that $\det X$ cannot change in the course of a continuous transformation from 1 to -1 without assuming the value 0 at some intermediate position. But $\det X = 0$ would imply the linear dependence of X_1, X_2, X_3 which cannot happen in the course of a rigid motion of mutually orthogonal vectors. Thus a rotation cannot change the orientation of the basis vectors. On the other hand, a reflection involves a change in sign of *one* of the basis vectors F_1, F_2, F_3. This changes the sign of $\det F$ and hence changes the orientation of the basis vectors. These results are summed up in the following statement.

Theorem 9.5. *Every proper orthogonal transformation of coordinates is a rotation of axes and conversely. Every improper orthogonal transformation of coordinates is either a reflection or a rotation of axes followed by a reflection.*

We can now give a geometric meaning to the orientation of a set of basis vectors. Let F_1, F_2, F_3 be an orthonormal basis. We say that these basis vectors are a right-hand system if to an observer at the terminal point of F_3 looking at the plane of F_1 and F_2 the direction of

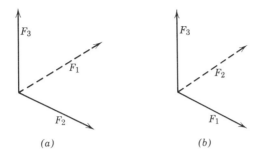

Fig. 9.1 (*a*) A left-hand system, (*b*) a right-hand system.

rotation from F_1 to F_2 through $90°$ is *counterclockwise*. If this direction is clockwise, we call F_1, F_2, F_3 a left-hand system. Note that if F_1, F_2, F_3 is a right-hand system, then F_1, F_2, $-F_3$ is a left-hand system. Thus a reversal in direction of any *one* of the basis vectors converts a right-hand system to a left-hand system and a left-hand system to a right-hand system.

Now suppose that the basis E_1, E_2, E_3 defined by (1) in terms of the original coordinate system is a right-hand system. It is clear that this property is not changed by a rotation for this is a continuous rigid motion of the basis vectors. Hence all bases obtained from E_1, E_2, E_3 by rotation (i.e., by proper orthogonal transformation) will be right-hand systems. On the other hand, as noted previously, a reflection changes a right-hand system to a left-hand system. Hence every improper orthogonal transformation will be a change from the basis E_1, E_2, E_3 to a left-hand system. Since E_1, E_2, E_3 are positively oriented, this means that every right-hand system is positively oriented and every left-hand system is negatively oriented. We can state these results as follows.

Theorem 9.6. *If one right-hand system of basis vectors is positively oriented, then all right-hand systems are positively oriented and all left-hand systems are negatively oriented.*

The notions of orientation, left-, and right-hand system are readily extended to bases that are not necessarily orthonormal. Similarly, a general transformation of coordinates with matrix P may be called proper or improper according as det P is positive or negative. It then follows that proper transformations preserve, but improper transformations change, the orientation of the basis vectors. If X_1, X_2, X_3 where $X_j = [x_{1j}, x_{2j}, x_{3j}]$ is any basis of $\mathcal{U}_3$, let X be the matrix of which $X_1{}^T$, $X_2{}^T$, $X_3{}^T$ are the first, second, and third columns. We know from Theorem 8.15 that $|\det X|$ is the volume of the fundamental parallelepiped defined by the basis vectors. Assuming that E_1, E_2, E_3 is a right-hand system we can now go further and say that this volume is $\det X$ if X_1, X_2, X_3 is a right-hand system and is $-\det X$ if X_1, X_2, X_3 is a left-hand system.

9.3 The axis of a rotation in $\mathcal{E}_3$

In this section we shall investigate points whose coordinates are not changed by a rotation of axes. Let P be the matrix of a rotation from the basis E_1, E_2, E_3 in (1) to a new basis F_1, F_2, F_3. Now the coordinates (x_1, x_2, x_3) and (y_1, y_2, y_3) of a point relative to the two coordinate systems are related by the equation

$$(3) \qquad\qquad X^T = PY^T.$$

Hence if there is a point (x_1, x_2, x_3) whose coordinates are unchanged by the rotation, the corresponding vector $X = [x_1, x_2, x_3]$ must, by (3), satisfy the equation $PX^T = X^T$ or

$$(4) \qquad\qquad (P - I)X^T = 0.$$

Now (4) is a system of three homogeneous equations in three unknowns x_1, x_2, x_3 with matrix $P - I$, that is (4) is equivalent to

$$
(5) \qquad
\begin{aligned}
(p_{11} - 1)x_1 + \quad & p_{12}x_2 + \quad && p_{13}x_3 = 0, \\
p_{21}x_1 + (p_{22} & - 1)x_2 + \quad && p_{23}x_3 = 0, \\
p_{31}x_1 + \quad & p_{32}x_2 + (p_{33} && - 1)x_3 = 0.
\end{aligned}
$$

These equations always have the trivial rotation $x_1 = x_2 = x_3 = 0$. (The origin has the same coordinates after a rotation.) A necessary and sufficient condition that there are nonzero solutions of (5) is that the matrix $P - I$ is singular, or by Theorem 8.12 that

$$(6) \qquad\qquad \det (P - I) = 0.$$

We now show that (6) holds for any proper orthogonal matrix P of order 3. For since P is proper orthogonal, $\det P^T = \det P = 1$. Hence

$$\det (P - I) = \det P^T \det (P - I)$$

$$= \det (P^T P - P^T) \quad \text{by Theorem 8.14}$$

$$= \det (I - P^T) \quad \text{since } P \text{ is orthogonal}$$

$$= \det (I - P)^T$$

$$= \det (I - P) = (-1)^3 \det (P - I) = -\det (P - I).$$

Hence $2 \det (P - I) = 0$ and (6) holds. Thus for any proper orthogonal matrix P of order 3 there is a nonzero vector X that satisfies (4). The terminal point (x_1, x_2, x_3) of this vector therefore has the same coordinates after the rotation as before. Since any scalar multiple kX of X also satisfies (4), the coordinates of every point on the line through the origin and (x_1, x_2, x_3) are also unchanged by the rotation. We have therefore proved the following theorem.

Theorem 9.7. *For every rotation of axes in* $\mathcal{E}_3$ *there is an* invariant line *l through the origin. The coordinates of every point on l are the same after the rotation as before.*

The invariant line corresponding to a rotation of axes is called the *axis* of the rotation. The effect of the rotation is to rotate the basis vectors about the axis of the rotation, preserving the angles they make with this axis.

EXERCISE 9.2

1. Show that the matrix of a rotation of axes in $\mathcal{E}_2$ is orthogonal.
2. Find three mutually perpendicular vectors one of which is $[3, 2, 1]$. Convert each of them to a unit vector by multiplying by a suitable scalar and hence construct an orthogonal matrix of which the first row is

$$\left[\frac{3}{\sqrt{14}} \quad \frac{2}{\sqrt{14}} \quad \frac{1}{\sqrt{14}} \right].$$

3. Construct an orthogonal matrix of which two column vectors are scalar multiples of $[2, 5, -1]$ and $[3, -2, -4]$.
4. Show that the transformation from the basis $E_1 = [1, 0, 0]$, $E_2 = [0, 1, 0]$, $E_3 = [0, 0, 1]$ to the basis $F_1 = [\frac{1}{3}, \frac{2}{3}, \frac{2}{3}]$, $F_2 = [\frac{2}{3}, -\frac{2}{3}, \frac{1}{3}]$, $F_3 = [\frac{2}{3}, \frac{1}{3}, -\frac{2}{3}]$ is a rotation. Find the axis of this rotation.

5. Write the matrix of a counterclockwise rotation through an angle θ
   (a) about the x_3-axis, (b) about the x_2-axis, (c) about the x_1-axis.
6. If P is an improper orthogonal matrix, show that the equations

$$PX^T = -X^T$$

   have a nonzero solution.
7. If B is the matrix defined in Problem 1, Exercise 9.1, find a nonzero vector
   such that $BX^T = -X^T$.

9.4   The general second-degree equation in x_1, x_2, x_3

In Chapter 6 we studied the quadric surfaces which arose as the graphs in $\mathcal{E}_3$ of various standard quadratic equations in the coordinates x, y, z. To facilitate the use of vector and matrix notation we continue to denote coordinates in $\mathcal{E}_3$ by x_1, x_2, x_3 rather than x, y, z. By means of suitable translations of axes it is easy to show that the graph of any equation of the form

(7) $ax_1{}^2 + bx_2{}^2 + cx_3{}^2 + dx_1 + ex_2 + fx_3 + k = 0,$

where not all of a, b, and c are zero, is one of the following:

(a) The empty set (e.g., $3x_1{}^2 + 7x_2{}^2 + x_3{}^2 + 8 = 0$).
(b) A single point or single line (e.g., $x_1{}^2 + 2x_2{}^2 + 4x_3{}^2 = 0$ or $x_1{}^2 + (x_2 - 3)^2 = 0$).
(c) Two (possibly coincident) planes (e.g., $x_1{}^2 - 4x_3{}^2 = 0$ or $x_1{}^2 = 0$).
(d) One of the quadric surfaces discussed in Chapter 6.

Our aim in this chapter is to show that any second-degree equation in x_1, x_2, x_3 (which in general will include terms in x_1x_2, x_1x_3 and x_2x_3) can be reduced to the form (7) by a suitable rotation of axes. It will then follow that the graph in $\mathcal{E}_3$ of any second-degree equation must be one of the preceding. We shall also show how to find the appropriate rotation of axes for any given equation and hence how to determine the nature of its graph.

A rotation of axes replaces the coordinates x_1, x_2, x_3 by linear homogeneous functions of the new coordinates y_1, y_2, y_3, namely,

$$x_1 = p_{11}y_1 + p_{12}y_2 + p_{13}y_3,$$

$$x_2 = p_{21}y_1 + p_{22}y_2 + p_{23}y_3,$$

$$x_3 = p_{31}y_1 + p_{32}y_2 + p_{33}y_3.$$

Such a transformation clearly takes second-degree terms in the x's into second-degree terms in the y's, and similarly for first-degree terms. The constant term is unchanged. Thus our problem is to show that the expression

(8) $\qquad ax_1^2 + bx_2^2 + cx_3^2 + 2hx_1x_2 + 2gx_1x_3 + 2fx_2x_3$

can be transformed by a rotation of axes into

(9) $\qquad \lambda_1 y_1^2 + \lambda_2 y_2^2 + \lambda_3 y_3^2.$

In the next section we restate this as a problem in matrix algebra.

9.5   Quadratic forms

The expression (8) is called a *quadratic form* in x_1, x_2, x_3. In general a quadratic form is a homogeneous quadratic polynomial in any number of variables x_1, x_2, . . . , x_n. There is a simple way of associating a matrix with a quadratic form. Since each term of such a form involves a product $x_i x_j$ of two of the variables, the coefficient a_{ij} of this product can be taken as the element in the ith row and jth column of a matrix. Since however $x_i x_j = x_j x_i$ we assign the *same element* to the ith row and jth column as to the jth row and ith column. Thus the form (8) can be written

$$ax_1x_1 + hx_1x_2 + gx_1x_3$$
$$+ hx_2x_1 + bx_2x_2 + fx_2x_3$$
$$+ gx_3x_1 + fx_3x_2 + cx_3x_3$$

and its associated matrix is

(10) $\qquad A = \begin{bmatrix} a & h & g \\ h & b & f \\ g & f & c \end{bmatrix}.$

Because we assign the same coefficient to $x_i x_j$ as to $x_j x_i$ the matrix A is symmetric about its main diagonal. Such a matrix satisfies the condition $A^T = A$ and is called a *symmetric matrix*. It is clear therefore that associated with every quadratic form in x_1, x_2, . . . , x_n is a uniquely determined symmetric matrix of order n and conversely.

The theorems that we are going to prove about quadratic forms and symmetric matrices are true for forms and matrices of any order n. However we shall give proofs only for the cases $n = 2$ and 3 since these are the cases we need for geometric applications. Proofs valid for any positive integer n may be found in [5], Chapters 7 and 8. We return therefore to the form (8) and its corresponding symmetric matrix A. If we compute the matrix product

$$XAX^T = [x_1, x_2, x_3]\begin{bmatrix} a & h & g \\ h & b & f \\ g & f & c \end{bmatrix}\begin{bmatrix} x_1 \\ x_2 \\ x_3 \end{bmatrix}$$

the result is a 1 by 1 matrix whose single element is precisely the form (8). We therefore identify the matrix product XAX^T with the quadratic form (8). We shall use the notation XAX^T for a quadratic form and it will be understood that the matrix A is symmetric.

Example 1. *Check the following by computing the matrix products:*

(a) $x^2 - 6xy + 8y^2 = [x, y]\begin{bmatrix} 1 & -3 \\ -3 & 8 \end{bmatrix}\begin{bmatrix} x \\ y \end{bmatrix}$

(b) $2x_1{}^2 + 8x_2{}^2 - x_3{}^2 + 3x_1x_2 + 6x_2x_3 - 10x_1x_3 =$

$$[x_1, x_2, x_3]\begin{bmatrix} 2 & \frac{3}{2} & -5 \\ \frac{3}{2} & 8 & 3 \\ -5 & 3 & -1 \end{bmatrix}\begin{bmatrix} x_1 \\ x_2 \\ x_3 \end{bmatrix}.$$

Theorem 9.8. *The quadratic form whose matrix is A is transformed by a transformation of coordinates with matrix P into a quadratic form with matrix $P^T A P$.*

Proof. The quadratic form with matrix A is XAX^T. The transformation with matrix P is $X^T = PY^T$ or, taking transposes, $X = YP^T$. Hence we have

$$XAX^T = (YP^T)A(PY^T) = Y(P^T AP)Y^T$$

which is a quadratic form in y_1, y_2, y_3 with matrix $P^T AP$. Moreover, since A is symmetric, $A^T = A$ and

$$(P^T AP)^T = P^T A^T P = P^T AP.$$

Hence $P^T AP$ is symmetric and the theorem is proved.

Now the quadratic form (9) is YDY^T where D is the diagonal matrix

(11)
$$D = \begin{bmatrix} \lambda_1 & 0 & 0 \\ 0 & \lambda_2 & 0 \\ 0 & 0 & \lambda_3 \end{bmatrix}.$$

Hence the problem of reducing (8) to (9) by an orthogonal transformation is equivalent to the following problem in matrix algebra: given a symmetric third-order matrix A with real elements, find an orthogonal matrix P such that $P^T A P = D$ where D is a diagonal matrix. Since P is orthogonal $P^T = P^{-1}$ and hence what is required is an orthogonal matrix P such that

(12)
$$AP = PD$$

where D is a diagonal matrix. In the next section we show how such a matrix P can be found.

9.6   Diagonalization of a real symmetric matrix of order 3

Let A be the real symmetric matrix (10). We wish to find a (real) orthogonal matrix P and diagonal matrix D that satisfy (12). We denote the column vectors of P by P_1^T, P_2^T, and P_3^T. If D is the matrix (11), the column vectors of PD are (Problem 8, Exercise 8.1) $\lambda_1 P_1^T$, $\lambda_2 P_2^T$, and $\lambda_3 P_3^T$. Equating these to the column vectors of AP we find that (12) is equivalent to

(13)
$$AP_1^T = \lambda_1 P_1^T,$$
$$AP_2^T = \lambda_2 P_2^T,$$
$$AP_3^T = \lambda_3 P_3^T.$$

The first equation of (13), written in full, is

(14)
$$\begin{bmatrix} a - \lambda_1 & h & g \\ h & b - \lambda_1 & f \\ g & f & c - \lambda_1 \end{bmatrix} \begin{bmatrix} p_{11} \\ p_{21} \\ p_{31} \end{bmatrix} = \begin{bmatrix} 0 \\ 0 \\ 0 \end{bmatrix}.$$

Thus P_1^T must be a solution vector of the system of homogenous equations (14) with matrix $A - \lambda_1 I$. The condition for the existence of a nonzero solution P_1^T of (14) is that the matrix $A - \lambda_1 I$ be singular, or by Theorem 8.12, that $\det (A - \lambda_1 I) = 0$. Similarly, the condition for the existence of nonzero vectors $P_2{}^T$ and $P_3{}^T$ satisfying (13) is that λ_2 and λ_3 satisfy $\det (A - \lambda_2 I) = 0$, $\det (A - \lambda_3 I) = 0$. It is now clear that the three numbers λ_1, λ_2, λ_3 must be chosen to satisfy the equation

$$(15) \qquad \det (A - xI) = \begin{vmatrix} a - x & h & g \\ h & b - x & f \\ g & f & c - x \end{vmatrix} = 0.$$

Since (15) is a cubic equation in x it has three (not necessarily distinct) roots* which we designate by λ_1, λ_2, and λ_3. We now introduce some new terminology to facilitate our discussion.

Definitions. *If A is a square matrix of order n, the matrix $A - xI$ obtained by subtracting x from each element of the main diagonal is called the* characteristic matrix *of A. The determinant $\det (A - xI)$ is a polynomial of degree n in x called the* characteristic polynomial *of A. The equation $\det (A - xI) = 0$ is called the* characteristic equation *of A and its roots are called the* eigenvalues *(or characteristic roots) of A. If λ is an eigenvalue of A, $A - \lambda I$ is singular and there exists a nonzero vector X such that $(A - \lambda I)X^T = 0$ or $AX^T = \lambda X^T$. Such a vector X is called an* eigenvector *of A corresponding to the eigenvalue λ.*

If X is an eigenvector of A corresponding to the eigenvalue λ so also is kX for any nonzero scalar k. Hence by choosing $k = 1/\|X\|$ we can always find an eigenvector of unit length corresponding to any eigenvalue. In order to complete the solution of our problem we now need to know two things: first that the eigenvalues λ_1, λ_2, λ_3 of A are real and second that the corresponding unit eigenvectors P_1, P_2, P_3 are mutually orthogonal so that P is then an orthogonal matrix. The remainder of this section will be devoted to proving these two facts.

Definition. *The matrices A and B are said to be* similar *if there exists a nonsingular matrix P such that $B = P^{-1}AP$.*

We note that this is a symmetric relationship since if $B = P^{-1}AP$, then $A = Q^{-1}BQ$ where $Q = P^{-1}$. Moreover, if $B = P_1{}^{-1}AP_1$ and $C = P_2{}^{-1}BP_2$, then

$$C = P_2{}^{-1}P_1{}^{-1}AP_1P_2 = (P_1P_2)^{-1}A(P_1P_2).$$

* See Theorem 10.5 in the next chapter.

Hence if A and B are similar and B and C are similar, then A and C are similar.

Lemma 9.1. *Similar matrices have the same characteristic polynomials and hence the same eigenvalues.*

Proof. By the distributive law,

$$P^{-1}(A - xI)P = P^{-1}AP - x(P^{-1}IP) = P^{-1}AP - xI.$$

Hence $\det (P^{-1}AP - xI) = \det P^{-1} \det (A - xI) \det P$

$$= \det (A - xI),$$

since $\det P^{-1} \det P = \det P^{-1}P = 1$. Hence A and $P^{-1}AP$ have the same characteristic polynomial and the same eigenvalues.

Lemma 9.2. *If A is a real symmetric matrix of order 3, then A has at least one real eigenvalue.*

Proof. The characteristic equation of A is of degree 3 and hence has at least one real root. We assume this fact here. The reason for it will be made clear in Chapter 10 (see Exercise 10.4, Problem 4).

Lemma 9.3. *The eigenvalues of a real symmetric matrix of order 2 are real.*

Proof.   If $A = \begin{bmatrix} p & r \\ r & q \end{bmatrix}$,

then

$$\det (A - xI) = \begin{vmatrix} p - x & r \\ r & q - x \end{vmatrix} = x^2 - (p + q)x + pq - r^2.$$

The discriminant of this quadratic is

$$(p + q)^2 - 4pq + 4r^2 = (p - q)^2 + 4r^2.$$

Since the discriminant is a sum of squares of real numbers, it is non-negative and the eigenvalues of A are therefore real.

Lemma 9.4. *If A is a real symmetric matrix of order 3 and λ is a real eigenvalue of A, then there exists a real orthogonal matrix P such that*

(16) $$P^T A P = P^{-1} A P = \begin{bmatrix} \lambda & 0 & 0 \\ 0 & p & r \\ 0 & r & q \end{bmatrix}.$$

Proof. Corresponding to the real eigenvalue λ is a real eigenvector of length 1, which we shall denote by P_1. Hence $AP_1{}^T = \lambda P_1{}^T$. We can now construct an orthogonal matrix P of which $P_1{}^T$ is the first column vector. For if $P_1 = [a_1, a_2, a_3]$, the second column $[b_1, b_2, b_3]^T$ is chosen as a unit solution vector of

$$a_1 x_1 + a_2 x_2 + a_3 x_3 = 0$$

and the third column vector is then chosen as a unit solution vector of the system

$$a_1 x_1 + a_2 x_2 + a_3 x_3 = 0,$$

$$b_1 x_1 + b_2 x_2 + b_3 x_3 = 0.$$

Now the first column of AP is (Exercise 8.1, Problem 17) $AP_1{}^T$ which is equal to $\lambda P_1{}^T$. Hence the first column of $P^T(AP)$ is $P^T(\lambda P_1{}^T) = \lambda P^T P_1{}^T$. Now the first row of P^T is P_1 itself (a unit vector) and the other two rows are orthogonal to P_1. Hence the first column of $P^T AP$, namely, $P^T P_1{}^T$, is

$$[\lambda, 0, 0]^T.$$

But since A is symmetric, $P^T AP$ is also symmetric (see Theorem 9.8). Hence the first row of $P^T AP$ is $[\lambda, 0, 0]$ and (16) follows.

Theorem 9.9. *The eigenvalues of a real symmetric matrix A of order 3 are real.*

Proof. By Lemma 9.2, A has a real eigenvalue λ_1 and by Lemma 9.4, there is an orthogonal matrix P such that

$$P^{-1}AP = \begin{bmatrix} \lambda_1 & 0 & 0 \\ 0 & p & r \\ 0 & r & q \end{bmatrix}.$$

The characteristic polynomial of $P^{-1}AP$ is clearly

$$(\lambda_1 - x) \begin{vmatrix} p - x & r \\ r & q - x \end{vmatrix}$$

and by Lemma 9.1 this is also the characteristic polynomial of A. The eigenvalues of A are therefore λ_1 and the two eigenvalues of the second-order matrix

$$\begin{bmatrix} p & r \\ r & q \end{bmatrix}$$

which are real by Lemma 9.3.

Theorem 9.10. *If A is a real symmetric matrix of order 2 with eigenvalues λ_1 and λ_2, there exists an orthogonal matrix P such that*

$$(17) \qquad P^{-1}AP = P^T AP = \begin{bmatrix} \lambda_1 & 0 \\ 0 & \lambda_2 \end{bmatrix}.$$

Proof. Let P_1 be a unit eigenvector corresponding to λ_1 and let P be an orthogonal matrix of which the first column vector is $P_1{}^T$. Exactly as in the proof of Lemma 9.4 we find (17) holds. The element λ_2 occuring in the lower right-hand corner of $P^{-1}AP$ is certainly an eigenvalue of $P^{-1}AP$ and hence of A by Lemma 9.1.

If we let D be the diagonal matrix $P^{-1}AP$, (17) is equivalent to

$$(18) \qquad\qquad AP = PD.$$

Equating column vectors on each side of (18) we get

$$AP_1{}^T = \lambda_1 P_1{}^T,$$
$$AP_2{}^T = \lambda_2 P_2{}^T,$$

where $P_2{}^T$ is the second column of P. Hence the column vectors of P are unit eigenvectors of A corresponding to λ_1 and λ_2, and we have proved the following.

Corollary. *A real symmetric matrix of order 2 has two mutually orthogonal unit eigenvectors.*

Theorem 9.11. *If A is a real symmetric matrix of order 3 with eigenvalues $\lambda_1, \lambda_2, \lambda_3$, there exists an orthogonal matrix R such that*

$$R^{-1}AR = R^T AR = \begin{bmatrix} \lambda_1 & 0 & 0 \\ 0 & \lambda_2 & 0 \\ 0 & 0 & \lambda_3 \end{bmatrix}.$$

Proof. Let λ_1 be any eigenvalue of A and let Q_1 be a unit eigenvector of A corresponding to λ_1. Since λ_1 is real so is Q_1 and we can construct as in Lemma 9.4 an orthogonal matrix Q, with $Q_1{}^T$ as its first column, such that

$$Q^{-1}AQ = Q^T AQ = \begin{bmatrix} \lambda_1 & 0 & 0 \\ 0 & p & r \\ 0 & r & q \end{bmatrix}.$$

The matrix

$$A_1 = \begin{bmatrix} p & r \\ r & q \end{bmatrix}$$

is symmetric with eigenvalues λ_2, λ_3 equal to the other two eigenvalues of A (and hence of $Q^{-1}AQ$). Hence there exists by Theorem 9.10 an orthogonal matrix

$$P = \begin{bmatrix} s & u \\ t & v \end{bmatrix}$$

such that

(19) $$P^{-1}A_1P = P^TA_1P = \begin{bmatrix} \lambda_2 & 0 \\ 0 & \lambda_3 \end{bmatrix}.$$

Now the matrix

$$S = \begin{bmatrix} 1 & 0 & 0 \\ 0 & s & u \\ 0 & t & v \end{bmatrix}$$

is orthogonal because P is orthogonal. Moreover, using (19) we find that

$$\begin{bmatrix} 1 & 0 & 0 \\ 0 & s & t \\ 0 & u & v \end{bmatrix}\begin{bmatrix} \lambda_1 & 0 & 0 \\ 0 & p & r \\ 0 & r & q \end{bmatrix}\begin{bmatrix} 1 & 0 & 0 \\ 0 & s & u \\ 0 & t & v \end{bmatrix} = \begin{bmatrix} \lambda_1 & 0 & 0 \\ 0 & \lambda_2 & 0 \\ 0 & 0 & \lambda_3 \end{bmatrix}.$$

or

(20) $$S^T(Q^TAQ)S = \begin{bmatrix} \lambda_1 & 0 & 0 \\ 0 & \lambda_2 & 0 \\ 0 & 0 & \lambda_3 \end{bmatrix}$$

Since Q and S are orthogonal, their product $R = QS$ is also orthogonal and we have from (20), since $R^T = S^TQ^T$,

$$R^{-1}AR = R^TAR = \begin{bmatrix} \lambda_1 & 0 & 0 \\ 0 & \lambda_2 & 0 \\ 0 & 0 & \lambda_3 \end{bmatrix}$$

and the theorem is proved.

Corollary. *A real symmetric matrix of order 3 has three mutually orthogonal unit eigenvectors.*

Proof. If we let D be the diagonal matrix $R^{-1}AR$, we have

(21) $$AR = RD$$

where

$$D = \begin{bmatrix} \lambda_1 & 0 & 0 \\ 0 & \lambda_2 & 0 \\ 0 & 0 & \lambda_3 \end{bmatrix}.$$

Equating column vectors on each side of (21),

$$AR_1{}^T = \lambda_1 R_1{}^T, \quad AR_2{}^T = \lambda_2 R_2{}^T, \quad AR_3{}^T = \lambda_3 R_3{}^T,$$

where $R_1{}^T$, $R_2{}^T$, and $R_3{}^T$ are the column vectors of R. Hence the columns of R are eigenvectors of A and are mutually orthogonal unit vectors since R is orthogonal.

The reduction of the quadratic form (8) to the form (9) by an orthogonal transformation is now complete. We sum up the method and then illustrate it with an example. First we write the symmetric matrix A corresponding to the quadratic form. Find the eigenvalues λ_1, λ_2, λ_3 of A and find three mutually orthogonal unit eigenvectors of A corresponding to λ_1, λ_2, λ_3. Let P be a (necessarily orthogonal) matrix of which these eigenvectors are the column vectors. Choose the order and sign of the column vectors of P so that det $P = 1$ and P is therefore proper orthogonal. The rotation of axes with matrix P will then reduce the form (8) to the form (9).

Example 1. *Find a proper orthogonal matrix P that will diagonalize the symmetric matrix*

$$A = \begin{bmatrix} 2 & -2 & -2 \\ -2 & 3 & 0 \\ -2 & 0 & 1 \end{bmatrix}.$$

Solution. The characteristic equation of A is

$$\det(A - xI) = \begin{vmatrix} 2-x & -2 & -2 \\ -2 & 3-x & 0 \\ -2 & 0 & 1-x \end{vmatrix} = 0$$

which simplifies, on expansion of the determinant, to

(22) $$x^3 - 6x^2 + 3x + 10 = 0.$$

By inspection $x = -1$ is a root (22). The left-hand side can therefore be divided by $x + 1$ and (22) is equivalent to

$$(x + 1)(x^2 - 7x + 10) = 0$$

or

$$(x + 1)(x - 2)(x - 5) = 0.$$

Thus the eigenvalues of A are -1, 2, 5. To find an eigenvector corresponding to $x = -1$ we must solve the equations

$$(A + I)X^T = \begin{bmatrix} 3 & -2 & -2 \\ -2 & 4 & 0 \\ -2 & 0 & 2 \end{bmatrix} \begin{bmatrix} x_1 \\ x_2 \\ x_3 \end{bmatrix} = \begin{bmatrix} 0 \\ 0 \\ 0 \end{bmatrix}.$$

Using the method of Section 8.2 we operate on the matrix $A + I$ as follows

$$
\begin{array}{l}
R_1 + R_2 \longrightarrow \\
\tfrac{1}{2}R_2 \longrightarrow \\
\tfrac{1}{2}R_1 \longrightarrow
\end{array}
\begin{bmatrix} 1 & 2 & -2 \\ -1 & 2 & 0 \\ -1 & 0 & 1 \end{bmatrix}
$$

$$
\begin{array}{l}
R_2 + R_1 \longrightarrow \\
R_3 + R_1 \longrightarrow
\end{array}
\begin{bmatrix} 1 & 2 & -2 \\ 0 & 4 & -2 \\ 0 & 2 & -1 \end{bmatrix}
$$

$$
\begin{array}{l}
\tfrac{1}{2}R_2 \longrightarrow \\
R_3 - \tfrac{1}{2}R_2 \longrightarrow
\end{array}
\begin{bmatrix} 1 & 2 & -2 \\ 0 & 2 & -1 \\ 0 & 0 & 0 \end{bmatrix}
$$

We can now read off the solution $x_2 = \tfrac{1}{2}x_3$ and $x_1 = -2x_2 + 2x_3 = x_3$. The general solution is therefore $[x_3, x_3/2, x_3]$ where x_3 is arbitrary. Since we want a unit eigenvector, we choose x_3 so that

$$x_3{}^2 + \frac{x_3{}^2}{4} + x_3{}^2 = 1$$

which yields $x_3 = \pm\tfrac{2}{3}$. A unit eigenvector corresponding to the eigenvalue -1 is therefore $[\tfrac{2}{3}, \tfrac{1}{3}, \tfrac{2}{3}]$. Similarly, as the student should verify, unit eigenvectors corresponding to the eigenvalues 2 and 5 are respectively $[\tfrac{1}{3}, \tfrac{2}{3}, -\tfrac{2}{3}]$, $[-\tfrac{2}{3}, \tfrac{2}{3}, \tfrac{1}{3}]$. We now choose for P a matrix with these three eigenvectors as columns and we order the columns so that $\det P = 1$. Thus we choose

$$(23) \qquad P = \begin{bmatrix} \tfrac{2}{3} & \tfrac{1}{3} & -\tfrac{2}{3} \\ \tfrac{1}{3} & \tfrac{2}{3} & \tfrac{2}{3} \\ \tfrac{2}{3} & -\tfrac{2}{3} & \tfrac{1}{3} \end{bmatrix}.$$

Our theory now tells us that

$$P^{-1}AP = P^{T}AP = \begin{bmatrix} -1 & 0 & 0 \\ 0 & 2 & 0 \\ 0 & 0 & 5 \end{bmatrix}.$$

The student verify this.

Example 2. *Find a rotation of axes that will reduce the equation*

(24) $\qquad 2x_1{}^2 + 3x_2{}^2 + x_3{}^2 - 4x_1x_2 - 4x_1x_3 = 20$

to one of the standard forms discussed in Chapter 6. Hence find what surface this equation represents.

Solution. The left-hand side of the equation is a quadratic form whose matrix is the symmetric matrix A of Example 1. Hence, using the results of Example 1 a rotation of axes $X^T = PY^T$ with matrix P given in (23) will transform equation (24) into

$$-y_1{}^2 + 2y_2{}^2 + 5y_3{}^2 = 20$$

or

$$-\frac{y_1{}^2}{20} + \frac{y_2{}^2}{10} + \frac{y_3{}^2}{4} = 1.$$

A discussion similar to that of Section 6.6 shows that this is an equation of a hyperboloid of one sheet.

The student should note that if there are no first-degree terms, as in Example 2, the standard equation of the quadric (in the sense of Chapter 6) is completely determined by the eigenvalues of the symmetric matrix. In this case it is not necessary to find the eigenvectors and the matrix of the rotation in order to determine the nature of the surface and its equation in the new coordinate system. This equation can be written down as soon as the eigenvalues are known.

EXERCISE 9.3

1. Find the matrix of a rotation of axes that will reduce the following equations to standard form. Write the standard form so obtained and identify the surface.

(a) $2x_1x_2 + 2x_1x_3 - 2x_2x_3 = 9$,

(b) $4x_1{}^2 + x_2{}^2 + 4x_3{}^2 - 4x_2x_3 - 4x_1x_2 + 8x_1x_3 - 6x_2 + 6x_3 = 5$.

2. Without actually finding the transformation, find a standard form of the following equation and hence identify the surface.

$$2x_1{}^2 - 6x_2{}^2 + 6x_1x_2 + 6x_1x_3 - 2x_2x_3 = 35.$$

3. Show that the equation

$$10x_1{}^2 + 11x_2{}^2 + 6x_3{}^2 - 12x_1x_2 - 8x_1x_3 + 4x_2x_3 = 36$$

represents an ellipsoid with semiaxes $\sqrt{12}$, $\sqrt{6}$, and $\sqrt{2}$.

4. Use the methods of this chapter to find rotations of axes that will reduce the following equations to standard equations of conics.

(a) $8x_1{}^2 - 12x_1x_2 + 17x_2{}^2 = 20$,
(b) $2x_1{}^2 - 12x_1x_2 - 3x_2{}^2 = 42$.

Hence identify these curves. Compare your solutions with Example 3, Section 7.6, and Problem 2, Exercise 7.6.

5. Consider the general quadratic equation (a, h, b not all zero).

$$ax_1{}^2 + 2hx_1x_2 + bx_2{}^2 + 2gx_1 + 2fx_2 + c = 0.$$

Show that

(a) If $h^2 - ab < 0$, the graph is either an ellipse, a circle, or the empty set.
(b) If $h^2 - ab > 0$, the graph is either a hyperbola or two intersecting lines.
(c) If $h^2 - ab = 0$, the graph is either a parabola or two parallel or two coincident straight lines.

Hint. Let $A = \begin{bmatrix} a & h \\ h & b \end{bmatrix}$. If $h^2 - ab < 0$, the eigenvalues of A have the same sign. If $h^2 - ab > 0$, the eigenvalues differ in sign. If $h^2 - ab = 0$, one eigenvalue is 0.

9.7   The n-dimensional case

It has been pointed out from time to time that nearly everything* we have done can be done in n-dimensional space as well as in the plane and in space of three dimensions.

If $X = [x_1, x_2, \ldots, x_n]$, $Y = [y_1, y_2, \ldots, y_n]$ are two vectors of V_n, their inner product $X \cdot Y$ is defined by

$$X \cdot Y = x_1y_1 + x_2y_2 + \cdots + x_ny_n.$$

---

*An exception to this statement is the vector product $X \times Y$ of two vectors which is a peculiarly three-dimensional concept and does not exist either in the plane or in space of dimension greater than three.

This can also be written as a matrix product $X \cdot Y = XY^T$. By analogy with the cases $n = 2$ and 3 we define the length $\|X\|$ of X to be

$$\|X\| = \sqrt{X \cdot X} = \sqrt{x_1^2 + x_2^2 + \cdots + x_n^2}.$$

If $\|X\| = 1$, we call X a unit vector. Similarly, we say X and Y are orthogonal (perpendicular) to each other if $X \cdot Y = 0$.

If $\mathcal{S}$ is any subspace of V_n of dimension r, it can be shown that there exist orthonormal bases in $\mathcal{S}$ consisting of r mutually orthogonal unit vectors. In fact, any set of mutually orthogonal unit vectors in $\mathcal{S}$ forms part of an orthonormal basis. This implies the existence of orthogonal matrices of any order n, defined as before by $P^T P = PP^T = I$. Moreover, the orthogonal matrices are exactly the matrices of the coordinate transformations from one orthonormal basis to another.

If X and Y are subjected to a transformation of coordinates with orthogonal matrix P, their new coordinates are PX^T and PY^T or in row vector form, XP^T and YP^T. The inner product of these transformed vectors is therefore

$$(XP^T) \cdot (YP^T) = XP^T(YP^T)^T = XP^TPY^T = XY^T = X \cdot Y$$

since $P^T P = I$. We see therefore that an orthogonal transformation of coordinates *leaves the inner product of two vectors unchanged*.

A quadratic form in $x_1, x_2, \ldots, x_n$ has the form XAX^T where A is a real symmetric matrix. Theorems 9.9 and 9.11 hold for symmetric matrices of any order and it follows that every quadratic form in $x_1, x_2, \ldots, x_n$ can be reduced by an orthogonal transformation $X^T = PY^T$ to the form

$$\lambda_1 y_1^2 + \lambda_2 y_2^2 + \cdots + \lambda_n y_n^2,$$

where $\lambda_1, \lambda_2, \ldots, \lambda_n$ are the eigenvalues of A and the column vectors of P are mutually orthogonal unit eigenvectors of A. For detailed proofs of these theorems in the general case the reader is referred to [5].

CHAPTER 10

| POLAR COORDINATES AND
| COMPLEX NUMBERS

10.1   Radian measure of angles

Consider two concentric circles with common center O and two rays drawn from O to cut the circles in P, Q, R, and S as shown in Fig. 10.1. Now let $OQ = r_1$ and $OS = r_2$ be the radii of the two circles and let s_1

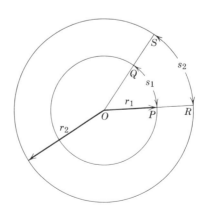

Fig. 10.1

and s_2 be the lengths of the arcs PQ and RS. Fundamental to what follows is this next theorem.

Theorem 10.1   *The lengths of the arcs cut from two concentric circles by two rays drawn from the center are proportional to the radii of the corresponding circles. In symbols, referring to Fig.* 10.1 *and the notation chosen above,*

$$\frac{s_2}{r_2} = \frac{s_1}{r_1}.$$

The proof of this theorem depends on the properties of similar triangles and on a careful definition of what is meant by the length of an arc of a circle. Since the definition of arc length depends on concepts which are normally discussed in books on calculus, the definition and the proof of Theorem 10.1 which depends on it will not be given here. We shall simply assume that the length of an arc of a circle *can* be defined in such a way that the theorem holds. It then follows that the ratio of the circumference of a circle to the radius r is a constant independent r. This constant, as is well known, is denoted by 2π and the length of the circumference is then $2\pi r$.

It follows from Theorem 10.1 that if s is the length of an arc PQ cut from a circle of radius r by two rays OP and OQ drawn from the center, then the ratio s/r is independent of the radius of the circle. Thus s/r depends only on the angle between the two rays and can be used as a measure of this angle. We write

$$\theta = \frac{s}{r}$$

and call θ the *radian measure* of the angle POQ subtended at the center of the circle by the arc PQ. An angle of 1 radian is the angle subtended at the center of a circle by an arc equal in length to the radius of the circle. If the angle POQ is $180°$, the corresponding arc length is πr, half the circumference of the circle. Hence we have

$$180° = \frac{\pi r}{r} = \pi \text{ radians},$$

whence

$$1° = \frac{\pi}{180} \text{ radians}$$

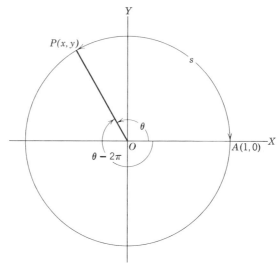

Fig. 10.2

and

$$1 \text{ radian} = \frac{180}{\pi} \text{ degrees.}$$

If $r = 1$, then $\theta = s$ and the radian measure of the angle is equal to the length of the corresponding arc. For reasons that become clear in the study of calculus, the radian is the usual unit for measurement of angles used in mathematics. However, in applications of mathematics to surveying, navigation, and so on, the degree is more commonly used.

Suppose we now choose rectangular coordinates in the plane ε_2, with equal units on the x- and y-axes, and consider the unit circle $x^2 + y^2 = 1$. This circle cuts the x-axis in the point $A(1, 0)$. Consider a point P that moves in the unit circle. If P starts from the position $A(1, 0)$ and moves in a *counterclockwise* direction to the position $P(x, y)$, we say that the vector $\overrightarrow{OP}$ sweeps out, or generates, an angle $\theta = s$ radians where s is the length of the arc traversed by P (see Fig. 10.2). There is no implication here that this arc is less than 2π, the circumference of the circle. The point P may go round the circle any number of times before stopping at $P(x, y)$ and hence the angle θ

(equal to the arc length s) may be any positive real number. If, however, we think of P starting from A and moving in a clockwise direction to the point $P(x, y)$, we say that OP generates a *negative* angle $\theta = -s$ radians where s is the length of the arc traversed by P in moving from $(1, 0)$ to (x, y). Again s can be any positive real number and hence we have provided for angles of θ radians where θ can be any real number. We call OA the *initial* side and OP, where P is the point (x, y), the *terminal* side of the angle θ. Finally let θ be an arbitrary angle with initial side OA and terminal side OP. Here θ may be any real number, positive, negative, or zero, and represents the radian measure of the angle. If (x, y) are the coordinates of P, we can define the sine and cosine functions* of θ by

$$\sin \theta = y$$

$$\cos \theta = x$$

Since $P(x, y)$ lies on the unit circle $x^2 + y^2 = 1$, it is clear that $\sin \theta$ and $\cos \theta$ both vary between -1 and 1 and satisfy the equation

$$\sin^2 \theta + \cos^2 \theta = 1$$

for all values of θ. Moreover, because angles that differ by a multiple of 2π radians have the same terminal side we have

$$\sin (\theta + 2n\pi) = \sin \theta$$

$$\cos (\theta + 2n\pi) = \cos \theta$$

for every integer n.

EXERCISE 10.1

1. Show that 1 radian is approximately equal to 57.29578 degrees.
2. Find the degree equivalents of the following angles which are expressed in radians: $\pi, \dfrac{\pi}{2}, \dfrac{\pi}{3}, \dfrac{5\pi}{6}, \dfrac{3\pi}{2}, 4\pi$.
3. Express the following angles in radians: $120°, 30°, 225°, 45°, 90°, 270°, 72°$. (Give the radian equivalent as a multiple of π.)
4. What is the length in feet of an arc of a circle of radius 1 mile that subtends an angle of $0.01°$ at the center?

---

* It is assumed that the student has already been introduced to the functions $\sin \theta$ and $\cos \theta$, at least when θ is an acute angle. We therefore do not include here a complete discussion of elementary trigonometry.

5. What is the angle, in degrees, subtended at the center of a circle of radius 10 feet by an arc of length 1 inch?

6. Verify each of the following by using the definitions of $\sin \theta$ and $\cos \theta$ given in Section 10.1:

(a) $\sin (-\theta) = -\sin \theta$,   (f) $\cos (2\pi - \theta) = \cos \theta$,

(b) $\cos (-\theta) = \cos \theta$,   (g) $\sin \dfrac{\pi}{2} = 1$,

(c) $\sin (\pi + \theta) = -\sin \theta$,   (h) $\cos \pi = -1$,

(d) $\cos (\pi + \theta) = -\cos \theta$,   (i) $\sin \dfrac{3\pi}{2} = -1$,

(e) $\sin (2\pi - \theta) = -\sin \theta$,   (j) $\sin \dfrac{\pi}{4} = \cos \dfrac{\pi}{4} = \dfrac{1}{\sqrt{2}}$.

10.2 Polar coordinates

Choose rectangular coordinates in the plane $\mathcal{E}_2$, with equal units on the x- and y-axes. Let $P(x, y)$ be any point in the plane. Let $r = \sqrt{x^2 + y^2}$ be the length of the segment OP and let θ be the angle between the vector $\overrightarrow{OP}$ and the positive ray OX of the x-axis measured counterclockwise from OX. The point P (see Fig. 10.3) is then determined by the two numbers (r, θ) which are called *polar coordinates* of P relative to the *origin* O and the *polar axis* OX. If we agree to the restrictions $r \geq 0$, $0 \leq \theta < 2\pi$, every point in the plane except the

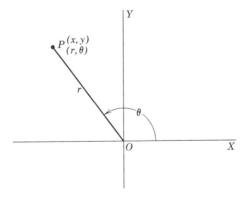

Fig. 10.3

origin has a unique pair of polar coordinates. The coordinates $(0, \theta)$ for any value of θ, will represent the origin.

However, for many purposes it is preferable to allow θ to assume any real value in which case the coordinates $(r, \theta + 2n\pi)$, n any integer, determine the same point as (r, θ). In general, we shall not assume any restriction on the values assumed by θ. Similarly, it is possible to allow the value of r to be negative if we identify the point $(-r, \theta)$ with the point $(r, \theta + \pi)$. This is unnecessary for many purposes but negative values of r cannot always be ignored. See, for example, Problem 5, p. 258.

If the point P has rectangular coordinates (x, y) and polar coordinates (r, θ) relative to the origin O and polar axis OX, it is clear that $(x/r, y/r)$ are the rectangular coordinates of the point in which the ray OP cuts the unit circle $x^2 + y^2 = 1$. Hence $x/r = \cos \theta$, $y/r = \sin \theta$ or

$$x = r \cos \theta$$
(1)
$$y = r \sin \theta.$$

Equations (1) relate the rectangular and polar coordinates of a point when the origins and axes coincide as described. Given an equation of a curve in $\mathcal{E}_2$ of the form

$$f(x, y) = 0,$$

a *polar equation* of this curve can be obtained in the form

$$f(r \cos \theta, r \sin \theta) = 0$$

by substituting equations (1) in $f(x, y) = 0$.

A polar equation of a curve may also be derived directly from a geometric definition of the curve.

Example 1. *If $a > 0$, find a polar equation of the circle with center at $(a, 0)$ and radius a.*

Solution. The circle is shown in Fig. 10.4. Let $P(r, \theta)$ be any point on the circle other than the origin. Since OA is a diameter of the circle, angle OPA is a right angle and we have

$$r = OA \cos \theta$$

or

(2)
$$r = 2a \cos \theta.$$

We note that this equation also holds when P is below the x-axis and θ is negative. The coordinates $(0, \pi/2)$ of the origin also satisfy (2),

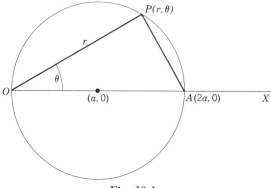

Fig. 10.4

although the coordinates $(0, 0)$ do not. Thus the graph of equation (2) is the given circle in that the circle consists of those points whose coordinates satisfy this equation.

Example 2. *Given the focus and directrix of a parabola, choose the origin at the focus and the polar axis OX perpendicular to the directrix but not intersecting it. Find a polar equation for the parabola.*

Solution. The parabola is shown in Fig. 10.5. Let $2a$ be the perpendicular distance from the focus to the directrix. Let $P(r, \theta)$ be any

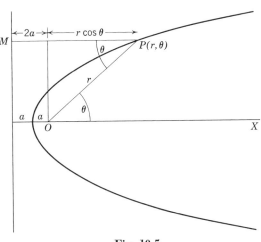

Fig. 10.5

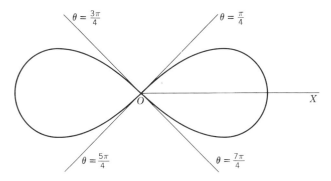

Fig. 10.6

point on the parabola and let M be the projection of P on the directrix. By the definition of the parabola, $OP = MP$ whence

$$r = 2a + r \cos \theta$$

or

(3) $$r = \frac{2a}{1 - \cos \theta}.$$

This is a polar equation for the parabola.

Example 3. *Sketch the graph of the polar equation $r^2 = \cos 2\theta$.*

Solution. The method is to consider what happens to $\cos 2\theta$ as θ varies from 0 to 2π and to sketch the resulting curve. When $\theta = 0$, $r = 1$. As θ increases from 0 to $\pi/4$, r^2 decreases from 1 to 0 and so therefore does r. Similarly, as θ goes from $-\pi/4$ to 0, $\cos 2\theta$ goes from 0 to 1 thus giving the right-hand loop shown in Fig. 10.6. For $\pi/4 < \theta < 3\pi/4$ we have $\pi/2 < 2\theta < 3\pi/2$. In this range $\cos 2\theta$ is negative and hence there are no points on the graph for $\pi/4 < \theta < 3\pi/4$. As θ increases from $3\pi/4$ to $5\pi/4$ and hence 2θ from $3\pi/2$ to $5\pi/2$, $\cos 2\theta$ goes from 0 to 1 (at $\theta = \pi$) and back to 0, giving the left-hand loop in Fig. 10.6. For $5\pi/4 < \theta < 7\pi/4$, $\cos 2\theta$ is again negative and there are no points on the curve. This curve is called a lemniscate.

Example 4. *Find a Cartesian equation for the lemniscate of Example 3.*

Solution. Choose O as origin and OX as positive x-axis. The polar equation $r^2 = \cos 2\theta$ can be written

$$r^2 = \cos^2 \theta - \sin^2 \theta$$

which is equivalent to

$$r^4 = r^2 \cos^2 \theta - r^2 \sin^2 \theta$$

because the origin (at which $r = 0$) is on the graph. By using equations (1), we see that this is equivalent to

$$(x^2 + y^2)^2 = x^2 - y^2$$

which is the Cartesian equation required.

EXERCISE 10.2

1. What are the graphs of the equations:

   (a) $r = a$
   (b) $\theta = \alpha$
   where a, α are constants?

2. Find a polar equation for the circle of radius a with center at $\left(a, \dfrac{\pi}{2} \right)$.

3. Use the polar equation (3) of a parabola to prove the result stated in Problem 12, Exercise 6.3.

4. Use the definition in Problem 8, Exercise 6.1, to derive a polar equation for an ellipse. Choose the origin at one focus and the line drawn from this focus through the other for the polar axis. Denote the distance from a focus to the corresponding directrix by p.

5. Choose coordinates and notation as in Problem 4 and use the definition given in Problem 11, Exercise 6.2 to derive the polar equation

$$r = \frac{pe}{1 - e \cos \theta}$$

for the hyperbola. Here e is the eccentricity. Show that this equation gives both branches of the hyperbola only if negative values of r are used.

6. Sketch graphs of the following polar equations:

   (a) $r = 5$, (b) $\theta = \dfrac{\pi}{6}$, (c) $r = \theta$, (d) $r = \sin \theta$, (e) $r = \sin 2\theta$,

   (f) $r = \sin 3\theta$, (g) $r^2 = 9 \sin 2\theta$. Allow negative values of r in part (e).

7. A circle of radius a rolls without slipping on a fixed circle of radius a. Find a polar equation for the curve traced by a point P on the moving circle. Choose the origin at a point O on the fixed circle and assume that the point P starts from the position O. Choose as polar axis the outward drawn ray normal to the fixed circle at O. The curve so defined is called a *cardioid*.

10.3   The complex numbers

If the only numbers available to us were the rational numbers the equation $x^2 - 2 = 0$ would have no solution, for there is no rational number whose square is 2. When confronted with this situation mathematicians did not hesitate to invent a new number $\sqrt{2}$ which *is* a solution of this equation. This particular invention was further motivated by the geometric need for a number which will measure the diagonal of a unit square. Similarly, if the only numbers available are the real numbers, the equation $x^2 + 4 = 0$ has no solution for there is no real number whose square is -4. To overcome this difficulty the complex numbers have been invented and have provided us with a number system in which every algebraic equation has a solution. Although they originated with this somewhat restricted problem of solving equations, the complex numbers have greatly enriched mathematics in all its branches, and have become an essential tool in both pure and applied mathematics. In this chapter we shall construct the complex numbers and study their basic properties.

Historically, complex numbers arose by adjoining to the real numbers a so-called imaginary number, $\sqrt{-1}$, usually denoted by i. The resulting new "numbers" of the form $a + bi$, a and b real, were then added and multiplied in the natural way by using the ordinary rules of algebra plus the additional rule $i^2 = -1$. The resulting formulas

$$(4) \qquad (a + bi) + (c + di) = (a + c) + (b + d)i$$

$$(5) \qquad (a + bi)(c + di) = (ac - bd) + (ad + bc)i$$

are easily verified.

We shall adopt a somewhat different point of view for which the historical approach provides the motivation.

By a *complex number* we shall mean a symbol of the form* $a + bi$ where a and b are arbitrary real numbers. We define the sum and product of two complex numbers by equations (4) and (5) and agree also to the following definition of equality:

$$(6) \qquad a + bi = c + di \qquad \text{if and only if } a = c \text{ and } b = d.$$

---

* It is sometimes more convenient to write $a + ib$. We do not distinguish between $a + bi$ and $a + ib$.

No particular meaning need be attached initially either to the symbol i or to the sign $+$ in the notation $a + bi$. In fact the complex number $a + bi$ could just as well be denoted by the symbol (a, b) for essentially it is merely an ordered pair of real numbers for which equality, addition, and multiplication are defined as in (4), (5), and (6). We prefer to retain the notation $a + bi$ not only because of its historical associations already mentioned, but also because this is the notation universally used except occasionally for purposes of the abstract definition of complex numbers as pairs of real numbers.

The next step is to prove the following.

Theorem 10.2. *The complex numbers form a field.*

Proof. The term *field* is used here in the sense defined in Section 1.2. The proof of Theorem 10.2 consists in verifying that the addition and multiplication defined in (4) and (5) satisfy the field postulates $A1$–5, $M1$–5 and $D1$ listed in Section 1.2. The commutative and associative laws for both addition and multiplication and the distributive law are easily verified and these verifications will be left as exercises. The complex number $0 + 0i$ acts as a zero and will be denoted by 0. It is clear that $z + 0 = z$ for every complex number z. Similarly, if $z = a + bi$ the complex number $-a + (-b)i$ will be denoted by $-z$ and we have $z + (-z) = 0$. Thus $A4$ and $A5$ of Section 1.2 are verified. If $w = c + di$, we define subtraction by

(7) $$z - w = z + (-w) = (a - c) + (b - d)i.$$

The complex number $1 + 0i$ acts as a unit, for by (5)

$$(a + bi)(1 + 0i) = a + bi.$$

We therefore denote $1 + 0i$ by 1 and we then have $z1 = z$ for all z. If $z = a + bi \neq 0$, then by (6) a and b are not both 0. In this case we wish to find a complex number $z^{-1} = x + yi$ such that $zz^{-1} = 1$. This implies that

$$(a + bi)(x + iy) = 1$$

or

$$(ax - by) + (bx + ay)i = 1 + 0i$$

whence by (6)

$$ax - by = 1$$

$$bx + ay = 0.$$

Eliminating y and x we get

$$(a^2 + b^2)x = a$$
$$(a^2 + b^2)y = -b$$

and
$$x = \frac{a}{a^2 + b^2}, \qquad y = \frac{-b}{a^2 + b^2}.$$

where $a^2 + b^2 \neq 0$ because a and b are not both zero. Hence

$$z^{-1} = \left(\frac{a}{a^2 + b^2}\right) + \left(\frac{-b}{a^2 + b^2}\right)i$$

and $M4$ and $M5$ of Section 1.2 are verified. If $z = a + bi$, $w = c + di$, and $z \neq 0$ we can now define the quotient w/z by

$$(8) \qquad \frac{w}{z} = wz^{-1} = \left(\frac{ac + bd}{a^2 + b^2}\right) + \left(\frac{ad - bc}{a^2 + b^2}\right)i.$$

This, together with Problem 7, Exercise 10.3, completes the proof of Theorem 10.2. The field of complex numbers will be denoted by $\mathcal{C}$.

Now consider the set of all complex numbers of the form $a + bi$ for which $b = 0$. Let $w = a + 0i$, $z = c + 0i$ be two of these. By (5), (6), (7), and (8) we have

$$w \pm z = (a \pm c) + 0i,$$
$$wz = ac + 0i,$$

and if $z \neq 0$,
$$\frac{w}{z} = \frac{a}{c} + 0i.$$

Thus the complex number $a + 0i$ acts exactly like the corresponding real number a as far as addition, subtraction, multiplication, and division are concerned. We therefore identify the complex number $a + 0i$ with the real number a, and in this sense the real numbers are included in the set of all complex numbers. It is clear that the sum of two real numbers is then the same whether they are added as real numbers or as complex numbers. The same applies to products. Thus $\mathcal{R}$ is a subfield of $\mathcal{C}$. We also write $a - bi$ for $a + (-b)i$ and we have the rules

$$a(c \pm di) = ac \pm adi,$$

$$\frac{c \pm di}{a} = \frac{c}{a} \pm \frac{d}{a} i, \qquad a \neq 0.$$

Similarly, a complex number of the form $0 + bi$ will be written simply bi. It is called a *pure imaginary number*. The real numbers a and b are called, respectively, the *real part* and the *imaginary part* of the complex number $a + bi$. When $b = 1$ the imaginary part is omitted and $a + 1i$ is written simply $a + i$. With these conventions we have by (5)

$$i^2 = (0 + 1i)(0 + 1i) = -1 + 0i = -1,$$

so that the rule $i^2 = -1$ is implicit in (5).

If $z = a + bi$, the complex number $a - bi$, denoted by $\bar{z}$, is called the *complex conjugate* or simply the *conjugate* of z. By (5) we have

$$z\bar{z} = (a + bi)(a - bi) = a^2 + b^2.$$

Hence the product of a complex number z and its conjugate is real and non-negative. It is zero only if $z = 0$. This fact provides the following alternative method for computing quotients of complex numbers:

$$\frac{w}{z} = \frac{w\bar{z}}{z\bar{z}} = \left(\frac{1}{z\bar{z}}\right)(w\bar{z}).$$

For example,

$$\frac{3 - i}{1 + 2i} = \frac{(3 - i)(1 - 2i)}{1 + 4} = \frac{1 - 7i}{5} = \frac{1}{5} - \frac{7}{5} i.$$

Theorem 10.3. *If w, z are complex numbers, then*

(a) $\overline{\bar{w}} = w$

(b) $\overline{w \pm z} = \bar{w} \pm \bar{z}$

(c) $\overline{wz} = \bar{w}\bar{z}$

(d) *If $w \neq 0$, $(\overline{w^{-1}}) = (\bar{w})^{-1}$ and hence $(\overline{w/z}) = \bar{w}/\bar{z}$.*

Proof. Each of these items is easily checked. For example, if $w = a + bi$, $z = c + di$, then by (5)

$$\overline{wz} = (ac - bd) - (ad + bc)i,$$

whereas

$$\bar{w}\bar{z} = (a - bi)(c - di)$$

$$= (ac - bd) - (ad + bc)i$$

and (c) is thus verified.

EXERCISE 10.3

1. Prove that $i^3 = -i$, $i^4 = 1$, and $i^5 = i$.
2. Prove that $1/i = -i$.
3. Prove that if r and s are integers $i^r = i^s$ if and only if $r - s$ is divisible by 4.
4. Using the result of Problem 3 prove that $i^{47} = i^3 = -i$.
5. Evaluate the following, that is, write in the form $a + bi$, where a and b are real.

(a) $(1 + 4i)(5 - 3i)$, (f) $(1 + i)^3$,
(b) $i(3 - 2i)$, (g) $(1 + i)^4$,
(c) $\dfrac{1 - i}{i}$, (h) $(1 + i)^9$,
(d) $i^{22} - i^{59}$ (i) $(-\frac{1}{2} + \frac{1}{2}\sqrt{3}\,i)^2$,
(e) $(1 + i)^2$, (j) $(-\frac{1}{2} + \frac{1}{2}\sqrt{3}\,i)^3$.

6. Evaluate:

(a) $\dfrac{1}{4 + 3i}$, (d) $\dfrac{2 + i}{3 - 2i}$,
(b) $\dfrac{(1 - i)(4 + 2i)}{3 + 5i}$, (e) $\dfrac{3 - 2i}{(2 + 5i)^2}$,
(c) $1 + i + i^2 + \cdots + i^{100}$.

7. Prove that the complex numbers satisfy the field postulates $A2$, $A3$, $M2$, $M3$, and $D1$ of Section 1.2.
8. Prove that a complex number z is real if and only if $\bar{z} = z$.
9. Prove by substitution that if $a \neq 0$ and $b^2 < 4ac$, the complex numbers

$$-\frac{b}{2a} \pm \left(\frac{\sqrt{4ac - b^2}}{2a} \right) i$$

are solutions of the equation $ax^2 + bx + c = 0$.
10. Find solutions in the form $a + bi$ of the following equations and verify your answers by substitution:

(a) $x^2 + 4x + 5 = 0$,
(b) $x^2 - x + 1 = 0$,
(c) $2x^2 + 8x + 51 = 0$.

11. Prove that if a polynomial equation

$$a_0x^n + a_1x^{n-1} + \cdots + a_n = 0$$

with real coefficients has a root $a + bi$, then $a - bi$ is also a root of this equation.

Hint. Let $f(x)$ be the left-hand side of the equation, and use Theorem 10.3 and Problem 8 to prove that

$$f(a - bi) = \overline{f(a + bi)}.$$

12. If a and b are real numbers, the mapping

$$a + bi \longleftrightarrow \begin{bmatrix} a & -b \\ b & a \end{bmatrix}$$

sets up a one to one correspondence between the set $\mathcal{C}$ of all complex numbers and a subset $\mathcal{S}$ of the set of real square matrices of order 2. Let w, z be complex numbers and let $A(w), A(z)$ be the corresponding matrices. Show that

$$A(w \pm z) = A(w) \pm A(z)$$

and

$$A(wz) = A(w)A(z).$$

If $z \neq 0$, find the matrix $A(z^{-1})$ and show that it is the inverse of $A(z)$. Show that $\mathcal{S}$ is a field under the operations of matrix addition and matrix multiplication.

10.4   Factorization of polynomials

If n is a non-negative integer, an expression of the form

(9) $$f(x) = a_0x^n + a_1x^{n-1} + \cdots + a_n,$$

where $a_0, a_1, \ldots, a_n$ are complex numbers is called a *polynomial* in x. If $a_0 \neq 0$ the polynomial $f(x)$ is said to be of *degree n*. The numbers $a_0, a_1, \ldots, a_n$ (which may of course be real) are called the *coefficients* of the polynomial. If $n = 0$, $f(x) = a_0$. Hence a nonzero complex number is a polynomial of degree 0. Two polynomials are said to be equal if and only if they have the same degree and the coefficients of like powers of x are equal. Polynomials are added, subtracted, and multiplied according to the rules of elementary algebra. If in (9) the symbol x is replaced by a complex number r, a complex number $f(r)$ results which is called the value of the polynomial at $x = r$.

If the polynomial $f(x)$ of degree n can be written as a product of two polynomials each of degree less than n, it is said to be factorable or reducible. If it cannot be so factored, $f(x)$ is said to be irreducible. Whether or not a polynomial can be factored depends on what kind of numbers are allowable as coefficients. For example, $x^2 - 2$ factors into $(x - \sqrt{2})(x + \sqrt{2})$ if real coefficients may be used but is irreducible if only rational coefficients are allowed. Similarly, $x^2 + 4$ is irreducible if all coefficients must be real but factors into $(x - 2i)(x + 2i)$ if complex coefficients are allowed. These facts are usually expressed by specifying a field—some subfield of the complex numbers—in which the coefficients are required to lie. Thus $x^2 - 2$ is irreducible in the rational field but factorable in the real field, whereas $x^2 + 4$ is irreducible in the real field but factorable in the complex field.

It is shown in more advanced books in algebra (see, for example, [7], Chap. 5) that every polynomial $f(x)$ with coefficients in a field $\mathfrak{F}$ can be factored into a product of irreducible polynomials in $\mathfrak{F}$ in an essentially unique way. By "essentially unique" is meant that if

$$f(x) = p_1(x)p_2(x) \cdots p_r(x) = q_1(x)q_2(x) \cdots q_s(x)$$

where

$$p_1(x), \ldots, p_r(x), \quad q_1(x), \ldots, q_s(x)$$

are all irreducible in $\mathfrak{F}$ and of degree greater than 0, then $r = s$ and the polynomials $p_i(x)$ and $q_i(x)$ can be so ordered that $q_i(x) = k_i p_i(x)$ where $k_i \in \mathfrak{F}$, $i = 1, 2, \ldots, r$.

A factor of $f(x)$ is said to be linear if it is of degree 1 in x. A basic property of the field of complex numbers is given by the following.

Theorem 10.4. *A polynomial with coefficients in the field $\mathbb{C}$ of complex numbers is irreducible in $\mathbb{C}$ if and only if it is linear. Hence every polynomial with coefficients in $\mathbb{C}$ can be factored into linear factors with coefficients in $\mathbb{C}$.*

The proof of this theorem is not easy and will not be given here. It is usually postponed until a course in functions of a complex variable, although more elementary proofs may be found in some books on theory of equations or, for example in [4], p. 269. It should be noted that since the field of real numbers is contained in the field of complex numbers, Theorem 10.4 tells us also that any polynomial with real coefficients can be factored into linear factors in the field of complex numbers.

Suppose the polynomial (9) has complex coefficients $a_0, \ldots, a_n$. (This does not exclude the case when the coefficients are all real!) Each linear factor of $f(x)$ will have the form $px - q$ or $p(x - r)$ where $r = q/p$ is a complex number. Hence the factored form of $f(x)$ can be written

$$(10) \qquad f(x) = a_0(x - r_1)(x - r_2) \cdots (x - r_n)$$

where the constant factor is a_0 since the coefficient of x^n must be the same on each side of the equation. It is clear from (10) that $f(r_1) = f(r_2) = \cdots = f(r_n) = 0$ and hence $r_1, r_2, \ldots, r_n$ are roots of the equation $f(x) = 0$. They are also called *roots* or *zeros* of the polynomial $f(x)$. Moreover, these n numbers are the only roots of $f(x)$ in $\mathbb{C}$. For if r is any complex number, by (10),

$$f(r) = a_0(r - r_1)(r - r_2) \cdots (r - r_n).$$

Since the complex numbers form a field, a product of complex numbers is 0 only if one of the factors is 0 (see Exercise 1.3, Problem 4). Thus, since, $a_0 \neq 0$, $f(r) = 0$ only if $r = r_j$ for at least one value of j, $1 \leq j \leq n$. If the same factor $x - r$ occurs m times in (10) but not $(m + 1)$ times, we say that r is a root of multiplicity m of $f(x)$. The next theorem follows from the preceding remarks and from Theorem 10.4.

Theorem 10.5. *A polynomial of degree n with complex coefficients has exactly n roots in the field of complex numbers provided that a root of multiplicity m is counted as m equal roots.*

As a consequence of this theorem it is not necessary to further enlarge the number system in order to find roots of polynomial equations. The complex numbers are sufficient for this purpose.

EXERCISE 10.4

1. If $r = a + bi$ and $b \neq 0$, show that $f(x) = (x - r)(x - \bar{r})$ is a quadratic polynomial with real coefficients and is irreducible in the field of real numbers.

2. Prove that every polynomial with real coefficients can be factored in the field of real numbers into linear and/or irreducible quadratic factors. *Hint:* Use Theorem 10.4, Problem 11, Exercise 10.3, and Problem 1 above.
3. Prove that a polynomial with real coefficients can only have an even number of nonreal roots. *Hint:* Use Problem 11, Exercise 10.3.
4. Prove that a polynomial of odd degree with real coefficients must have an odd number of real roots. Deduce, therefore, that such a polynomial has at least one real root.
5. (For students with a knowledge of calculus.) Let $f(x)$ be a polynomial with real coefficients and let $f'(x)$ be its derivative. Prove that $f(x)$ has a root of multiplicity 2 or greater if and only if $f(x)$ and $f'(x)$ have a factor (and hence a root) in common.

10.5   Geometric representation of the complex numbers

It is clear that the mapping

$$x + yi \longleftrightarrow (x, y)$$

sets up a one-to-one correspondence between the set $\mathbb{C}$ of all complex numbers and the points of the plane $\mathcal{E}_2$. We therefore choose a rectangular coordinate system in the plane and represent the complex number $x + yi$ by the point (x, y). Under this scheme a real number x corresponds to the point $(x, 0)$ on the x-axis which we therefore call the *real axis*. Similarly, a pure imaginary number yi corresponds to the point $(0, y)$ on the y-axis which is called the *imaginary axis*. The xy-plane, with each of its points designated in this way by a complex number, will be called the *complex plane*. If z is any complex number we shall speak of the point z, meaning the point of the complex plane corresponding to z.

If $z = x + yi$ and if (r, θ), where $r \geq 0$, are polar coordinates of the point z, we have, by (1), $x = r \cos \theta$, $y = r \sin \theta$, and hence

(11) $$z = r(\cos \theta + i \sin \theta).$$

The right member of equation (11) is called the *polar form* of the complex number z. The number r, which is equal to $\sqrt{x^2 + y^2}$, is called the *absolute value* of z and is denoted by $|z|$. If z is real, there is no conflict with the previously defined absolute value of a real number. For in this case $y = 0$ and $|z| = \sqrt{x^2} = |x|$. The absolute value of z is clearly equal to the distance of the point z from the origin.

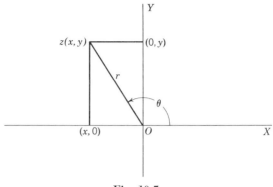

Fig. 10.7

The angle θ in (11) is usually taken to be the angle shown in Fig. 10.7. It is clear however, that θ may be replaced by $\theta + 2n\pi$, where n is any integer, without affecting the value of z or the position of the corresponding point in the complex plane. The angle θ, or any one of the angles $\theta + 2n\pi$, is called the amplitude* of z and is written am z. It is assumed here, as it usually will be, that θ is measured in radians. We have now proved the following.

Theorem 10.6. *If $z \neq 0$ is a complex number, there exists a unique positive real number r (the absolute value of z) and an angle θ (called the amplitude of z) such that $z = r(\cos \theta + i \sin \theta)$.*

Although the amplitude θ is not uniquely determined, it can always be chosen in the interval $0 \leq \theta < 2\pi$ and any two values of the amplitude differ by a multiple of 2π.

Example. *Find the polar form of the complex number $3 - 2i$.*

Solution. Since $|3 - 2i| = \sqrt{9 + 4} = \sqrt{13}$, we have $r = \sqrt{13}$ and

$$z = \sqrt{13} \left(\frac{3}{\sqrt{13}} - \frac{2}{\sqrt{13}} i \right) = \sqrt{13} \, (\cos \theta + i \sin \theta)$$

where θ is determined by

$$\cos \theta = \frac{3}{\sqrt{13}}, \qquad \sin \theta = - \frac{2}{\sqrt{13}}.$$

---

* In some books the term *argument* of z is used instead of amplitude and is abbreviated arg z.

It follows that θ is a fourth quadrant angle and, from a trigonometric table,

$$\theta = 360° - 33.7° = 326.3° = 5.69 \text{ radians, approximately.}$$

The polar form is therefore $\sqrt{13}$ (cos 5.69 + i sin 5.69).

Theorem 10.7. *If w, z are any two complex numbers, then*
 (a) $|wz| = |w|\,|z|$,
 (b) *if $w \neq 0$ and $z \neq 0$, then am wz = am w + am z.*

Proof. If either $w = 0$ or $z = 0$, then $wz = 0$ and

$$|wz| = 0 = |w|\,|z|$$

so that (a) holds in this case. We therefore assume $w \neq 0$, $z \neq 0$. Let

$$w = r_1(\cos\theta + i\sin\theta)$$
$$z = r_2(\cos\phi + i\sin\phi)$$

be the polar forms of w and z. Multiplying we get

$$wz = r_1 r_2[(\cos\theta\cos\phi - \sin\theta\sin\phi) + i(\sin\theta\cos\phi + \cos\theta\sin\phi)]$$
$$= r_1 r_2[\cos(\theta + \phi) + i\sin(\theta + \phi)].$$

This is the polar form of wz and therefore

$$|wz| = r_1 r_2 = |w|\,|z|$$

and

$$\text{am } wz = \theta + \phi = \text{am } w + \text{am } z$$

and the theorem is proved.

Corollary 1. *If $z \neq 0$, $|z^{-1}| = \dfrac{1}{|z|}$.*

Proof. Since $zz^{-1} = 1$, we have $|z|\,|z^{-1}| = |1| = 1$ and the result follows.

Corollary 2. *If $z \neq 0$, $\left|\dfrac{w}{z}\right| = \dfrac{|w|}{|z|}$.*

Proof. $\left|\dfrac{w}{z}\right| = |wz^{-1}| = |w|\,|z^{-1}| = \dfrac{|w|}{|z|}$, by Corollary 1.

Corollary 3. *If* $z \neq 0$, am $z^{-1} = -$ am z.

Proof. Since am $z +$ am $z^{-1} =$ am $zz^{-1} =$ am $1 = 0$, we have

$$\text{am } z^{-1} = -\text{ am } z.$$

Note that if $0 <$ am $z < 2\pi$, then $2\pi -$ am z is the value of am z^{-1} that satisfies these inequalities.

Corollary 4. *If* $z \neq 0$, $w \neq 0$, *then* am $(w/z) =$ am $w -$ am z.

Proof. am $w/z =$ am $wz^{-1} =$ am $w +$ am $z^{-1} =$ am $w -$ am z.

10.6   Complex numbers and vectors

Since the complex number $x + yi$ is essentially an ordered pair (x, y) of real numbers, if a rectangular coordinate system is chosen in $\mathcal{E}_2$ we can set up a one-to-one correspondence

(12) $a + bi \longleftrightarrow [a, b]$

between the complex numbers and the vectors in $\mathcal{E}_2$. Here the complex number $a + ib$ is represented geometrically as the vector $[a, b]$ drawn from the origin to the point (a, b). The correspondence (12) preserves addition for if

$$c + di \longleftrightarrow [c, d],$$

it is clear that the sum of the complex numbers on the left corresponds to the sum of the vectors on the right, namely,

$$(a + c) + (b + d)i \longleftrightarrow [a + c, b + d].$$

From this it follows that complex numbers, when represented geometrically on the complex plane, can be added by the parallelogram law. Thus if w, z are complex numbers, and hence also points of the complex plane, the point $w + z$ is the fourth vertex of the parallelogram (Fig. 10.8, left) of which Ow and Oz are adjacent sides. Similarly, the point $z - w$ is the fourth vertex of the parallelogram (Fig. 10.8, right) of which Ow and wz are adjacent sides.

Theorem 10.8. *If* w, z *are any two complex numbers, the distance between the points* w *and* z *in the complex plane is* $|w - z|$.

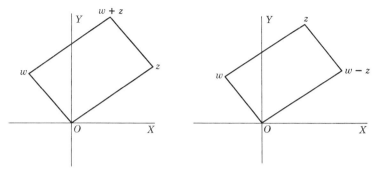

Fig. 10.8

The truth of this theorem is obvious from Fig. 10.8 (right) because $|z - w|$ is the distance from the origin to the point $z - w$.

EXERCISE 10.5

1. Write each of the following complex numbers in polar form and plot them on the complex plane.

   (a) $1 - i$,
   (b) $1 + i$,
   (c) $4i$,
   (d) $-2i$,

   (e) $-3 + 4i$,
   (f) $-5 - 12i$,
   (g) $-1 + \sqrt{3}\, i$,
   (h) -1.

2. Plot the points $w = 2 - 3i$ and $z = 5 + 2i$ on the complex plane and find geometrically the points $w + z$, $z - w$, $3w$, $2z$, $3w + 2z$.
3. Prove Theorem 10.8 by using the distance formula, Section 2.4.
4. Find the lengths of the sides of the triangle whose vertices are the points:

   (a) $3 + 8i$, $1 - 2i$, $11 + 5i$,
   (b) $-1 + 2i$, $3 - i$, $-2 - 2i$.

5. If a is a fixed complex number and z is a complex number such that $|z - a| < 2$, draw a sketch of the region of the complex plane in which z can lie. Do the same for the region of the complex plane defined by the inequalities $3 < |z - (3 + 2i)| < 5$.
6. If a and b are fixed complex numbers, identity the curves consisting of all points z for which:

   (a) $|z - a| = 6$
   (b) $|z - a| + |z - b| = 6$.

7. If $w = u + vi$, $z = x + yi$, prove directly from the definition of absolute value that $|wz| = |w|\,|z|$.

8. Prove that $|z|^2 = z\bar{z}$, and use this fact and Theorem 10.3c to prove that $|wz| = |w|\,|z|$.

9. If w, z are two complex numbers, prove geometrically that $|w + z| \le |w| + |z|$. Use this fact to prove that $|z - w| \ge |z| - |w|$.

10. Let w, z denote two complex numbers and also the corresponding points in the complex plane. Draw a ray OQ (see Fig. 10.9) so that the angle XOQ is equal to am $z +$ am w. Join z to the point 1. Draw a line through w to cut OQ in P, making the angle OwP equal to the angle $O1z$. Prove that P is the point corresponding to the complex number wz. *Hint:* Use the polar form of w and z and Theorem 10.7.

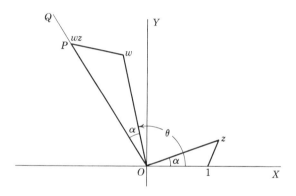

Fig. 10.9

11. Give a construction similar to that in Problem 10 that will locate the point w/z when the points w and z are given.

12. If $z \ne 0$, show that the points O, w, z lie on a straight line if and only if w/z is real.

13. Show that three distinct points z_1, z_2, z_3 lie on a straight line if and only if $(z_1 - z_3)/(z_2 - z_3)$ is real.

14. If z_1, z_2, z_3 are three distinct points of the complex plane, prove that the angle θ subtended at z_3 by the segment joining z_1 and z_2 is given by either

$$\theta = \operatorname{am}\left(\frac{z_1 - z_3}{z_2 - z_3}\right) \quad \text{or} \quad \theta = \operatorname{am}\left(\frac{z_2 - z_3}{z_1 - z_3}\right).$$

15. Find the interior angles of the two triangles given in Problem 4.

16. If a is a complex number such that $|a| = 1$ and z is any complex number, show that the effect of multiplying z by a is to rotate the vector Oz about the origin through an angle equal to am a.

17. Use the result of Problem 16 to show that if the vector $[x, y]$ is rotated counterclockwise through an angle θ, it is transformed into the vector $[u, v]$ where

$$u = x \cos \theta - y \sin \theta$$

$$v = x \sin \theta + y \cos \theta.$$

Hint: By Problem 16, $u + iv = (x + iy)(\cos \theta + i \sin \theta)$.

18. If the vector $[5, 2]$ is turned counterclockwise through (a) 30°, (b) 45°, (c) 90°, find in each case the vector into which it is transformed.

19. If z_1, z_2 lie on the unit circle with center at the origin, show that z_1^2, z_1^{-1}, $z_1 z_2$ and z_1/z_2 all lie on the same circle. Explain how to locate each of these points geometrically when z_1 and z_2 are given.

10.7   Powers and roots of complex numbers

It is clear that Theorem 10.7 can be extended to products of any finite number of complex numbers. Thus if

$$z_1 = r_1(\cos \theta_1 + i \sin \theta_1),$$

$$z_2 = r_2(\cos \theta_2 + i \sin \theta_2),$$

$$\cdot \cdot \cdot \cdot \cdot \cdot \cdot \cdot \cdot \cdot \cdot \cdot \cdot \cdot$$

$$z_n = r_n(\cos \theta_n + i \sin \theta_n),$$

then

$$z_1 z_2 \cdot \cdot \cdot z_n = r_1 r_2 \cdot \cdot \cdot r_n[\cos \phi + i \sin \phi],$$

where

$$\phi = \theta_1 + \theta_2 + \cdot \cdot \cdot + \theta_n.$$

If we apply this to the special case in which $r_1 = r_2 = \cdot \cdot \cdot = r_n = 1$ and $\theta_1 = \theta_2 = \cdot \cdot \cdot = \theta_n = \theta$ we get the following.

Theorem 10.9 (De Moivre's theorem). *If n is any positive integer, then*

$$(\cos \theta + i \sin \theta)^n = \cos n\theta + i \sin n\theta.$$

Corollary. *De Moivre's theorem also holds if n is a negative integer or zero.*

Proof. The case $n = 0$ is obvious if we retain the definition $z^0 = 1$ for complex numbers. Now let $n = -m$ where m is a positive integer.

Then

$$(\cos \theta + i \sin \theta)^n = \frac{1}{(\cos \theta + i \sin \theta)^m} = \frac{1}{\cos m\theta + i \sin m\theta}$$

$$= \frac{\cos m\theta - i \sin m\theta}{\cos^2 m\theta + \sin^2 m\theta} = \cos m\theta - i \sin m\theta$$

$$= \cos (-m\theta) + i \sin (-m\theta) = \cos n\theta + i \sin n\theta.$$

Let p/q, where p and q are integers with $q > 0$, be an arbitrary rational number. By Theorem 10.9 we have

$$[\cos (p\theta/q) + i \sin (p\theta/q)]^q = \cos p\theta + i \sin p\theta$$

$$= (\cos \theta + i \sin \theta)^p,$$

and therefore $\cos (p\theta/q) + i \sin (p\theta/q)$ is a qth root of $(\cos \theta + i \sin \theta)^p$. Hence by analogy with the ordinary algebra of exponents we define rational powers of $\cos \theta + i \sin \theta$ by

$$(\cos \theta + i \sin \theta)^{p/q} = \cos (p\theta/q) + i \sin (p\theta/q).$$

Thus if $z = r(\cos \theta + i \sin \theta)$, we have

$$z^{p/q} = \sqrt[q]{r^p} \, [\cos (p\theta/q) + i \sin (p\theta/q)].$$

We now consider the problem of finding nth roots of a complex number. If we let $a = r(\cos \theta + i \sin \theta)$, it is clear from De Moivre's theorem that

$$z_1 = r^{1/n}[\cos (\theta/n) + i \sin (\theta/n)]$$

is an nth root of a because $z_1{}^n = r(\cos \theta + i \sin \theta) = a$. Here $r^{1/n}$ is the uniquely determined positive real nth root of r. However, θ can be increased by multiples of 2π without changing a. Hence the following are also nth roots of a:

$$z_2 = r^{1/n} \left[\cos \frac{\theta + 2\pi}{n} + i \sin \frac{\theta + 2\pi}{n} \right],$$

$$z_3 = r^{1/n} \left[\cos \frac{\theta + 4\pi}{n} + i \sin \frac{\theta + 4\pi}{n} \right],$$

$$\cdots \cdots \cdots \cdots \cdots \cdots \cdots \cdots \cdots$$

$$z_n = r^{1/n} \left[\cos \frac{\theta + 2(n-1)\pi}{n} + i \sin \frac{\theta + 2(n-1)\pi}{n} \right].$$

These n complex numbers $z_1, z_2, \ldots, z_n$ are all different. Since by Theorem 10.5 the equation $z^n - a = 0$ has exactly n roots, we have found all the complex nth roots of a in this way. We have therefore proved the following.

Theorem 10.10. *Every nonzero complex number* $a = r(\cos \theta + i \sin \theta)$ *has exactly* n *nth roots which are given by the formula*

$$r^{1/n} \left[\cos \frac{\theta + 2(j-1)\pi}{n} + i \sin \frac{\theta + 2(j-1)\pi}{n} \right], \quad (j = 1, 2, \cdots, n).$$

Example 1. *Find the three cube roots of* $-2 + 2i$.

Solution. If $a = -2 + 2i$, $|a| = \sqrt{8}$ and am $a = 135° = \dfrac{3\pi}{4}$ radians.

Then $a = \sqrt{8} \left(\cos \dfrac{3\pi}{4} + i \sin \dfrac{3\pi}{4} \right)$ and the cube roots are

$$\sqrt{2} \left(\cos \frac{\pi}{4} + i \sin \frac{\pi}{4} \right) = 1 + i,$$

$$\sqrt{2} \left[\cos \left(\frac{\pi}{4} + \frac{2\pi}{3} \right) + i \sin \left(\frac{\pi}{4} + \frac{2\pi}{3} \right) \right] = \sqrt{2} \left(\cos \frac{11\pi}{12} + i \sin \frac{11\pi}{12} \right),$$

$$\sqrt{2} \left[\cos \left(\frac{\pi}{4} + \frac{4\pi}{3} \right) + i \sin \left(\frac{\pi}{4} + \frac{4\pi}{3} \right) \right] = \sqrt{2} \left(\cos \frac{19\pi}{12} + i \sin \frac{19\pi}{12} \right).$$

Example 2. *Find the six sixth roots of unity (i.e., the solutions of* $z^6 = 1$) *and plot them on the complex plane.*

Solution. Since $1 = \cos 0 + i \sin 0$, by Theorem 10.10 the sixth roots of 1 are

$$\cos \frac{2(j-1)\pi}{6} + i \sin \frac{2(j-1)\pi}{6}, \qquad (j = 1, 2, \ldots, 6).$$

Thus the six sixth roots all have absolute value 1 and the amplitudes are $\pi/3$, $2\pi/3$, π, $4\pi/3$, $5\pi/3$, 2π. The corresponding points in the complex plane are all on the unit circle and are the vertices of a regular hexagon (see Fig. 10.10).

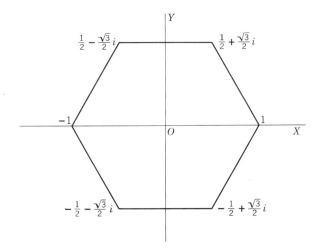

Fig. 10.10

EXERCISE 10.6

1. Find the two square roots of

   (a) i, (b) $-i$, (c) $1 - i$, (d) $-\frac{1}{2} + \dfrac{\sqrt{3}}{2}\, i$.

2. Find the three cube roots of -1 and plot them on the complex plane.
3. Find all the twelfth roots of 1 and plot them on the complex plane.
4. Use the results of Problems 1 and 2, Exercise 10.4, and Problem 3 above to factor $x^{12} - 1$ into its irreducible factors in the field of real numbers.
5. If w, z are nth roots of 1 prove that wz, $1/z$ and w/z are nth roots of 1.
6. If z is an nth root of 1, show that $\bar{z} = 1/z$.
7. Let z be the nth root of 1 with least positive amplitude, namely, $2\pi/n$. Prove that every nth root of 1 is a power of z and that all nth roots of 1 are given by

$$1,\, z,\, z^2,\, \ldots,\, z^{n-1}.$$

8. Since $\cos 2\theta + i \sin 2\theta = (\cos \theta + i \sin \theta)^2$

$$= \cos^2 \theta - \sin^2 \theta + (2 \sin \theta \cos \theta)i,$$

we have, on equating real and imaginary parts,

$$\cos 2\theta = \cos^2 \theta - \sin^2 \theta, \qquad \sin 2\theta = 2 \sin \theta \cos \theta.$$

Apply a similar procedure to $\cos 3\theta + i \sin 3\theta$ to derive formulas for $\cos 3\theta$ and $\sin 3\theta$ in terms of $\cos \theta$ and $\sin \theta$.

10.8   Mappings of the complex plane

Let $\mathcal{C}$ be the set of all complex numbers and let f be a function from $\mathcal{C}$ to $\mathcal{C}$, with domain $\mathfrak{D}$ and range $\mathfrak{K}$. The function f defines a mapping of the set $\mathfrak{D}$ onto the set $\mathfrak{K}$. If $z \in \mathfrak{D}$, we plot the point z on one complex plane (the z-plane) and the image point $w = f(z)$ on another complex plane (the w-plane). Many simpler functions have properties of continuity that ensure that as z traces a curve C in the z-plane, the image point $w = f(z)$ traces a curve C' in the w-plane which is called the map, or image, of the curve C under f.

Consider, for example, the function with domain $\mathcal{C}$ and range $\mathcal{C}$ defined by $f(z) = z^2$. If we let $z = x + iy$, we have

$$w = z^2 = (x^2 - y^2) + (2xy)i = u + iv,$$

where

$$u = x^2 - y^2$$

$$v = 2xy.$$

Thus x, y are the coordinates of the point z in the z-plane and u, v the coordinates of the point w in the w-plane (see Fig. 10.11). Now as z traces the rectangular hyperbola $x^2 - y^2 = k$ in the z-plane, w will trace the line $u = k$ in the w-plane. The hyperbola is therefore mapped onto this line by the function f. Similarly, the hyperbola $2xy = k$ is mapped by f onto the line $v = k$ parallel to the real axis on the w-plane.

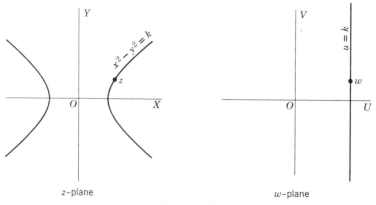

Fig. 10.11

Note also that the points z and $-z$ have the same image on the w-plane. Thus the upper half of the z-plane is mapped onto the whole of the w-plane by f. The study of the mapping of one complex plane on another by a function f is in a sense a generalization of the study of graphs. For the graph of a real function f from $\Re$ to $\Re$ is simply a picture of the mapping of one real line (the x-axis) into another real line (the y-axis).

It is of course possible to identify the w-plane with the z-plane and to consider the function f as a mapping or (alibi) transformation of the z-plane into itself. This point of view is especially convenient when the mapping is one to one. We now discuss several important but simple examples of this type.

Example 1. *Let $z_0 = a + ib$ be any fixed complex number and let f be the function (domain $\mathbb{C}$ and range $\mathbb{C}$) such that $f(z) = z + z_0$. Describe the mapping defined by f.*

Solution. The point $z = x + iy$ is mapped by f onto the point $w = (x + a) + i(x + b)$. From the rectangular coordinate point of view this means the point (x, y) is mapped on $(x + a, y + b)$ and the mapping is clearly a translation of the complex plane in the direction of the vector $[a, b]$. (Cf. alibi translations of the plane discussed in Section 4.1).

Example 2. *Let f be the function (domain $\mathbb{C}$, range $\mathbb{C}$) defined by $f(z) = rz$ where r is real and positive. Describe the mapping defined by f.*

Solution. The point $x + iy$ is mapped onto $rx + ryi$. Thus the absolute value of z is multiplied by r but its amplitude is unchanged. Such a mapping is called a magnification. Its only effect is to multiply the distance of each point from the origin by a fixed positive number r.

Example 3. *Let f be the function (domain $\mathbb{C}$, range $\mathbb{C}$) defined by $f(z) = (\cos \alpha + i \sin \alpha)z$, where α is fixed. Describe the mapping defined by f.*

Solution. If $z = r(\cos \theta + i \sin \theta)$ is the polar form of z, we have

$$f(z) = r(\cos \theta + i \sin \theta)(\cos \alpha + i \sin \alpha)$$
$$= r[\cos (\theta + \alpha) + i \sin (\theta + \alpha)].$$

Thus z is mapped onto the point with the same distance from the origin (same absolute value) but with amplitude increased by α. Thus the effect of the transformation is to rotate the entire z-plane about the origin, counterclockwise through an angle α.

Example 4. *Let $z_0 = r_0(\cos \alpha + i \sin \alpha)$ be any fixed nonzero complex number. Describe the mapping defined by the function f (domain $\mathbb{C}$, range $\mathbb{C}$) such that $f(z) = z_0 z$.*

Solution. If $r_0 > 0$, which may always be assumed, this mapping is clearly a rotation through an angle α followed by a magnification by the factor r_0. The order of these two operations may be reversed.

Example 5. *Let f be the function (domain $\mathbb{C}$, range $\mathbb{C}$) defined by $f(z) = \bar{z}$. Describe the mapping defined by f.*

Solution. Since f maps the point $x + iy$ onto $x - iy$, it is a reflection of the z-plane in the real axis.

Example 6. *Let f be the function (domain and range the set of all nonzero complex numbers) defined by $f(z) = 1/z$. Describe the mapping defined by f.*

Solution. If $z = r(\cos \theta + i \sin \theta)$, then

$$f(z) = z^{-1} = r^{-1}(\cos \theta - i \sin \theta).$$

Thus the point in the z-plane with polar coordinates (r, θ) is mapped onto the point $(1/r, -\theta)$. We now give a geometric construction for the point z^{-1} in the case that z is a point outside the unit circle with center at the origin (see Fig. 10.12).

From z draw tangents to the unit circle $|z| = 1$ and let p, q be the points of contact of the tangents. Join pq and Oz and let z' be their point of intersection. Then $1/z = \bar{z}'$, the reflection of z' in the real axis. To prove this we note that the triangles Opz' and Ozp are similar and hence

$$\frac{Oz'}{Op} = \frac{Op}{Oz}.$$

But since $Op = 1$, $Oz' = 1/Oz$ or $|z'| = |z|^{-1} = 1/r$. Since also am $\bar{z}' = -$ am $z' = -$ am $z = -\theta$, the polar coordinates of $\bar{z}'$ are $(1/r, -\theta)$ as required.

The transformation of the z-plane defined by $f(z) = 1/z$ is called an inversion with respect to the unit circle with center at the origin. We note the following properties of f.

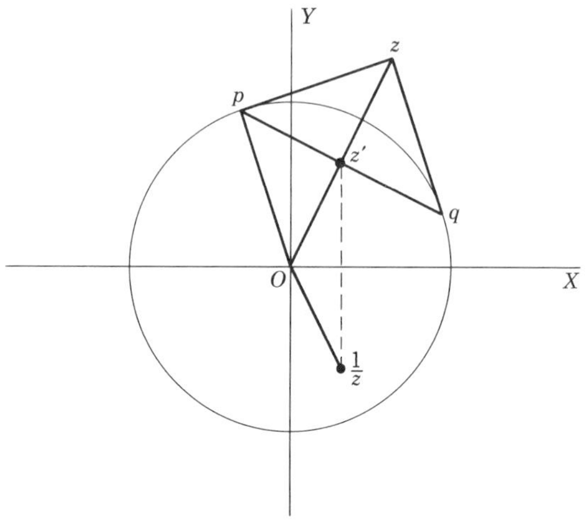

Fig. 10.12

(a) A point on the unit circle $|z| = 1$ is mapped onto its complex conjugate.

(b) A point outside the circle $|z| = 1$ in the upper (lower) half of the z-plane is mapped by f onto a point inside the circle in the lower (upper) half of the z-plane.

(c) A point inside the circle $|z| = 1$ in the upper (lower) half of the z-plane is mapped onto a point outside the circle in the lower (upper) half of the z-plane.

Example 7. *Let a, b, c, d be complex numbers such that*

$$\begin{vmatrix} a & b \\ c & d \end{vmatrix} \neq 0.$$

Let f be the function with domain the set of all complex numbers z for which $cz + d \neq 0$, *defined by*

$$f(z) = \frac{az + b}{cz + d}.$$

Describe the mapping defined by f.

Solution. The transformation defined by f is called a linear transformation of the complex plane. We shall show that such a transformation is equivalent to a succession of translations, rotations, magnifications, and inversions. It is easy to check the identity (if $c \neq 0$)

$$\frac{az + b}{cz + d} = \frac{a}{c} + \left(\frac{bc - ad}{c}\right)\left(\frac{1}{cz + d}\right).$$

Thus f is equivalent to the following succession of mappings:

(1) $\qquad\qquad z_1 = cz,$

(2) $\qquad\qquad z_2 = z_1 + d,$

(3) $\qquad\qquad z_3 = \dfrac{1}{z_2},$

(4) $\qquad\qquad z_4 = \left(\dfrac{bc - ad}{c}\right) z_3,$

(5) $\qquad\qquad f(z) = z_5 = z_4 + \dfrac{a}{c}.$

Now (1) is a magnification followed by a rotation as in Example 4, (2) represents a translation, (3) an inversion, (4) a magnification and rotation, and (5) a translation. These five transformations applied successively in the order named are equivalent to f. Of course, special values, such as 0 and 1, of some of the constants may mean omission of one or more of the five transformations. The above analysis was based on the assumption that $c \neq 0$. If $c = 0$, then $d \neq 0$ because

$$\begin{vmatrix} a & b \\ c & d \end{vmatrix} \neq 0.$$

Then $f(z) = (a/d)z + b/d$ and f is equivalent to a magnification followed by a rotation and a translation.

It can be proved that every circle and straight line in the z-plane is transformed by a linear transformation into a circle or a straight line. The method is to prove this for each of the component transformations, namely translations, rotations, magnifications, and inversions.

EXERCISE 10.7

1. If z is a point inside the unit circle $|z| = 1$, give details of a geometric construction that will locate the point $1/z$.

2. State detailed instructions for locating the point $1/(z - a)$ geometrically when z and a are known and $a \neq 0$.

3. If a and b are complex numbers and f is the function with domain $\mathbb{C}$ defined by $f(z) = az + b$, prove that (a) f maps any circle in the z-plane onto a circle and (b) f maps any straight line in the z-plane onto a straight line.

4. Prove that the inversion defined by $f(z) = 1/z$

   (a) maps every circle in the z-plane that does not pass through the origin onto a circle.

   (b) maps every straight line in the z-plane that does not pass through the origin onto a circle through the origin.

5. Try to discover the effect of the inversion $f(z) = 1/z$ on lines and circles that pass through the origin. Note that $z = 0$ is not in the domain of f.

REFERENCES

1. Apostol, Tom M. *Calculus*. Blaisdell, New York, 1961.
2. Beaumont, Ross A., and Richard S. Pierce. *The Algebraic Foundations of Mathematics*. Addison-Wesley, Reading, Mass., 1963.
3. Birkhoff, Garrett, and Saunders MacLane. *A Survey of Modern Algebra*, revised edition. Macmillan, New York, 1953.
4. Courant, Richard, and Herbert Robbins. *What Is Mathematics?* Fourth edition. Oxford University Press, New York, 1947.
5. Murdoch, D. C. *Linear Algebra for Undergraduates*. Wiley, New York, 1957.
6. Polya, G. *Mathematics and Plausible Reasoning*, Vol. 1. Princeton University Press, Princeton, N. J., 1954.
7. Weiss, Marie J. *Higher Algebra for the Undergraduate*. Second edition, revised by Roy Dubisch. Wiley, New York, 1962.

ANSWERS TO EXERCISES

Exercise 1.1

1. (a) $A' = \{1, 2, 3, 4, 5, 6\}$.
        $A \cap B = \{7, 8, 9\}$.
        $A \cap B' = $ all natural numbers greater than 9.
        $A \cup B = $ set of all natural numbers.
        $A' \cap B' = \emptyset$.
  (b) The set of all multiples of 60.
5. (b) $A \cap B' \cap C$.   (d) $A \cap [(B \cap C') \cup (B' \cap C)]$.
6. (a) $A \cap B' \cap C' = $ set of all blonde unmarried females.
  (b) Eight categories.

Exercise 1.3

6. (a) $x > 5$.   (b) $-5 < x < 5$.   (c) $3 < x < 7$.
  (d) $-1 < x < \frac{5}{3}$.   (e) $-2 < x < 2$.
  (f) $\sqrt{2} \leq x \leq \sqrt{6}$ or $-\sqrt{6} \leq x \leq -\sqrt{2}$.
  (g) $x < 1$ or $x > 2$.   (h) $0 < x < \frac{5}{3}$.
10. (b) All values of x except $x = \frac{3}{2}$ such that $-1 < x < 4$.
  (c) $x > 6$.

Exercise 2.1

3. (a) $(x, 0)$.   (b) $(0, y)$.   4. (a) x-axis 6, y-axis 5.
5. (a) $|x_1 - x_2|$.   (b) $|y_1 - y_2|$.   7. (a) 6.   (c) 10.
8. (b) On the axis.   (d) On the xz-plane.   (f) On the y-axis.
9. (a) All on a plane parallel to the yz-plane.
  (b) All on a straight line parallel to the y-axis.
11. (a) Projection on xy-plane $(2, -1, 0)$.
  (b) Projection on plane parallel to xy-plane $(2, -1, -3)$.
13.   Projection on xy-plane $(x, y, 0)$; on x-axis, $(x, 0, 0)$.
17. (a) $(8, 0)$.   (c) $(0, 0)$.   (f) $\left(0, \dfrac{y_1 + y_2}{2}\right)$.
22. (a) $(3, 4)$.   (c) $(\frac{9}{2}, -\frac{7}{2}, 2)$.

24. $(a_1 + b_1, a_2 + b_2)$.   **26.** $(x_1 + x_2, y_1 + y_2, z_1 + z_2)$.
27. $(12, 8)$.

Exercise 2.2

1. (a) $\sqrt{29}$.   (c) $\sqrt{106}$.   **4.** radius $= 5$.
7. $(-\frac{13}{5}, 0)$.   **9.** center $(2, -3)$, radius 5.
10. (a) $\sqrt{65}$.   (b) $\sqrt{14}$.   (e) $a\sqrt{3}$.
15. $(-\frac{29}{6}, 0, 0)$; no.   **16.** $\left(x, \dfrac{2 - 2x}{3}, 0 \right)$ for arbitrary x.

Exercise 2.3

3. Domain and range the set $\mathfrak{R}$ of all real numbers.
5. Domain $\mathfrak{R}$, range $\mathcal{I}$, the set of all integers.
6. Domain $-2 \leq x \leq 2$ range $0 \leq x \leq 2$.
8. Domain all nonzero real numbers, range the same.
11. $f(-1) = 5, f(10) = 9.4$.
13. $f(0, 0, 1) = 0, f(-1, -1, 3) = 10$. Domain: all triples (x, y, z) of real numbers for which $x + y + z \neq 0$.

Exercise 2.4

1. (a) All points in $\mathcal{E}_2$ above the line that bisects the angle between the positive rays of the coordinate axes.
    (c) All points (x, y) for which $2 \leq x \leq 4$.
    (e) All points on a circle with center at $(4, -3)$ and radius 2.
    (g) All points inside the 4 by 8 rectangle, center at the origin, with side of length 4 parallel to the x-axis and side of length 8 parallel to the y-axis.
    (i) All points (x, y) inside the circle with center at the origin and radius 3 for which the ordinate is greater than 2.
4. (a) All points on the sphere with center at the origin and radius 5 which are 4 units above the xy-plane.
    (b) Includes (a) and the points on the sphere 4 units below the xy-plane.
6. (a) The null set.   (b) The null set.
10. Sphere with center at $(2, 0, 0)$ and radius 2.

Exercise 3.1

1. $x + 6y = 13, 4x + 9y = 7, x + y = 3$.
3. $8x + 18y = 29$.
4. $x + 6y < 13, x + y < 3, 4x + 9y > 7$.
6. The null set.

Exercise 3.2

1. (a) $-\frac{8}{3}, \frac{10}{3}, \frac{1}{3}$.   (c) $10x - 3y + 25 = 0$.
    (e) $4x - 3y + 1 = 0, 2x + 3y - 13 = 0, x = 2$.
3. $7x + 3y - 55 = 0$.
9. (a) $x - 25y = 0$.   (b) $21x + 7y = 76$.   (c) $13x - 24y = 43$.

Exercise 3.3

1. (a) $(0, 0), \sqrt{20}$.   (c) $(-\frac{5}{2}, \frac{11}{2}), \frac{1}{2}\sqrt{274}$.   (d) $(1, -\frac{5}{3}), \frac{1}{3}\sqrt{97}$.
3. (a) $x^2 + y^2 - 28x - 20y + 71 = 0$.

(b) $x^2 + y^2 - 2x + 4y = 20$.

(c) $x^2 + y^2 - x + 5y = 2$.

(d) $7x^2 + 7y^2 - 20x + 32y = 227$.

12. $3x^2 + 3y^2 - 44x - 50y + 283 = 0$; center $(\frac{22}{3}, \frac{25}{3})$, radius $\dfrac{2\sqrt{65}}{3}$.

Exercise 4.1

1. $x' = x - 3, y' = y + 4$.   2. $x' = x + 3, y' = y - 4$.

4. $x' = x + 5, y' = y + 9$; no.

6. (a) New origin $(3, -1)$; $x'^2 + y'^2 = 24$.

   (c) New origin $(-2, \frac{5}{2})$; $16x'^2 + 4y'^2 = 105$.

Exercise 4.2

1. (a) $[7, 5, -5]$; $3\sqrt{11}$; $\dfrac{7}{3\sqrt{11}}$, $\dfrac{5}{3\sqrt{11}}$, $-\dfrac{5}{3\sqrt{11}}$.

   (b) $[-7, -5, 5]$; $3\sqrt{11}$; $-\dfrac{7}{3\sqrt{11}}$, $-\dfrac{5}{3\sqrt{11}}$, $\dfrac{5}{3\sqrt{11}}$.

   (c) $[2, 2, 1]$; 3; $\frac{2}{3}, \frac{2}{3}, \frac{1}{3}$.

3. $(5, -6, 9)$.

Exercise 4.3

1. $x' = x + 2, y' = y - 1, z' = z + 7$; $(5, 3, 6)$.

5. $(7, 16, -3)$, $(-1, 2, 5)$, $(3, -12, 11)$.

10. (a) $[\frac{4}{5}, -\frac{3}{5}]$.   (b) $[\frac{2}{3}, -\frac{1}{3}, \frac{2}{3}]$ (answer not unique).

11. (a) $\cos\theta = \frac{4}{5}$.   (c) $\cos\theta = -\dfrac{6}{\sqrt{14}\sqrt{65}}$.

Exercise 4.4

1. Any scalar multiples of $[3, -2]$.

3. $[\pm 2\sqrt{3}, \pm\sqrt{3}]$.

5. $\cos\theta = \dfrac{7}{\sqrt{170}}$.   6. (a) $\dfrac{4\sqrt{5}}{5}$.   (b) $\dfrac{18\sqrt{5}}{5}$.

7. 3.   9. $\frac{48}{13}$.   11. $(\frac{5}{3}, 3)$.

13. $\cos A = \dfrac{37}{\sqrt{113}\sqrt{52}}$, $A = 61°9'$ approx.

15. $\cos\theta = \dfrac{2}{\sqrt{6}}$, $\theta = 35°16'$ approx.

17. $x = 2 + 3t, y = -7 + 12t$ (not unique).

21. $\left(\dfrac{x_1 + x_2 + x_3}{3}, \dfrac{y_1 + y_2 + y_3}{3}, \dfrac{z_1 + z_2 + z_3}{3}\right)$.

25. $\dfrac{16}{\sqrt{69}}$.

Exercise 5.1

1. (a) $3x - y + 4z = 9$.   (c) $3x - 7y + z = 18$.

   (e) $5x + 5y + 2z = 34$.

3. $p = \left| \dfrac{ax_1 + by_1 + cz_1 - d}{\sqrt{a^2 + b^2 + c^2}} \right|.$

5. $\cos \theta = \dfrac{1}{\sqrt{246}},$ $\theta = 86°39'$ approx.

6. $\dfrac{150}{31}, \dfrac{145}{31}, \dfrac{-3}{31}.$

8. $x = 3t, y = -1 - t, z = 5 + 9t.$

Exercise 5.2

1. $3x - y + 6z = 10.$
3. $x - 6y + 2z = 0.$
5. $8x - 13y - 7z + 12 = 0.$
7. $2x + y + 3z = 26.$

Exercise 5.3

1. 84 acres wheat, 236 acres oats, 40 acres corn; return \$11,680.
2. Yes. 320 bu.
4. 290 acres wheat, 30 acres oats. No.
5. Beefex 2.5, cerelina 0, vegetone 6.5; 1225 calories; \$5.10.

Exercise 5.4

1. (a) $x^2 + y^2 + z^2 - 6x = 0.$
2. (a) Center $(\frac{7}{2}, 0, 2)$ radius $\frac{1}{2} \sqrt{145}.$
3. Center $(-6, 3, \frac{1}{3})$, radius $\frac{14}{3}.$

Exercise 6.1

1. (a) $a^2x^2 + (a^2 - c^2)y^2 = a^2(a^2 - c^2).$ (c) $3x^2 - 2xy + 3y^2 = 8.$

   (b) $\dfrac{(x - 1)^2}{36} + \dfrac{(y - 4)^2}{20} = 1.$

3. $a = 8, b = 4, 2c = 8 \sqrt{3}.$
6. $\frac{10}{3}$ ins.

Exercise 6.2

2. (a) $(c^2 - a^2)y^2 - a^2x^2 = a^2(c^2 - a^2).$
   (b) $4x^2 - 5y^2 - 16x + 20y + 16 = 0.$ (c) $2xy = 1.$

5. Center $(-3, 1)$, $e = \dfrac{2\sqrt{10}}{3},$ $2c = 4\sqrt{5}$, asymptotes $x + 3y = 0,$

   $x - 3y + 6 = 0.$

Exercise 6.3

2. (a) $x^2 = 16y.$ (b) $y^2 - 8y - 16x - 48 = 0.$ (c) $x^2 + 12y = 0.$
   (d) $x^2 - 6x - 8y + 33 = 0.$ (e) $x^2 - 2xy + y^2 + 8x + 8y = 16.$
6. (b) Vertex $(0, 6)$, focus $(0, 9)$. (d) Vertex $(\frac{1}{8}, 3)$, focus $(\frac{17}{8}, 3)$.

Exercise 6.4

1. (a) $(y - 2)^2 + (z + 1)^2 = 25.$ (c) $y^2 + z^2 = m^2x^2.$
2. $20x^2 + 125y^2 - 43z^2 - 84xz - 126yz + 252xy = 0.$
5. (a) $x^2 + 4y^2 + 2z^2 = 100$; ellipsoid.
   (b) $x^2 + y^2 = 8z$ elliptic paraboloid.
   (c) $4x^2 + y^2 - z^2 = 18.$

Exercise 6.5

1. (a) On xy-plane: $2x^2 + 2xy + 2y^2 = 9$, $z = 0$.
   (b) On xz-plane: $x + z = 0$, $y = 0$.
   On yz-plane: $y^2 + 2z^2 = 9$, $x = 0$.
   (c) On xy-plane: $(x^2 + y^2)^2 = 16(x^2 + 4y^2)$, $z = 0$.

3. $2x - 6y + 4z = 25$; center $(\frac{2\,5}{2\,8}, -\frac{7\,5}{2\,8}, \frac{5\,0}{2\,8})$; radius $\dfrac{5\sqrt{31}}{2\sqrt{14}}$.

Exercise 7.1

2. (a), (c), and (f).

Exercise 7.2

3. (a) $X_1 + X_2 - 2X_3 = 0$. (e) $37X_1 + 30X_2 + X_3 - 85X_4 = 0$.
   (c) $5X_1 + 0X_2 + 0X_3 = 0$.

11. (a) $t = -\frac{6}{7}$. (b) $t = -\frac{14}{13}$.

Exercise 7.3

8. $[2, -3, -1]$, $[4, 1, -1]$ (not unique).
9. $[1, -11, -3]$ or any nonzero scalar multiple.
14. $[\frac{4}{7}, \frac{19}{7}, 1, 0]$, $[\frac{3}{7}, -\frac{5}{7}, 0, 1]$; dimension 2.

Exercise 7.4

7. (a) $[\frac{1}{3}, 1, 0, 0]$, $[-\frac{1}{3}, 0, 1, 0]$, $[\frac{2}{3}, 0, 0, 1]$.
   (c) $[\frac{3}{5}, -\frac{4}{5}, 1, 0, 0]$, $[-1, 1, 0, 1, 0]$, $[-1, 0, 0, 0, 1]$.
   (e) $[-5, 4, 3]$.

Exercise 7.5

1. (a) $x_1 = 2y_1 - y_2$, (c) $x_1 = \dfrac{y_1 - y_2}{\sqrt{2}}$,

   $x_2 = y_1 + 3y_2$. $x_2 = \dfrac{y_1 + y_2}{\sqrt{2}}$.

2. (a) $5y_1^2 + 2y_1y_2 + 10y_2^2 = 9$.
   (b) $5y_1^2 + 2\sqrt{5}\,y_1y_2 + 5y_2^2 = 45$. (c) $y_1^2 + y_2^2 = 9$.
3. $y_1^2 + y_2^2 = 1$.
6. Choose unit points at the points $(a, 0, 0)$, $(0, b, 0)$ and $(0, 0, c)$.

Exercise 7.6

1. (a) $y_1^2 - y_2^2 = 8$. (c) $5\sqrt{5}\,y_1^2 + 11y_1 - 8y_2 = 0$.
   (b) $y_1^2 + \sqrt{2}\,y_2 = 0$. (d) $3y_2^2 - 13y_1^2 - 12y_1y_2 = 25$.

Exercise 8.1

1. $AB = \begin{bmatrix} 4 & 7 \\ 11 & -23 \end{bmatrix}$, $BA = \begin{bmatrix} -3 & 31 \\ 7 & -16 \end{bmatrix}$, $A^2 = \begin{bmatrix} 3 & 8 \\ -8 & 35 \end{bmatrix}$.

4. $A^{57} = \begin{bmatrix} \cos 57\theta & -\sin 57\theta \\ \sin 57\theta & \cos 57\theta \end{bmatrix}$.

5. $A^2 = \begin{bmatrix} 0 & -1 \\ 1 & 0 \end{bmatrix}$, $A^4 = \begin{bmatrix} -1 & 0 \\ 0 & -1 \end{bmatrix}$, $A^8 = \begin{bmatrix} 1 & 0 \\ 0 & 1 \end{bmatrix}$.

A is the matrix of a rotation through $45°$.

6. $A^{12} = \begin{bmatrix} 1 & 0 \\ 0 & 1 \end{bmatrix}$.   11. $X = \begin{bmatrix} \frac{5}{13} & \frac{1}{13} \\ -\frac{3}{13} & \frac{2}{13} \end{bmatrix}$.

12. (a) No.   (b) Yes. Infinitely many.   (c) Yes. One.

Exercise 8.2

1. (a) $x = \frac{13}{4}, y = -\frac{1}{4}$ (b) $x = \frac{79}{30}, y = -\frac{29}{30}, z = \frac{31}{6}$.
3. (a) $x = t, y = t, z = -t$ (b) $x = 10z - 10w, y = 17w - 19z$.

   (c) $x = \dfrac{43 + 3t}{8}, y = \dfrac{13 + 5t}{8}, z = t$ (d) $x = -11t, y = 6t, z = 8t, w = 5t$.

6. $A^{-1} = \begin{bmatrix} 1 & 1 \\ 2 & 2.5 \end{bmatrix}$, $B^{-1} = \begin{bmatrix} 3 & -4 & 2 \\ -4 & 5 & -2 \\ 3 & -3 & 1 \end{bmatrix}$.

Exercise 8.6

1. 22.   2. 21.   4. $\sqrt{3059}$.   5. $10\sqrt{77}$.
9. $(-4, 10, 11), (5, 5, 14), (-4, 3, 7), (-2, 8, 17)$; vol. $= 368$.

Exercise 9.1

1. A proper.   2. $AB = \frac{1}{21} \begin{bmatrix} 16 & -13 & 4 \\ 11 & 16 & 8 \\ 8 & 4 & -19 \end{bmatrix}$
   B improper.

Exercise 9.2

3. $\begin{bmatrix} \dfrac{2}{\sqrt{30}} & \dfrac{3}{\sqrt{29}} & \dfrac{22}{\sqrt{870}} \\ \dfrac{5}{\sqrt{30}} & -\dfrac{2}{\sqrt{29}} & -\dfrac{5}{\sqrt{870}} \\ -\dfrac{1}{\sqrt{30}} & -\dfrac{4}{\sqrt{29}} & \dfrac{19}{\sqrt{870}} \end{bmatrix}$ 4. $x = 2t, y = t, z = t$.

5. (a) $\begin{bmatrix} \cos\theta & -\sin\theta & 0 \\ \sin\theta & \cos\theta & 0 \\ 0 & 0 & 1 \end{bmatrix}$ 7. $X = [-1, 5, 1]$.

Exercise 9.3

1. (a) $\begin{bmatrix} \dfrac{2}{\sqrt{6}} & 0 & \dfrac{1}{\sqrt{3}} \\ \dfrac{1}{\sqrt{6}} & -\dfrac{1}{\sqrt{2}} & -\dfrac{1}{\sqrt{3}} \\ \dfrac{1}{\sqrt{6}} & \dfrac{1}{\sqrt{2}} & -\dfrac{1}{\sqrt{3}} \end{bmatrix}$, $y_1^2 + y_2^2 - 2y_3^2 = 9$. Hyperboloid of one sheet. Matrix not unique.

   (b) $\begin{bmatrix} \frac{2}{3} & \frac{2}{3} & -\frac{1}{3} \\ -\frac{1}{3} & \frac{2}{3} & \frac{2}{3} \\ \frac{2}{3} & -\frac{1}{3} & \frac{2}{3} \end{bmatrix}$, $9y_1^2 + 6y_1 - 6y_2 = 5$. Parabolic cylinder. Matrix unique except for order and sign of column vectors.

2. $\left(\dfrac{-3 + \sqrt{145}}{2}\right) y_1{}^2 + \left(\dfrac{-3 - \sqrt{145}}{2}\right) y_2{}^2 - y_3{}^2 = 35$; Hyperboloid of two sheets.

Exercise 10.1

2. $180°, 90°, 60°, 150°, 270°, 720°$.

3. $\dfrac{2\pi}{3}, \dfrac{\pi}{6}, \dfrac{5\pi}{4}, \dfrac{\pi}{4}, \dfrac{\pi}{2}, \dfrac{3\pi}{2}, \dfrac{2\pi}{5}$.

5. $\dfrac{3}{2\pi}$ degrees.

Exercise 10.2

1. (a) Circle, center at origin, radius a.
   (b) The ray with initial point O making angle α with OX.

2. $r = 2a \sin \theta$.

4. $r = \dfrac{pe}{1 - e \cos \theta}$.

7. $r = 2a(1 - \cos \theta)$.

Exercise 10.3

5. (a) $17 + 17i$.   (c) $-1 - i$.   (e) $2i$.   (g) -4.   (i) $-\frac{1}{2} - \dfrac{\sqrt{3}}{2} i$.

6. (a) $\dfrac{4 - 3i}{25}$.   (b) $\dfrac{4 - 18i}{17}$.   (c) 1.

10. (a) $-2 \pm i$.   (b) $\frac{1}{2} \pm \dfrac{\sqrt{3}}{2} i$.

Exercise 10.5

1. (a) $\sqrt{2}\left[\cos \dfrac{7\pi}{4} + i \sin \dfrac{7\pi}{4}\right]$.   (e) $5(\cos \theta + i \sin \theta)$, $\theta = 125°55'$.

   (c) $4\left(\cos \dfrac{\pi}{2} + i \sin \dfrac{\pi}{2}\right)$.   (h) $\cos \pi + i \sin \pi$.

4. (a) $\sqrt{104}, \sqrt{149}, \sqrt{73}$.

5. (a) Circle, center at a, radius 6.
   (b) Ellipse, foci at a and b, major axis 6.

15. (a) Angles between 0 and 180° defined by $\tan \alpha = \frac{4\,3}{4\,5}$, $\tan \beta = \frac{4\,3}{7}$, and $\tan \gamma = \frac{8\,6}{5\,9}$.

Exercise 10.6

1. (a) $\dfrac{1 + i}{\sqrt{2}}, \dfrac{-1 - i}{\sqrt{2}}$.   (c) $\sqrt{2}\left(\cos \dfrac{7\pi}{8} + i \sin \dfrac{7\pi}{8}\right)$ and $\sqrt{2}\left(\cos \dfrac{15\pi}{8} + i \sin \dfrac{15\pi}{8}\right)$.

3. $1, \frac{1}{2} + \dfrac{\sqrt{3}}{2} i, \dfrac{\sqrt{3}}{2} + \frac{1}{2}i, i, -\dfrac{\sqrt{3}}{2} + \frac{1}{2}i, -\frac{1}{2} + \dfrac{\sqrt{3}}{2} i$, and -1 times each of these.

8. $\cos 3\theta = 4 \cos^3 \theta - 3 \cos \theta$.

INDEX

291